The National **Numeracy** *Strategy*

Framework for teaching mathematics from Reception to Year 6

Contents

Department for Education and Employment

Introducing the Framework

Foreword

Numeracy is a key life skill. Without basic numeracy skills, our children will be disadvantaged throughout life. That is why we have set a target of 75% of 11-year-olds reaching the standard of mathematics expected for their age by 2002. And, through the National Numeracy Strategy, we have made funding available to provide training and support for schools as they work towards this target. The National Numeracy Strategy will be launched in schools this September and will build on the experience of the National Literacy Strategy. Through these two mutually reinforcing initiatives, we want children to achieve a secure foundation in literacy and numeracy as we move into the next millennium.

This *Framework for Teaching Mathematics from Reception to Year 6* is a key part of the package of support available for teachers, headteachers and governors. Schools which have already tested it out have found that the yearly teaching programmes, key objectives and planning grids greatly assist them in planning and teaching their mathematics lessons. I believe that the Framework has much to offer every school.

We recognise the crucial importance of giving teachers the support they need to raise standards. But the success of both the Literacy and Numeracy Strategies depends on the commitment and enthusiasm of teachers themselves. I hope that all schools will use the Framework to make a real difference.

The Rt Hon David Blunkett MP
Secretary of State for Education and Employment
March 1999

1

1

Introducing the **Framework**

Introduction

Over the past few years an accumulation of inspection, research and test evidence has pointed to a need to improve standards of literacy and numeracy. The Government's targets for 2002 are that 80% of all 11-year-olds achieve at least level 4 in the National Curriculum tests for English, and 75% achieve at least level 4 in the tests for mathematics. The National Literacy Strategy has been launched, with a *Framework for Teaching Literacy* in a daily literacy hour, and a programme of in-service training and support for schools.

The National Numeracy Strategy will complement the Literacy Strategy. From September 1999, schools will provide a structured daily mathematics lesson of 45 minutes to one hour for all pupils of primary age. Teachers will teach the whole class together for a high proportion of the time, and oral and mental work will feature strongly in each lesson.

This *Framework for Teaching Mathematics from Reception to Year 6* is a key element of the training materials that will support the Numeracy Strategy.

The Framework illustrates the intended range and balance of work in primary mathematics to make sure that pupils become properly numerate. It is intended mainly for day-to-day reference by class teachers and has been tested extensively and successfully in schools of different types and sizes. Its purpose is to help primary and middle schools, and special schools with primary-age pupils, to set appropriately high expectations for their pupils and understand how pupils should progress through the primary years. Teachers working with older pupils who have more severe or complex special educational needs might also find its contents relevant.

Good school leadership is vital for teachers to be successful in the classroom. The Framework should also be read and used by headteachers and governors as they manage the improvement of standards of mathematics, monitor progress and support the staff. Parents too may be interested to see it.

The contents of the Framework

The National Curriculum Order describes what must be taught in each key stage. This Framework provides guidance to supplement the Order. It has been developed alongside the proposals for the revised National Curriculum so that it is compatible with them.

The Framework contains a set of **yearly teaching programmes** illustrating how mathematics can be planned and taught from Reception to Year 6. It includes guidance on the daily mathematics lesson in which this teaching will take place and on the assessment of pupils' progress.

The objectives in the yearly teaching programmes cover all aspects of the National Curriculum for mathematics in Key Stages 1 and 2. The programme for Reception takes account of the Early Learning Goals for 3- to 5-year-olds, and provides a bridge from the Goals to the National Curriculum.

Some of the objectives in the yearly programmes are more critical than others if children are to become numerate. These **key objectives** are listed in a separate section and are also highlighted in bold type in the yearly teaching programmes. They are central to all pupils' achievements in relation to the National Curriculum level descriptions, and hence to their performance in teacher assessments and tests. Teachers should give priority to these key objectives when they are planning work and assessing pupils' progress.

Each yearly teaching programme is accompanied by grids to help teachers to plan a term's lessons in outline. The **planning grids** show how mathematical topics can be grouped in units of work throughout the term. A recommended number of lessons is given for each unit. Time is built in for half-termly assessment and review.

After the yearly teaching programmes and planning grids come **supplements of examples**, for Reception, Years 1–3 and Years 4–6. These examples are not intended to be covered as a 'scheme of work', or used as a 'textbook' or for worksheets. Their purpose is to illustrate, for each teaching objective, a selection of what pupils should know, understand and be able to do by the end of each school year. Over time, teachers should add to and replace the examples with those that they find most useful and cross-reference them to other resources, including information and communications technology (ICT), to form a working document.

The section on planning starting on page 38 discusses in detail the key objectives, yearly teaching programmes, planning grids and examples, and explains how to use them.

Related publications

For schools that are starting to prepare for the National Numeracy Strategy there are a number of other publications to accompany the Framework.

- *The Implementation of the National Numeracy Strategy* This final report of the Numeracy Task Force, published in July 1998 by the DfEE, gives a practical agenda for action to implement the National Numeracy Strategy. It can be obtained from DfEE Publications, tel: 0845 6022260.
- *Mathematical Vocabulary* This 32-page booklet lists the important vocabulary for each year group. An introductory section discusses questioning strategies. Further copies of the booklet can be obtained from DfEE Publications, tel: 0845 6022260.
- *Teaching Mental Calculation Strategies: Guidance for Teachers at Key Stages 1 and 2* This book has been produced by the Qualifications and Curriculum Authority (QCA) to support the National Numeracy Strategy. It describes approaches to the teaching of mental calculations and the role of calculators in Key Stages 1 and 2. Further copies can be obtained from QCA Publications, tel: 01787 884444; fax: 01787 312950.
- *Standards in Mathematics: Exemplification of Key Learning Objectives from Reception to Year 6* This book, also produced by the QCA, describes the key learning objectives for each age group from Year 1 to Year 6 and illustrates them with examples of children's work. Further copies can be obtained from QCA Publications, tel: 01787 884444; fax: 01787 312950.

What is numeracy?

Numeracy is a proficiency which involves confidence and competence with numbers and measures. It requires an understanding of the number system, a repertoire of computational skills and an inclination and ability to solve number problems in a variety of contexts. Numeracy also demands practical understanding of the ways in which information is gathered by counting and measuring, and is presented in graphs, diagrams, charts and tables.

As a teacher you can help children to acquire this proficiency by giving a sharp focus to the relevant aspects of the programmes of study for mathematics. The outcome should be numerate pupils who are confident enough to tackle mathematical problems without going immediately to teachers or friends for help. Your pupils should:

- have a sense of the size of a number and where it fits into the number system;
- know by heart number facts such as number bonds, multiplication tables, doubles and halves;
- use what they know by heart to figure out answers mentally;
- calculate accurately and efficiently, both mentally and with pencil and paper, drawing on a range of calculation strategies;
- recognise when it is appropriate to use a calculator, and be able to do so effectively;
- make sense of number problems, including non-routine problems, and recognise the operations needed to solve them;
- explain their methods and reasoning using correct mathematical terms;
- judge whether their answers are reasonable and have strategies for checking them where necessary;
- suggest suitable units for measuring, and make sensible estimates of measurements; and
- explain and make predictions from the numbers in graphs, diagrams, charts and tables.

Factors that promote high standards of numeracy

As part of the National Literacy Strategy your school will have considered ways of promoting higher standards of literacy. The action that you have already taken will help you when you come to consider ways of promoting pupils' numeracy skills, since many of the same factors will apply.

Where **school management** is concerned, better numeracy standards occur when:

- the headteacher is well-informed, provides active leadership and sets high expectations for what can be achieved by staff and pupils;
- a co-ordinator for mathematics has the expertise, opportunity and support needed to influence practice;
- a desire to secure high standards through effective teaching and learning pervades the whole school;
- there are clear, realistic targets for raising standards, and a manageable plan for achieving them, with regular evaluation of the school's progress towards the targets – including effective arrangements, which take account of national standards, for assessing the progress of whole year groups and each class;

- there is systematic monitoring and self-review, under the headteacher's direction, of teachers' planning, teaching and assessment;
- there is a whole-school approach to the professional development of teachers and other staff involved in the teaching of mathematics, with emphasis on developing knowledge of the primary mathematics curriculum and appropriate teaching methods;
- classroom assistants take part in planning and are used effectively to support teachers in mathematics lessons;
- parents are kept well-informed and encouraged to be involved through discussions at school and sometimes in work with pupils at home; and
- governors are involved actively in policy, monitoring and evaluation.

Taking the **curriculum and assessment** in the school as a whole, better numeracy standards occur when:

- staff share a common understanding of numeracy and how best to promote it;
- there is a daily, dedicated mathematics lesson in every class, with lesson time extended through out-of-class activities and regular homework;
- the teaching programme is based on identified learning objectives, and is planned thoroughly, to ensure high expectations, consistent approaches and good progression throughout the school;
- the foundations of mental calculation and recall of number facts are established thoroughly before standard written methods are introduced;
- assessments are used to identify pupils' strengths and difficulties, to set group and individual targets for them to achieve and to plan the next stage of work;
- assessments include informal observations and oral questioning, regular mental tests, and half-termly planned activities designed to judge progress; and
- recording systems give teachers the information that they need to plan and report successfully, but are not too time-consuming to maintain.

Where **teaching** is concerned, better numeracy standards occur when teachers:

- structure their mathematics lessons and maintain a good pace;
- provide daily oral and mental work to develop and secure pupils' calculation strategies and rapid recall skills;
- devote a high proportion of lesson time to direct teaching of whole classes and groups, making judicious use of textbooks, worksheets and ICT resources to support teaching, not to replace it;
- demonstrate, explain and illustrate mathematical ideas, making links between different topics in mathematics and between mathematics and other subjects;
- use and give pupils access to number lines and other resources, including ICT, to model mathematical ideas and methods;
- use and expect pupils to use correct mathematical vocabulary and notation;
- question pupils effectively, including as many of them as possible, giving them time to think before answering, targeting individuals to take account of their attainment and needs, asking them to demonstrate and explain their methods and reasoning, and exploring reasons for any wrong answers;
- involve pupils and maintain their interest through appropriately demanding work, including some non-routine problems that require them to think for themselves;
- ensure that differentiation is manageable and centred around work common to all the pupils in a class, with targeted, positive support to help those who have difficulties with mathematics to keep up with their peers.

The approach to calculation

An ability to calculate mentally lies at the heart of numeracy. You should emphasise mental methods from the early years onwards with regular opportunities for all pupils to develop the different skills involved. These skills include:

- remembering number facts and recalling them without hesitation;
- using the facts that are known by heart to figure out new facts: for example, a fact like $8 + 6 = 14$ can be used to work out $80 + 60 = 140$, or $28 + 6 = 34$;
- understanding and using the relationships between the 'four rules' to work out answers and check results: for example, $24 \div 4 = 6$, since $6 \times 4 = 24$;
- drawing on a repertoire of mental strategies to work out calculations like $81 - 26$, 23×4 or 5% of £3000, with some thinking time;
- solving problems like: 'Can I buy three bags of crisps at 35p each with my £1 coin?' or: 'Roughly how long will it take me to go 50 miles at 30 m.p.h.?'

An emphasis on mental calculation does not mean that written methods are not taught in the primary years but the balance between mental and written methods, and the way in which pupils progress from one to the other, is very important.

The first stages

In the early years children will use oral methods, in general moving from counting objects or fingers one by one to more sophisticated mental counting strategies. Later they will use a number line or square to work out their answers in different ways, depending on the numbers involved. After giving them experience of a variety of situations, real and imagined, you should teach them to remember and recall simple number facts such as 5 add 3 is 8 or that 7 taken from 9 leaves 2. Posing problems and expressing relationships in different ways, and encouraging children to use this language when they talk about mathematics, is an important stage in developing their calculation strategies and problem-solving skills.

These early stages of mental calculation are not, however, at the exclusion of written recording. Alongside their oral and mental work children will learn first to read, interpret and complete statements like $5 + 8 = \square$ or $13 = \square + 5$, and then to record the results of their own mental calculations in the correct way, using a horizontal format like $43 - 8 = 35$. They should also be taught addition and subtraction alongside each other so that they are able to write the subtraction corresponding to a given addition sum, and vice versa.

The first stage of recording calculations

Pupils learn to read number statements and interpret signs and symbols. They write answers only, to develop or practise rapid recall. For example:

$6 + 4 =$ $\qquad \square + 10 = 17$

$26 + 4 =$ $\qquad 17 - \square = 10$

$36 + 4 =$

Larger numbers and informal jottings

As pupils progress to working with larger numbers they will learn more sophisticated mental methods and tackle more complex problems. They will develop some of these methods intuitively and some you will teach explicitly.

Through a process of regular explanation and discussion of their own and other people's methods they will begin to acquire a repertoire of mental calculation strategies. At this stage, it can be hard for them to hold all the intermediate steps of a calculation in their heads and so informal pencil and paper notes, recording some or all of their solution, become part of a mental strategy. These personal jottings may not be easy for someone else to follow but they are an important staging post to getting the right answer and acquiring fluency in mental calculation.

The next steps in recording calculations

Pupils make jottings to assist their mental calculations: e.g. 47 + 26

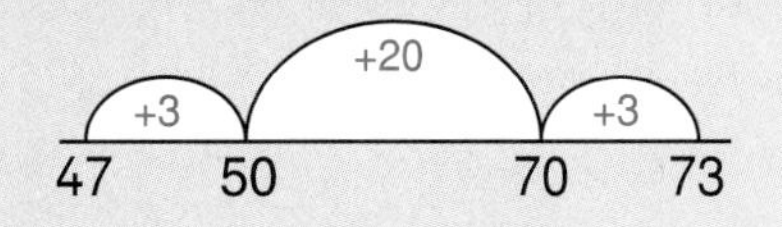

Pupils record steps so that you and they can see what they have done: e.g.

36 + 27

36 + 20 → 56   56 + 7 → 63

or

30 + 20 → 50 and 6 + 7 → 13

50 + 13 → 63

Not everyone does a mental calculation like 81 – 26 in the same way (nor is it necessary for them to do so) but some methods are more efficient and reliable than others. By explaining, discussing and comparing different part written, part mental methods, you can guide pupils towards choosing and using the methods which are most efficient and which can be applied generally. At this point, the need for more formal recording of calculation methods emerges.

Standard written methods

Standard written methods are reliable and efficient procedures for calculating which, once mastered, can be used in many different contexts. But they are of no use to someone who applies them inaccurately and who cannot judge whether the answer is reasonable. For each operation, at least one standard written method should be taught in the later primary years but the progression towards these methods is crucial, since they are based on steps which are done mentally and which need to be secured first. For example, the calculation of 487 + 356, done by the method which has been taught traditionally, requires the mental calculations 7 + 6 = 13, 8 + 5 + 1 = 14 and 4 + 3 + 1 = 8, while a division calculation such as 987 ÷ 23 can involve mental experiment with multiples of 23 before the correct multiple is chosen.

Most countries, and in particular those which are most successful at teaching number, avoid the premature teaching of standard written methods in order not to jeopardise the development of mental calculation strategies. The bridge from recording part written, part mental methods to learning standard methods of written calculations begins only when children can add or subtract reliably any pair of two-digit numbers in their heads, usually when they are about 9 years old.

Using standard written methods

Pupils write to work out complex calculations that they cannot do mentally: e.g.

```
   253
   576
 + 843
  1672
```

```
     232
  7)1624
```

When they have reached the stage of working out more complex calculations using pencil and paper you should still expect your pupils to practise and develop their mental calculation strategies. When faced with any calculation, no matter how large or how difficult the numbers may appear to be, the first question pupils should always ask themselves is: 'Can I do this in my head?' They then need to ask themselves: 'Do I know the approximate size of the answer?' so that they can be reasonably sure their calculation is right.

The role of calculators

The calculator is a powerful and efficient tool. It has a strong part to play in subjects such as geography, history or science, since it allows children of primary age to make use of real data – often numbers with several digits – that they have gathered in their research or experiments, perhaps to work out a percentage, or to compare totals or proportions.

In the primary years, the calculator's main role in mathematics lessons is not as a calculating tool, since children are still developing the mental calculation skills and written methods that they will need throughout their lives. But it does offer a unique way of learning about numbers and the number system, place value, properties of numbers, and fractions and decimals. For example, you could use an overhead projector calculator for whole-class demonstration purposes so that the class can predict what happens when they multiply by 10 or divide by 10, or individual pupils might use a calculator to find two consecutive numbers with a given product and then discuss their different approaches.

If children are to use the basic facilities of a calculator constructively and efficiently, you need to teach them the technical skills they will require: the order in which to use the keys; how to enter numbers such as sums of money, measurements or fractions; how to interpret the display; how to use the memory... Children need to learn when it is, and when it is not, appropriate to use a calculator, and their first-line strategy should involve mental calculations wherever possible. For example, you might show pupils that they can 'beat the calculator' if they can recall number facts rapidly. They should also have sufficient understanding of the calculation in front of them to be able to decide which method to use – mental, pencil and paper, or calculator. When they do use a calculator they should be able to draw on well-established skills of rounding numbers and calculating mentally to gain a sense of the approximate size of the answer, and have strategies to check and repeat the calculation if they are not sure whether it is right.

For these reasons schools should not normally use the calculator as part of Key Stage 1 mathematics but should emphasise oral work and mental calculation. But by the end of Key Stage 2, pupils should have the knowledge and competence to use a calculator to work out, say, $(56 + 97) \div (133 - 85)$ and round the answer to one decimal place. They should also recognise that an approximate answer is $150 \div 50$, or 3, and use this to check their calculation.

Laying the foundations for algebra

Algebra is a compact language which follows precise conventions and rules. Formal algebra does not begin until Key Stage 3 but you need to lay the foundations in Key Stages 1 and 2 by providing early algebraic activities from which later work in algebra can develop. These activities include:

- **Forming equations** When you are questioning your class you might at times ask them to give more than single word or single number answers. For example, you might sometimes expect the response to short questions such as: 'What is 16 add 8?' to be expressed as a complete statement: 'sixteen add eight equals twenty-four', which children can repeat in chorus. You might also invite a child to the board to write the same equation in symbolic form: $16 + 8 = 24$.
- **Solving equations** By asking questions such as: 'Complete $3 + \square = 10$' you can introduce children to the idea that a symbol can stand for an unknown number. You can also ask questions in the form: 'I double a number, then add 1, and the result is 11. What is the number?' By considering equations with two unknowns, such as $\square + \triangle = 17$, or inequalities like $1 < \square < 6$, you can lead children towards the idea that the unknown is not necessarily one fixed number but may also be a variable.
- **Using inverses** Another important idea in both number and algebra is the use of an inverse to 'reverse' the effect of an operation. For example, the inverse of doubling is halving, of adding 7 is subtracting 7, and of multiplying by 6 is dividing by 6. Once they have grasped this idea, pupils can use their knowledge of an addition fact such as $4 + 7 = 11$ to state a corresponding subtraction fact: $11 - 7 = 4$. Similarly, pupils should be able to use their knowledge of a multiplication fact such as $9 \times 6 = 54$ to derive quickly a corresponding division fact: $54 \div 6 = 9$.
- **Identifying number patterns** Encourage children to look for and describe number patterns as accurately as they can in words and, in simple cases, to consider why the pattern happens. For example, they could explore the patterns made by multiples of 4 or 5 in a 10 by 10 tables square, or extend and describe simple number sequences such as 2, 7, 12, 17... and, where appropriate, describe and discuss how they would set about finding, say, the 20th term.
- **Expressing relationships** When discussing graphs drawn, say, in science, ask children to describe in their own words the relationships revealed: for instance, 'every time we added another 20 grams the length of the elastic increased by 6 centimetres'. They can also be asked to use and make their own simple word equations to express relationships such as:

  $$\text{cost} = \text{number} \times \text{price}$$

  By Year 6, pupils should be ready to express relationships symbolically: for example, if cakes cost 25p each then $c = 25 \times n$, where c pence is the total cost and n is the number of cakes.
- **Drawing graphs** As well as drawing graphs which display factual information, teach older pupils to draw and use graphs which show mathematical relationships, such as those of the multiplication tables, or conversions from pounds to foreign currency. Games like Battleships can be used to introduce the idea of co-ordinates to identify spaces and, later, single points. It is then possible to record graphically, for example, pairs of numbers that add up to 10.

- **Developing ideas of continuity** Another foundation stone for algebra is laid in Years 5 and 6 when you help children to appreciate that between any two decimal numbers there is always another, and that the number line is continuous. They also need to understand that quantities like heights and weights are never exact. In growing from 150 cm to 151 cm, say, every possible value in that interval has been attained because measures too are continuous.
- **Finding equivalent forms** You should emphasise from the very beginning the different ways of recording what is effectively the same thing. For example:
  - $24 = 20 + 4 = 30 - 6$;
  - $30 = 6 \times 5 = 3 \times 2 \times 5$;
  - $15 + 4 = 19$ implies that $15 = 19 - 4$, and $3 \times 4 = 12$ implies that $12 \div 3 = 4$;
  - $\frac{1}{2} = \frac{2}{4} = \frac{3}{6}$... and each of these is equivalent to 0.5 or 50%.
- **Factorising numbers** Factorising 30 as $2 \times 3 \times 5$ is a precursor of the idea of factorising in algebra. It is also a useful strategy for multiplication and division. For example, since $12 = 6 \times 2$, the product 15×12 can be calculated in two steps, first $15 \times 6 = 90$, then $90 \times 2 = 180$. Similarly, $273 \div 21$ can be worked out by using the factors of 21, first $273 \div 3 = 91$, then $91 \div 7 = 13$.

  Encourage pupils to factorise numbers as far as is possible. To factorise 24 as 6×4 is not as complete as $2 \times 2 \times 2 \times 3$.
- **Understanding the commutative, associative and distributive laws** Pupils do not need to know the names of these laws but you need to discuss the ideas thoroughly since they underpin strategies for calculation and, later on, algebraic ideas.

  Children use the commutative law when they change the order of numbers to be added or multiplied because they recognise from practical experience that, say:

  $4 + 8 = 8 + 4$ and $2 \times 7 = 7 \times 2$

  The associative law is used when numbers to be added or multiplied are regrouped without changing their order: for example,

  $(4 + 3) + 7 = 4 + (3 + 7)$ and $(9 \times 5) \times 2 = 9 \times (5 \times 2)$

  An example of the distributive law would be a strategy for calculating 99×8:

  $99 \times 8 = (100 - 1) \times 8 = 100 \times 8 - 8$

  Another example of the distributive law is a method for 'long multiplication' which prepares the way for the standard written method. In this multiplication method each part of the first number is multiplied by each part of the second, and then the products are added to find their total. So 35×24 is split up as:

	30	5
20	600	100
4	120	20

  $600 + 100 + 120 + 20 = 840$

  As well as illustrating clearly how the multiplication method works, this method provides a foundation for the later idea of multiplying out a pair of brackets:

  $(30 + 5)(20 + 4) = (30 \times 20) + (5 \times 20) + (30 \times 4) + (5 \times 4)$

Pupils who have a secure understanding of all these important ideas by the age of 11 will be in a sound position to start work on more formal algebra in Key Stage 3.

Teaching mathematics

The approach to teaching recommended by the National Numeracy Strategy is based on four key principles:

- dedicated mathematics lessons every day;
- direct teaching and interactive oral work with the whole class and groups;
- an emphasis on mental calculation;
- controlled differentiation, with all pupils engaged in mathematics relating to a common theme.

This section and the next, 'School and class organisation: some questions answered', give you, as a class teacher, some practical guidance on how to put this approach into practice.

Teaching time

To ensure that there is adequate time for developing numeracy skills, each class teacher is expected to provide a daily lesson for mathematics, which should last about 45 minutes in Key Stage 1 and 50 to 60 minutes in Key Stage 2.

It is also important to find time in other subjects for pupils to develop and apply their mathematical skills. For example, you could plan regular opportunities for measuring in science and design and technology, using properties of shapes and patterns in art, and collecting and presenting data in history, geography and ICT (see also 'Making links between mathematics and other subjects', on pages 16 and 17).

You will also need to build in time to discuss progress with individual pupils (see the section on assessment starting on page 33).

The focus on direct teaching

During each lesson you should aim to spend as much time as possible in direct teaching and questioning of the whole class, a group of pupils, or individuals.

High-quality direct teaching is oral, interactive and lively. It is not achieved by adopting a simplistic formula of 'drill and practice' and lecturing the class, or by expecting pupils to teach themselves from books. It is a two-way process in which pupils are expected to play an active part by answering questions, contributing points to discussions, and explaining and demonstrating their methods to the class.

Good direct teaching is achieved by balancing different elements:

- **Directing:** sharing your teaching objectives with the class, ensuring that pupils know what to do, and drawing attention to points over which they should take particular care, such as how a graph should be labelled, the degree of accuracy needed when making a measurement, or how work can be set out…
- **Instructing:** giving information and structuring it well: for example, describing how to multiply a three-digit number by a two-digit number, how to interpret a graph, how to develop a mathematical argument…

- **Demonstrating:** showing, describing and modelling mathematics using appropriate resources and visual displays: for example, showing how to scribe numerals, showing how to measure using a metre stick or a protractor, demonstrating on a number line how to add on by bridging through 10, using a thermometer to demonstrate the use of negative numbers…
- **Explaining and illustrating:** giving accurate, well-paced explanations, and referring to previous work or methods: for example, explaining a method of calculation and discussing why it works, giving the meaning of a mathematical term, explaining the steps in the solution to a problem, giving examples that satisfy a general statement, illustrating how the statement $7 - 3 = 4$ can represent different situations…
- **Questioning and discussing:** questioning in ways which match the direction and pace of the lesson and ensure that all pupils take part (if needed, supported by apparatus or a communication aid, or by an adult who translates, signs or uses symbols), listening carefully to pupils' responses and responding constructively in order to take forward their learning, using open and closed questions, skilfully framed, adjusted and targeted to make sure that pupils of all abilities are involved and contribute to discussions, allowing pupils time to think through answers before inviting a response…
- **Consolidating:** maximising opportunities to reinforce and develop what has been taught, through a variety of activities in class and well-focused tasks to do at home, asking pupils either with a partner or as a group to reflect on and talk through a process, inviting them to expand their ideas and reasoning, or to compare and then refine their methods and ways of recording their work, getting them to think of different ways of approaching a problem, asking them to generalise or to give examples that match a general statement…
- **Evaluating pupils' responses:** identifying mistakes, using them as positive teaching points by talking about them and any misconceptions that led to them, discussing pupils' justifications of the methods or resources they have chosen, evaluating pupils' presentations of their work to the class, giving them oral feedback on their written work…
- **Summarising:** reviewing during and towards the end of a lesson the mathematics that has been taught and what pupils have learned, identifying and correcting misunderstandings, inviting pupils to present their work and picking out key points and ideas, making links to other work in mathematics and other subjects, giving pupils an insight into the next stage of their learning…

Direct teaching and good interaction are as important in group work and paired work as they are in whole-class work but organising pupils as a 'whole class' for a significant proportion of the time helps to maximise their contact with you so that every child benefits from the teaching and interaction for sustained periods.

Class organisation

From Year 1, all pupils should have a dedicated mathematics lesson every day, so that work is not mixed with other subjects as it is in an 'integrated day' approach. Direct teaching is not compatible with an integrated day. If you spent your time teaching and interacting with each group doing mathematics throughout an integrated day, there would be little time for direct teaching of any other subject.

Dedicated lessons also make it easier for you to secure a good balance between whole-class work, group teaching and individual practice, and to make the most of any support for mathematics from classroom assistants. Dedicated lessons allow you to establish routines that pupils get used to, so that you can maximise the time you spend teaching the class, as against managing it. The overall pattern of lessons will generally be the same for all classes so you will also have a common structure for developing ideas and sharing planning and teaching with other colleagues.

Teaching in Reception is discussed in question 8 of the next section (pages 26–29).

A typical lesson

A typical 45 to 60 minute lesson in Years 1 to 6 will be structured like this:

- **oral work and mental calculation** (about 5 to 10 minutes)
  whole-class work to rehearse, sharpen and develop mental and oral skills
- **the main teaching activity** (about 30 to 40 minutes)
  teaching input and pupil activities
  work as a whole class, in groups, in pairs or as individuals
- **a plenary** to round off the lesson (about 10 to 15 minutes)
  work with the whole class to sort out misconceptions and identify progress, to summarise key facts and ideas and what to remember, to make links to other work and discuss the next steps, and to set work to do at home

Oral work and mental calculation

The first 5 to 10 minutes of a lesson can be used in a variety of ways to rehearse and sharpen skills, sometimes focusing on the skills that will be needed in the main part of the lesson. On different days you might choose to do one or more of these:

- counting in steps of different sizes, including chanting as a whole class and counting round the class;
- practising mental calculations and the rapid recall of number facts in varied ways (for example, by playing an interactive number game, by giving examples of 'a number one less than a multiple of 5' or 'a calculation with the answer 12');
- figuring out new facts from known facts and explaining the strategies used;
- building on a previous strategy, and then developing it;
- identifying facts which children can learn by heart and discussing ways of remembering them;
- reviewing an activity done at home.

In this first part of the lesson you need to:

- get off to a clear start and maintain a brisk pace;
- provide a variety of short oral and mental activities throughout each week;
- prepare a good range of open and closed questions to ask the class;
- ensure that all children can see you easily and can and do take part;
- target individuals, pairs or small groups with particular questions;
- use pupils' responses to make an informal assessment of their progress;
- brief any support staff to position themselves and give discreet help to any children who need particular support;
- avoid disruption from too much movement of pupils about the room;
- avoid running over time and move smoothly to the next part of the lesson.

The main teaching input and pupil activities

The main part of the lesson provides time for:

- ◆ introducing a new topic, consolidating previous work or extending it;
- ◆ developing vocabulary, using correct notation and terms and learning new ones;
- ◆ using and applying concepts and skills.

In this part of the lesson you need to:

- ◆ make clear to the class what they will learn;
- ◆ make links to previous lessons, or to work in other subjects;
- ◆ tell pupils what work they will do, how long it should take, what, if anything, they need to prepare for the plenary session and how they are to present it;
- ◆ maintain pace and give pupils a deadline for completing their work.

When you are working directly with the **whole class** you need to:

- ◆ demonstrate and explain using a board, flip chart, computer or OHP;
- ◆ involve pupils interactively through carefully planned questioning;
- ◆ ensure that pupils with particular learning needs in mathematics are supported effectively with appropriate resources and wall displays, and adult help;
- ◆ identify and correct any misunderstandings or forgotten ideas, using mistakes as positive teaching points;
- ◆ highlight the meaning of any new vocabulary, notation or terms, and get pupils to repeat these and use them in their discussions and written work;
- ◆ ask pupils to offer their methods and solutions to the whole class for discussion.

When you are working directly with **groups** you need to:

- ◆ have a manageable number of groups (usually a maximum of four), so that you know what each group should be doing at any time;
- ◆ decide how groups will be introduced to tasks and how the group work will end;
- ◆ control the degree of differentiation (for example, provide tasks on the same theme and usually at no more than three levels of difficulty);
- ◆ provide activities, tasks and resources that don't involve children in a long wait for turns and which keep them all interested, motivated and on-task;
- ◆ sit and work intensively with one or two of the groups, not flit between them all;
- ◆ brief any support staff or adult helpers about their role, making sure that they have plenty to do with the pupils they are assisting and will not interrupt you;
- ◆ avoid interruption by pupils by making sure that those working independently in a group know where to find further resources, what to do before asking you for help and what to do if they finish early.

When you are providing work for **individuals or pairs** you need to:

- ◆ keep the class working on related activities, exercises or problems;
- ◆ target individuals or pairs for particular questioning and support;
- ◆ during paired work, encourage discussion and co-operation between pupils.

The plenary session

The plenary is an important part of the lesson. It is a time when you can help pupils to assess their developing knowledge and skills against any targets they have been set and to see for themselves the progress they are making. It is also a time when you can relate mathematics to their work in other subjects: for example, how their work on calculation will be used in science, or how their measuring skills will be practised in physical education.

For example, this part of the lesson can be used to:

- ask pupils to present and explain their work, or mark a written exercise done individually during the lesson, so that you can question pupils about it, assess it informally and rectify any misconceptions or errors;
- discuss and compare the efficiency of pupils' different methods of calculation;
- help pupils to generalise a rule from examples generated by different groups, pairs or individuals;
- draw together what has been learned, reflect on what was important about the lesson, summarise key facts, ideas and vocabulary, and what needs to be remembered;
- discuss the problems that can be solved using the ideas and skills that have been learned;
- make links to other work and discuss briefly what the class will go on to do next;
- remind pupils about their personal targets and highlight the progress made;
- provide tasks for pupils to do at home to extend or consolidate their class work.

In this part of the lesson you need to:

- have a clear idea of the purpose of the plenary session and what you want to achieve in it;
- make sure that the main part of the lesson does not over-run, so that there is enough time for the plenary;
- plan carefully how pupils are to present their work, if they are to do this, and how long it will take;
- bring the lesson to a close and evaluate its success.

The outline structure of a typical lesson should not be seen as a mechanistic recipe to be followed. You should use your professional judgement to determine the activities, timing and organisation of each part of the lesson to suit its objectives.

In the main part of the lesson, in particular, there is scope for considerable variety and creativity, with a different mix of work with the whole class, groups, pairs and individuals on different days, although each lesson should include direct teaching and interaction with the pupils, and activities or exercises that pupils do. Overall, there should be a high proportion of work with the whole class but there may be more in some lessons than in others. For example, at the start of a new unit of work you might need more time for explanation and discussion with everyone together for the whole lesson, and the plenary may be very short. On the other hand, where you have identified general errors or misunderstanding during the main part of a lesson, you might need a longer plenary to sort them out. At the end of a unit of work it can be useful to use the plenary to look back with the whole class over a number of lessons to draw together what has been learned and to identify the key points and methods that you want pupils to remember and use in the future. For this kind of plenary session, you may need a much longer time than usual.

Out-of-class work and homework

Your daily mathematics lessons provide opportunities for children to practise and consolidate their skills and knowledge, to develop and extend their techniques and strategies, and to prepare for their future learning. You can extend these opportunities through out-of-class activities or homework.

Not all out-of-class work needs to be written work which then has to be marked. You can equally well ask your class to:

- do an activity which makes use of the home context, such as tipping out a purse and counting what is in it, or weighing things on the kitchen or bathroom scales;
- play a number game or work on a number puzzle;
- learn some number facts or multiplication tables by heart;
- gather information to use in the next lesson: for example, collect data or take measurements;
- think about how they might solve a problem;
- prepare their contribution to a group presentation to the class.

For older children, work outside the normal lesson can be completing a short written exercise or task which consolidates and develops from work done in class, with modifications of the presentation for any children who need them (see question 2 in 'School and class organisation: some questions answered', pages 19 and 20). You then need to mark the work promptly and thoroughly so you can give children some feedback on their progress. For example, an exercise at the end of a unit of work, or a few days after it, and which pupils do independently, can give you useful diagnostic information on who has learned what and who needs extra support. Sometimes you might set a quiz with a mix of short questions which you expect children to do quickly and successfully. At the start of the next lesson you can read out answers and children can mark their own work. You should then go through any questions that proved to be difficult.

Out-of-class activities need to be frequent, short and focused. They should be varied, interesting and fun so that they motivate children, stimulate their learning and foster different study skills.

But whatever work you set, you should give children feedback to show them that their work is important and their efforts are valued. You should also indicate whether and how their work might be improved. For example, you might discuss a problem briefly in the plenary part of a lesson and ask the children to tackle it in preparation for the next lesson. This could start with sharing and refining methods and solutions, which are then used to inform the main teaching activity, when you give similar or linked problems to each group. Or you could use the plenary to introduce a game which helps children to practise the recall of number facts and which they can play with their families or friends. In the mental and oral work at the start of the next lesson you could focus on the recall of these facts, so that you can see through your interactions with the children which of them have good recall and which need some additional support.

Making links between mathematics and other subjects

You need to look for opportunities for drawing mathematical experience out of a wide range of children's activities. Mathematics contributes to many subjects of the primary curriculum, often in practical ways. Activities such as recording the growth of a plant or an animal, measuring temperature and rainfall, or investigating the cog wheels in a bicycle can provide data or starting points for discussion in your mathematics lessons as well as opportunities to apply and use mathematics in real contexts.

English Mathematics lessons can help to develop and support pupils' literacy skills: for example, by teaching mathematical vocabulary and technical terms, by asking children to read and interpret problems to identify the mathematical content, and by encouraging them to explain, argue and present their conclusions to others. Equally, the literacy hour can support your daily mathematics lesson. For example, in Reception and Key Stage 1, stories, rhymes and songs can be chosen which rely for their appeal on the pleasure of counting, the sequencing of events, and the use of everyday words such as 'on' and 'under', 'up' and 'down' to describe position or direction. In Key Stage 2, the literacy hour can be used to read non-fiction in which mathematical vocabulary, graphs, charts and tables have to be interpreted.

Science Almost every scientific investigation or experiment is likely to require one or more of the mathematical skills of classifying, counting, measuring, calculating, estimating, and recording in tables and graphs. In science pupils will, for example, order numbers, including decimals, calculate simple means and percentages, use negative numbers when taking temperatures, decide whether it is more appropriate to use a line graph or bar chart, and plot, interpret and predict from graphs.

Art, design and technology Measurements are often needed in art and design and technology. Many patterns and constructions are based on spatial ideas and properties of shapes, including symmetry. Designs may need enlarging or reducing, introducing ideas of multiplication and ratio. When food is prepared a great deal of measurement occurs, including working out times and calculating cost; this may not be straightforward if only part of a packet of ingredients has been used.

Information and communications technology Children will apply and use mathematics in a variety of ways when they solve problems using ICT. For example, they will collect and classify data, enter it into data handling software, produce graphs and tables, and interpret and explain their results. Their work in control includes the measurement of distance and angle, using uniform non-standard then standard measures. When they use computer models and simulations they will draw on their abilities to manipulate numbers and identify patterns and relationships.

History, geography and religious education In history and geography children will collect data by counting and measuring and make use of measurements of many kinds. The study of maps includes the use of co-ordinates and ideas of angle, direction, position, scale and ratio. The pattern of the days of the week, the calendar and recurring annual festivals all have a mathematical basis. For older children historical ideas require understanding of the passage of time, which can be illustrated on a time line, similar to the number line that they already know.

Physical education and music Athletic activities require measurement of height, distance and time, while ideas of counting, time, symmetry, movement, position and direction are used extensively in music, dance, gymnastics and ball games.

The key to making the most of all these opportunities is to identify the mathematical possibilities across the curriculum at the planning stage. You should also draw children's attention to the links between subjects by talking frequently about them, both in mathematics and in other lessons.

School and class organisation: some questions answered

1 Can we plan work for groups of children?

All pupils gain from working in groups, in pairs or as individuals from time to time.

Whether you have group work may depend on where you are in a series of lessons. For example, you might introduce a new unit of work with a main teaching activity that is mostly with the whole class while you explain, demonstrate, ask questions and discuss answers. Short tasks for pupils to do, perhaps in pairs, and a short written exercise that children tackle individually, may also be appropriate in this lesson. Another possibility when you introduce a new unit of work is to begin the main part of the lesson with some teaching input to the whole class, then to start the more confident pupils on an activity or exercise while you continue to teach the rest. When they too are ready to work independently, set them going while you support the one or two pupils who are likely to have the most difficulty with the task.

In the next couple of lessons, the main activity might consist of group work on the same theme, although your lesson will still begin and end with the whole class. Occasionally, group work should allow pupils at all levels of attainment to work with each other on an equal footing, but grouping pupils by attainment – perhaps two groups in the middle range, one of higher achievers and one of those who find mathematics more difficult – allows for a controlled degree of differentiated work on the topic being taught to the whole class, with a simplified task for some pupils and a harder challenge for others.

If, for example, you have four groups, you can teach two of them during a lesson for about 15 minutes each, giving positive direction and guidance; in the next lesson you can teach the other two groups. In the groups working independently children can, of course, work on the group task as individuals or in smaller groups of up to four. In your plenary, if different groups are giving feedback, they have a common interest since they have all been working on the same topic, albeit at different levels of difficulty. You can draw together ideas that all pupils have worked on and make an informal assessment of their understanding to help you plan the next lesson.

The final lesson of a unit of work might centre around one or more open-ended problems, games or puzzles for the whole class which allow responses at different levels. After you have introduced an activity to everyone, children can continue it in pairs. During the paired work you can support and teach particular pairs or individuals you wish to target, such as pupils who have been absent.

You need to prepare your class for these ways of working, so that pupils and adult helpers don't interrupt you when you are teaching a group. Pupils need to know how their lesson time is to be used and what routines they should follow when they are working independently before they ask an adult for help: for example, how to collect and return any resources that they need, what to do if they have finished something or are 'stuck', and so on. There may also be implications for how you arrange tables and chairs (see question 9, page 29).

2 Are there other ways of providing differentiated work?

The children in each class should, as far as possible, work together through the year's programme described in the Framework, so that all children participate when a new unit of work starts and can take part in the plenary. When classes taking part in the National Numeracy Project were taught in this way, all groups of pupils made significant progress, including the most able, but those who made more progress relative to other groups were the pupils who initially had achieved the lowest test scores.

There are several ways in which the needs of particular pupils can be met, partly through the differentiated group work and open-ended tasks described under question 1, and partly through other teaching strategies.

Differentiation during whole-class oral work

For your daily session of oral work and mental calculation with the whole class, think about the questions you will ask, planning some with particular children in mind. Your first few questions might be at a level that all children can manage, to get them involved and interested. When children are counting round the class, for example, you might point to the child who should say the next number; for the smaller, easier numbers point to those who tend to struggle and leave larger, harder numbers for higher achievers. When you are directing questions to the whole class, build in enough 'wait time' for all children to think before expecting the class as a whole to answer your questions. This benefits everyone. Ask the whole class to repeat a correct answer together using a complete sentence, so that all pupils, including those learning English as an additional language or with special educational needs, get to say larger numbers aloud and use mathematical vocabulary correctly.

You can also use open questions that allow all children to take part: for example, 'What numbers can you make using each of the digits 2, 3 and 4 once, and any operations?' Encourage the class to discuss their answers in pairs before they give you a response. You can also target individuals or groups: 'Louise, can you make 9?' 'Winston, can you make 17?' 'Can this group make 5 in three different ways?'

Even closed questions such as 'What is 30×25?' can be opened up by discussing the methods used. For example, some pupils may first do 3×25 and then multiply the result by 10, others may do 30×20 first and then add 30×5, while others may multiply 30 by 100 then divide the result by 4. Some may be helped by jotting down the interim stages of these calculations, while some will be able to do the entire calculation mentally. The answer $30 \times 25 = 750$ can lead to discussion of other statements that can now be deduced, such as 3×25, or 300×25, or $750 \div 30$, …

It is important that all pupils can take part in the discussion. Make sure that they can all see or hear what is being done, and can respond orally, or through number cards, symbols or tactile materials, or with support from an adult.

Differentiation during written work or homework

There are several ways in which the presentation of written work or homework can be adapted to suit particular needs, without varying either the task or the level of difficulty. For example, it can be presented on an audio tape rather than a written page, or in enlarged print or by using tactile materials. For some children all that is needed is simplified vocabulary, or extra diagrams or illustrations to illuminate key points. Others may need the task broken down into a series of guided steps. There may also be children who continue to need apparatus to support their thinking while others manage without. For instance, with the addition and subtraction of larger numbers, some children will continue to use a number line, while others will already be able to do the calculations mentally. The freedom for children to choose their own support materials is therefore important, and you should ensure that suitable resources are on hand. At the same time you need to encourage them to dispense with the apparatus when you judge that they are ready.

Some children work faster than others, perhaps because they use short-cuts, or are generally more confident and more able. They may need to do fewer examples and be moved on to extension or enrichment tasks linked to the theme of the lesson so that they use and apply their skills in more challenging contexts, including those which ICT can offer. Others may need longer to practise and consolidate what they have been learning. For them, problems in which they use and apply skills, and the use of ICT, are also an important part of their learning, but the problems may need to be simpler and sometimes left until later in a unit of work, or when a unit is revisited, or in extra time outside the lesson.

3 Should we set the pupils for mathematics lessons?

Larger schools with parallel classes sometimes deal with a range of attainment by organising 'ability sets' for mathematics lessons. The advantage is that planning can be easier if the attainment gap in a class is not too wide. It is also possible to set across, say, Years 5 and 6, if both years are timetabled for their mathematics lessons at the same time, although you need to ensure that when the Year 5 pupils move into Year 6 they do not simply repeat the previous year's activities.

Any setting arrangements need to be flexible to allow easy transfer of pupils between sets. On its own, setting does not necessarily help to close the attainment gap across the year group over time. Children are quick to spot and interpret the significance of this kind of provision.

The success of setting depends on very careful monitoring, close team work and co-operative planning among staff to make sure that expectations for all pupils are suitably high and that lower expectations are not justified simply because pupils are in a 'lower set'. Governors and parents need to know why classes are set for mathematics, especially if pupils are not taught in sets for other subjects.

As standards improve over time, the range of attainment in each year group ought to reduce so that it becomes possible to cater for the diversity of needs by grouping pupils within the same class.

4 How can we cater for pupils who are very able?

Nearly all able pupils will be taught with their own class, whether it be a higher-ability set or a mixed-ability class. They can be stretched through differentiated group work, harder problems for homework, and extra challenges – including investigations using ICT – which they do towards the end of a unit of work when other pupils are doing consolidation exercises.

When you are working with the whole class, you can direct some questions towards the most able pupils, just as you can direct some specifically towards the children who find mathematics most difficult.

The yearly teaching programmes described in the Framework leave about one week in each term unallocated, when pupils who are very able can, for example, carry out a sustained mathematical investigation and continue it at home. There are many good publications to support this kind of work and schools with access to the Internet can also download suitable material from a problem-solving web-site.

Pupils who are exceptionally gifted in many subjects, and who are sufficiently mature, are sometimes promoted to work with an older age group. They are able to deal with abstract mathematics much earlier than other children and, for them, some acceleration is desirable. Very occasionally, a pupil is exceptionally gifted in mathematics, but not in other subjects. Special arrangements are sometimes made for these pupils. For example, by timetabling Year 3 and Year 4 mathematics lessons at the same time, an exceptionally gifted pupil in Year 3 can be taught the subject with the Year 4 class and benefit from discussion with other pupils working at a similar level. Where this is not possible, exceptionally gifted pupils can follow individualised programmes at appropriate times in the daily mathematics lesson, with far fewer practice examples and many more challenging problems to tackle.

5 How do we cater for pupils with particular needs?

The daily mathematics lesson is appropriate for almost all pupils. You should aim to ensure that everyone makes progress and gains positively from the lesson, and to plan lessons so that all pupils can be included, rather than over-differentiate.

Individual needs do not necessarily warrant individual attention. The needs of pupils regarded as 'special' are not essentially different from those of other children. Instead of focusing on differences, you might emphasise the links with the needs of all learners, and use them productively to improve learning opportunities for all children. The key things are to give greater emphasis to children's language during mathematics lessons and to encourage all pupils to learn by working together.

All children can benefit from oral work. In whole-class sessions, plan some questions specifically for pupils at the earlier stages of learning English as an additional language (EAL), and others for those with special educational needs (SEN), and ask named children to respond. At times you may want to place those with particular needs close to you, so that they can be given some discreet help: for example, when children discuss an answer in pairs before responding. Pupils with hearing impairments may also need to sit closer to you, or be helped to take part in the activity through signing or support given by another adult.

Reading difficulties or lack of familiarity with English can slow some children's progress with mathematics. Use flash cards and illustrated wall displays to show the specific mathematical vocabulary for a unit of work. Minimise any written instructions and explanations on worksheets and written exercises. Remember that mathematics has a strong visual element and capitalise on this wherever you can to illuminate meaning. Make frequent use of a number line, 100 square, number apparatus, pictures, diagrams, graphs, computer programs... and games and puzzles where the rules are picked up quickly by watching a demonstration.

Teachers can involve and support all pupils through the strategies for differentiation described under questions 1 and 2 (see pages 18–20). Beyond this, the assumption is that appropriate support will be dedicated to help those pupils who need it to make progress at the appropriate rate. You should take quick action to help them, as it is much easier to catch children early on than to struggle later with a backlog of problems. Use the dedicated time each half term to assess and review children's progress and make sure that the key learning objectives are secure. Use the week of unallocated teaching time each term for extra consolidation for pupils who need it, focusing on the misconceptions or weaknesses you have identified. You could also aim to recruit parents to help their children in specific ways.

Where schools are able to offer lunch-time or after-school activities, teachers or other adults might offer extra support so that particular pupils can either be prepared for or consolidate their learning from the daily lesson. For example, pupils with hearing impairments, or EAL pupils, could be introduced to the new vocabulary they will meet in the next week's oral work; mentoring sessions may be needed for children whose behaviour causes concern; others may benefit from practising skills and making individual use of suitable computer software.

Other points related to pupils learning English as an additional language

Take care not to underestimate what children can do mathematically simply because they are new learners of the English language. The expectation should be that they progress in their mathematical learning at the same rate as other pupils of their age. Whole-class sessions can provide helpful adult models of spoken English, and opportunities for careful listening, oral exchange and supportive, shared repetition. Group work provides opportunities for intensive, focused teaching input. You will probably need to repeat instructions for EAL pupils and to speak more clearly, emphasising key words, particularly when you are describing tasks that they are to do independently. Put picture cues on worksheets or puzzle cards and simplify the words used, but not the mathematics (except where an EAL pupil also has special educational needs that warrant this).

Peer-group talk is important in helping children to make sense of and apply mathematical ideas. It helps if English language beginners can converse with other children or adults who speak the same home language when they are doing practical group activities, playing mathematical games or working with a computer.

Don't ask individual children who are in the early stages of learning English as an additional language to present their work orally before they are ready. Allow them time to watch and listen to those fluent in English explaining and demonstrating their methods to the class using a board or flip chart. Invite them too to demonstrate, on the board or with apparatus – they will often show capabilities that are as good if not better than their peers – but without any pressure to accompany their demonstration with an oral explanation in English before they are ready.

Encourage them to join in things that all children do in chorus: counting, reading aloud whole number sentences, chanting, finger games, songs about numbers, and so on. The structure of rhymes, and the natural rhythm in songs and poems, play an important part in developing number sense in any culture. Try to use stories and rhymes that will support access to meaning for pupils from a range of cultural backgrounds. As soon as English language beginners are reasonably confident at saying something together with others, ask them to say it again on their own. Give them plenty of time and much praise for doing so, and also check for understanding.

Emphasise the importance early on of children learning to understand, say, read and write numbers in English, also signs such as plus (+) and minus (–) and words such as 'add' and 'subtract'. They may well be familiar with the meanings of such words in their home language. Get them to show the class the ways that numbers are spoken and written in their home language, and to demonstrate any board games or playground games that they know and which involve numbers. Children who speak and read only English are often fascinated by the similarities with the number system that they are familiar with and they too gain from the experience.

Pupils with special educational needs and individual education plans

All teachers will have in their class some children whose progress warrants special consideration. Their difficulties may have physical, sensory, behavioural, emotional or neurological causes, or may stem from a legacy of poor learning that inhibits their current learning. Some of the one in six pupils identified by primary schools as having special educational needs may have problems with mathematics, often but not always in association with literacy problems caused by difficulties of varying degrees of complexity. It is not possible in this document to give detailed advice covering every type of special educational need, but as a general guide you should aim to include all these pupils fully in your daily mathematics lesson, so that they benefit from the emphasis on oral and mental work and participating in watching and listening to other children demonstrating and explaining their methods.

For example, there is no good reason why pupils with physical or sensory disabilities should work on any sort of separate programme. For most of them it is simply a question of access, and materials, equipment and furniture should be adapted to meet their particular needs so that they can work alongside their peers. They need to work on the objectives for their year if these are within their grasp, with the emphasis on access and support. Adaptations that may be necessary are, for example, preparation for the oral and mental part of the lesson and the pace at which it is conducted, the use of signing, Braille and symbols, and the provision of a range of tactile materials, technological aids and adapted measuring equipment.

Pupils with emotional or behavioural difficulties can benefit from the structure and routines of the daily mathematics lesson. Adaptations are usually needed during the main teaching activity, with a shorter time for independent group work if adult support is not available. Learning to work independently with increasing self-confidence is important for these pupils but it has to be introduced slowly, cultivated deliberately and rewarded. Tasks and timings are critical; you need to consider them carefully if you are to maintain the pupils' motivation and interest.

Where pupils' learning difficulties extend to mathematics, use the Framework to identify suitable objectives to be incorporated into individual education plans (IEPs), tracking back to earlier stages if it is appropriate to do so. Keep these objectives in mind when you are planning group work, when you can address special needs through simplified or modified tasks and the use of support staff to consolidate key points. Where appropriate, you could develop a more manageable 'group education plan' with common objectives and learning targets for a group.

A pupil whose difficulties are severe or complex may need to be supported with an individualised programme in the main part of a lesson. Consult any staff who are giving support to the pupil, then use your judgement to decide whether this is appropriate, bearing in mind the lesson's aims and the short-term aims in the IEP.

Spell out in all pupils' IEPs not only who will provide adult support but when and how it will be used. For example, children with hearing impairments may need an adult to prepare them for whole-class oral work and sign for them during it, or those with learning difficulties may need to be guided during group work in the use of apparatus to support their thinking. IEPs which address behavioural issues can set useful objectives about appropriate behaviour in independent group time.

How can the Framework be used in special schools?

Many of the Framework's principles are applicable to special schools, such as planning from clear teaching objectives, with an emphasis in lessons on oral work and mental calculation, visual interest, involvement and interaction, and keeping pupils working together as far as possible. Special schools are encouraged to adopt the Framework but should also adapt arrangements to suit their particular circumstances.

For example, the notion of 'whole-class teaching' can be modified, as it is different when there are 10 to 14 pupils in a class, and the teacher is at times supported by other staff. There may be times when all the pupils are taught together for their daily mathematics lesson, just as in a mainstream school, but others when two 'whole-class lessons' are taking place in the same room, with the class teacher teaching one half of the class, and a support assistant working with the other half.

It is possible that in some special schools all or nearly all of the pupils in a class have learning difficulties that extend to mathematics. In this case it may be best to base the work for Key Stages 1 and 2 on the teaching programmes for Reception and Years 1 to 2, taking two years to cover what will be taught in one year in a mainstream school. Extra 'small steps' can be inserted, and contexts for practical work and problem-solving adapted for the pupils' ages. There will then be plenty of time for consolidation without sacrificing the breadth of the teaching programmes or the principle of planning from clearly defined objectives. The routine of the daily mathematics lesson is best built up over a period of weeks. Aim first to establish the daily oral and mental work. Then introduce routines for the main part of the lesson and the plenary, concentrating on a strong oral or communication technique that promotes interaction, combined with a good range of practical activities.

Similar principles apply where pupils have severe learning difficulties. The pupils may first need to work at levels earlier than those in the Framework, and then have further extensions to the pace at which the yearly teaching programmes are covered and to the extra 'small steps'.

6 How is it best to use classroom assistants, including support for SEN and EAL?

The role of support staff is to help you make sure that each child plays a full part in every lesson. You should give them copies of this Framework and involve them in planning lessons. You will need to brief them very thoroughly about each lesson and their particular role in it. Make sure that they know not only what children are to do but what children are to learn. Draw their attention to the booklet *Mathematical*

Vocabulary (see page 3) and identify the words they might focus on in a particular unit of work.

During any whole-class oral work, ask support staff to position themselves close to any children who need special help and provide this discreetly by, for example:

- prompting shy or reticent pupils;
- signing or translating core vocabulary or phrases;
- helping children to use specific individual resources to find an answer, such as personal number cards or table-top number lines;
- operating individualised ICT resources as indicated in children's IEPs.

They should also observe carefully the responses of the children they will be working with later in the lesson to inform the support they will give.

If you have a general classroom assistant and are organising group work with four groups in the main part of the lesson, explain that you will work with two of the groups, and that the assistant should oversee the other two. Ask the assistant to:

- ensure that children interpret instructions correctly, concentrate and behave responsibly;
- remind children of teaching points made earlier in the lesson;
- question children and encourage their participation (you will need to suggest the questions and prompts that would be appropriate, and any particular children whom they should focus on);
- look for and note any common difficulties that children have, or mistakes that they make, so that you can address these in the plenary and in future lessons;
- use and make available to children a number line and/or 100 square, visual or practical aids, or a computer with suitable software, especially when they are helping children with difficulties or misunderstandings.

Include assistants and other adult helpers in whole-school training days and draw their attention to the training offered through the specialist teacher assistant (STA) scheme, if your LEA is taking part in this.

7 How do we organise and plan for mixed-age classes?

Often mixed-age classes are unavoidable because of the size of the school but if there are parallel mixed-age classes in your school you could try to reorganise them for mathematics lessons into year groups or even 'ability sets'. This helps to reduce the attainment gap in each class so that planning is easier for you.

Classes of children from two year groups can be taught in the same way as classes with a single year group. The Framework is designed to make sure that during the main part of the lesson all the children in the class can work on the same topic at the same time, if necessary at different levels during differentiated group work. You can use the termly planning grid for either age group, since there are relatively few changes in the balance of topics from one year to the next, or you can design your own, but choose objectives from the teaching programmes for each of the two years.

When you are questioning the class as a whole, include some questions targeted at individual children, sometimes the younger ones and sometimes the older. When you are organising group work, say with a Year 3 and Year 4 class, aim for four groups, one upper and one middle group for Year 4, and one middle group and one lower group for Year 3. The two middle groups can usually do the same work, so that you still plan activities at three levels. In the following year, when the Year 4 pupils have left the class, the two Year 3 groups are promoted to form a new upper group and one of the middle groups. In this way, they don't repeat activities when you revisit units of work.

Very small schools

In very small schools with three or more year groups in the same class, it is still possible to have a profitable oral and mental starter with the whole class. This can focus on counting and practising mental strategies previously taught to most of the class. You should use the full range of strategies for differentiation described under question 2 (pages 19–20), including open-ended examples that encourage the rehearsal of known number facts, such as: 'Give me two numbers which make …'

When you introduce a new topic in the main part of the lesson, further work with the whole class is sometimes possible. If the range of attainment is too wide, the class can be divided into two for direct teaching purposes. However, older pupils benefit from explaining what they know already about a topic to younger ones, with prompts from the teacher. For them, the whole-class session is useful revision and consolidation. For the younger children the work will be new and demanding, and should be reinforced by further direct teaching. While you do this with the group of younger children, the middle age group can work on an introductory activity. The older, higher-attaining pupils can continue with consolidation exercises based on their previous work on that topic. On the next day you can introduce the older pupils to more advanced work, and then the middle group.

Children in classes of three or more year groups are often allocated to a group according to the activity which is suitable for them rather than their age. It is better to aim for no more than four groups and, as in larger schools, all children should be able to work independently on tasks when you are working with another group. Pupils with special needs may need some adaptations to their group activity, especially if they find recording difficult.

For the plenary, younger children can explain the hardest examples they had to do. Older pupils can be challenged to explain the easiest examples they worked on but in such a way that the youngest pupils can understand. As in other schools, you should establish clearly in the plenary what has been learned, and identify and put right any misunderstandings. Where necessary, hold the plenary with half the class on alternate days. If one half has received most or all of the direct teaching in a particular lesson, then your attention can be given to the other half in the plenary.

The key is flexibility and capitalising on what you have learned from the Literacy Strategy. You need to make arrangements which work for your particular situation, bearing in mind the need for regular opportunities for oral and mental work and sustained direct teaching for all children.

8 How can we work in Reception?

Some children will be just four when they start in Reception in September. Others will start in January or April at rising five and will complete only one or two terms in the class before moving to Year 1. Some will have been to nurseries or playgroups and some will not. Teaching needs to include a wide range of techniques to ensure effective learning for this range.

A Reception class is typically organised to promote the social skills and developing mathematical understanding of young children through stories, songs, rhymes and finger games, board games, sand and water, construction on a large and small scale, imaginative play, outdoor play and 'playground' games, cooking and shopping, two- and three-dimensional creative work with a range of materials, and by observing numbers and patterns in the environment and daily routines.

Given this organisation, your daily mathematics lesson can be planned like this:

- an introduction with the whole class, usually involving some counting, with finger games, number rhymes and songs;
- some teaching of the whole class on the main mathematics topic for the day;
- group activities:

  either for everyone in small groups simultaneously: for example, in an outdoor lesson with skittles, bean bags, hoops... with scoring built into the activities, or in an indoor lesson with shapes to be made from different media;

  or one or more play activities, linked to the theme of the lesson, worked on by groups in turn during the day, usually supported by an adult: for example, exploring 'one more' when buying stamps in the class post office, when finger painting, when making jumps in outdoor play;
- a plenary with the whole class after the group activities are ended, to consolidate and extend through discussion and questioning what they have been learning and to praise progress.

Your aim should be to prepare children, by the end of Reception, for the dedicated mathematics lesson of about 45 minutes that will be part of each day in Year 1. For example, you will need to help them to learn how to listen, how to show and talk about what they have been doing in front of other children, how to find and use the equipment that they need, how to take turns, and so on.

What teaching approaches are appropriate in Reception?

If you base your teaching on the objectives in the Framework for Reception, you can feel confident that you are working towards the Early Learning Goals and preparing children for starting the National Curriculum in Year 1. You can then plan interesting, linked activities and talking points with your chosen objectives in mind. In this way, your teaching is focused on the mathematics and is not left to chance.

On some days you can introduce mathematical ideas because they are interesting and worthwhile in themselves. For example, you might ask all the children to play a game to identify shapes, or a dice game which involves counting or adding. A story such as *The Tiger Who Came to Tea* or *Kipper's Toy Box* could be the focus for a class lesson on counting. Or you might go outside to teach about shape and space by getting children to explore the shapes they make with their bodies, and the space they use in moving. In these lessons, mathematics is the particular focus, and all children work on it at the same time.

On other days you can plan opportunities for learning in contexts which children find relevant and interesting. For example, you might put objects to encourage counting in the sand and water trays, such as speckled frogs, a lily pad and a 'pool'.

An opportunity like this can be introduced to the whole class. In this example, it may be by singing and acting different versions of *Five Little Speckled Frogs*, then showing the frogs in the sand and water trays. After the introduction, small groups can be scheduled to play freely in the 'opportunity' area but you or an assistant need to intervene in the play to question the children and develop their understanding in ways that you have planned in advance.

Ordinary classroom routines such as taking the register, changing for PE or lining up are also good opportunities for counting and reinforcing mathematical ideas. Objects that children bring to school can trigger discussions about numbers or shapes. Capitalise on such opportunities wherever you can to supplement your 'daily mathematics lesson', linking the ideas to other work the children have done.

Where can we start with Reception children?

The supplement of examples for Reception illustrates what a child who reaches the age of 5 in the autumn term, and who spends a full year in the class, should know and be able to do. Variations of knowledge and experience for those who spend less time in the class are kept in mind by the use of expressions such as:

'Begin to...' 'Show awareness of...' 'Start to use in a practical context...'

and by regular revisiting of topics term by term to absorb children who join the class throughout the year.

Because their pre-school experiences are so varied, and because their ages are so relatively different, children will start school with very mixed experiences and understanding. It is better to find out about and build on the awareness children already have than to start with an assumption of a lack of knowledge. Most children will have their own personal experience of numbers, such as the ages of people in their family, their door number, bus number, telephone number, family lottery numbers, the time of their favourite TV programme and their bed time, and so on.

Records from nurseries and playgroups can provide information about the children's performance in relation to the Early Learning Goals. Your school will also have baseline assessments to give you information about each child's starting points. All this is important information on which to build your planning.

You should also listen to what parents tell you about their child's mathematical progress. They are often anxious to know how to help. Keep them fully informed about how their children are being taught and suggest mathematical games and activities that they can play with their child at home. Make sure that each family has copies of *Count and Figure it out Together* distributed by the Basic Skills Agency.

Although there may be differences in the capabilities of a child who has spent a year in Reception and who is nearly six, and one who is just five and has been there for only one term, these differences usually lessen gradually during Key Stage 1.

Forging links with Year 1

Children in Year 1 follow the National Curriculum. Some Reception children may be under statutory school age so the emphasis of the Framework for Reception is different from that for Year 1. It is expected that children in Reception will receive some direct teaching and talk about mathematical ideas, and will explore those ideas through structured play and practical work, sometimes recording informally what they have done with objects or drawings. The main emphasis is on different aspects of counting, such as knowing the number names, putting numbers in order, counting for a purpose, adding and subtracting by counting on and counting back, and so on, with little or no 'reading' or 'writing', other than learning to recognise and trace the first few numerals.

Summer-born children may start school in Year 1 without spending any time in Reception. Year 1 teachers can use the Framework for Reception to inform their teaching of these and any other children who have not had a complete year in a Reception class. Equally, Reception teachers and assistants should refer regularly to the Framework for Year 1 so that they are clear about where the work is heading. This should help to ensure that all children have made a sound start on the National Curriculum for mathematics by the end of Year 1.

9 How might we arrange the furniture?

How you arrange the furniture will depend on the size and shape of your room but each child needs to be able to see you, the board and their table top easily when they are seated, for both whole-class and group work. Seating arrangements for mathematics don't need to dictate the arrangements for other subjects. In mainstream classes there are children who are capable of moving the tables and chairs and they soon get used to a brisk routine of doing so.

- One solution is to arrange clumps of three or four tables in rectangles, with the narrow ends of the rectangles towards the front. Six to eight pupils can then sit in a U-shape round three sides of the rectangle so that no child has his or her back to the front. When you sit down to teach the group you can work from the vacant short edge, so aim to keep a spare chair there.
- Another solution is to arrange the tables in one large U-shape. This has the advantage that all the pupils can see each other as well as you, and the central area can be used for floor demonstrations. Or you could arrange one U-shape within another, with the inner U reserved for those who might need to sit closer to you or the board, or who showed misunderstandings in a previous lesson.

It is not essential for a class of any age to sit in a carpeted area for part of their mathematics lessons. They can just as easily sit at tables. Bear this in mind when you are organising your classroom, especially if it is small. If you do teach in a carpeted area, make sure that a board or flip chart is available on which you and the class can demonstrate and explain, and that there is enough space for pupils to do so without climbing over others. Make sure too that any pupils whose special needs warrant that they sit in particular positions are well placed. Where necessary an assistant should give discreet support by using a small, hand-held white board to mirror the work on the main board.

10 What resources do we need?

Beside a board, each classroom should have a large, long **number line** for teaching purposes, perhaps below the board, and at a level at which you and the children can touch it. A 'washing line' of numbers strung across the room, and which can be added to or altered, is useful. Provide table-top number lines, marked and unmarked, for individual use. For Reception and Year 1, **number tracks** with the spaces numbered to 20, rather than number lines with the points numbered, are helpful, including those made from carpet tiles. You could also have a floor 'snake' for children to move along in corridors, the hall and the playground. For Year 2, lines need to extend to 100; by Year 4 they should include negative numbers; Years 5 and 6 need marked and unmarked lines on which decimals and fractions can be placed.

Equip each child with their own pack of **digit cards** 0 to 9 to hold up when answering questions in a whole-class setting. Two-digit numbers can be formed from cards held side-by-side. Younger children can use their fingers, both for counting and for showing answers to questions.

Place value cards are equally useful. With nine cards printed with multiples of 100 from 100 to 900, nine with multiples of 10 from 10 to 90, and ten with the numbers 0 to 9, two- or three-digit numbers can be built up by overlapping cards of different widths.

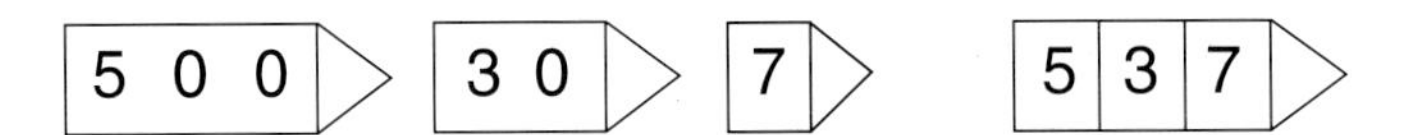

Also useful are bundles of **addition and subtraction cards** for number bonds, first bonds to 5, then to 10, extending to 20. Children can use these, for example, to find all the cards with an answer of 7, setting them out systematically. They can also be used to form equations or inequations: for example, $3 + 7 = 2 + 8$, or $5 + 4 > 10 - 2$. **Symbol cards** for +, –, × and ÷ can be held up in response to questions about the operation needed to solve a problem.

A large **100 square**, displayed where children can touch it, is essential for work in Years 2 to 4 on patterns such as 43 + 8, 43 + 18, 43 + 28, 43 + 38… or to illustrate addition or subtraction of two-digit numbers: for example, when 38 + 23 is treated as 38 + 10 + 10 + 3. Similarly, 72 – 47 can be treated by counting back first 4 tens then 7 ones to reach 25. Another way to illustrate 72 – 47 is to count up from 47 to 67 in tens, then from 67 to 72 in ones.

From resources kept in each classroom it ought to be possible to equip each group with **small apparatus** such as counters, interlocking cubes, wooden cubes, pegs and pegboard, straws, rulers, coins, dominoes, dice, and calculators when needed. Each class needs ready access to a variety of **squared paper**, and a good range of **number games, measuring equipment, sets of shapes and construction kits**.

Base-10 apparatus can be used to show the relative sizes of 1, 10, 100 and 1000, and partitioning of numbers: for example, how to break 374 into 300 + 70 + 4, or into 300 + 60 + 14. However, some children learn to manipulate the pieces without ever transferring their understanding to the number system. Always use digit cards alongside the pieces to help overcome this. The same applies to a **spike abacus**.

Your library corner might have some **interest books on mathematics** and **mathematical dictionaries** suitable for the age of the children. For activities and practice exercises for class work and homework there are many useful books of suggestions for teachers and pupils produced by educational publishers, mathematical associations, local education authorities and others. You may need particular equipment, books and materials for pupils with special needs.

Don't forget that the aim is for children to become less reliant on fingers and apparatus and to calculate mentally. Try to develop an approach in which mental methods are always considered first. Use strategies like: 'First think, and try to work it out in your head. Now check on your number line.' Or: 'Close your eyes and imagine five counters on the table... a number line on the wall... two dice you have shaken... a bag of silver coins...'

Information and communications technology (ICT)

ICT includes the calculator (see page 8) and extends to the whole range of audio-visual aids, including audio tape, video film and educational broadcasts. You can use ICT in various ways to support your teaching and motivate children's learning. For example, by using a computer pupils in Key Stages 1 and 2 can:

- explore, describe and explain number patterns: for example, by watching a counting 'meter' with sequences of numbers shown slowly one at a time, or experimenting with patterns of multiples highlighted on different number grids;
- practise and consolidate their number skills: for example, by using software designed to 'teach' or practise a particular skill and give rapid assessment feedback to you and them;
- explore and explain patterns in data: for example, by accessing, displaying and interpreting ready-made sets of data, displaying quickly a bar chart or pictogram showing the outcome of a class vote, or using a sensor connected to a computer to measure, display and show trends in room temperature;
- estimate and compare measures of length or distance, angle, time, and so on: for example, by devising a sequence of instructions to move a floor robot or screen 'turtle' along a path, then modifying their instructions in the light of the robot's response;
- experiment with and discuss properties of patterns in shape and space: for example, by using software to transform shapes and create geometric patterns, or watching a film of a square being halved in different ways;
- develop their mathematical vocabulary, logical thinking and problem-solving skills: for example, by using a 'branching tree' computer program to sort shapes or numbers, or exploring a simple simulation to discover the mathematical relationship that underpins it.

An aim of the daily mathematics lesson is to keep the class working together and to link but limit to no more than three the number of different activities going on during group work. Most schools with pupils in Key Stages 1 and 2 don't have enough computers for all the children in a class to do the same activity simultaneously. But you or another adult can make good use of a single computer in the daily lesson by working with the whole class, if the monitor's screen is large enough. An alternative is for you to work with part of the class – perhaps a group of six to eight pupils. As with other ways of teaching mathematics, your role is to demonstrate, explain and question, stimulate discussion, invite predictions and interpretations of what is displayed and ask individual children to come to the keyboard to enter an instruction or a response.

A small group of pupils working together can also make effective use of one or two computers in the daily mathematics lesson, provided that the activity is consistent with the lesson's objectives, the activities of other groups and the overall number of activities. You need to intervene in the computer work from time to time to teach and develop the children's learning, and make sure that they are all participating. You should also invite them to contribute to the plenary part of the lesson.

Individual use of computer programs is usually inappropriate in the daily lesson, except where pupils with profound special educational needs or exceptional ability are doing individualised work. But programs which allow any pupil to practise number skills independently, or to investigate a mathematical problem with a partner, have a valuable part to play in breaks and after-school clubs, and at home.

You should use computer software in your daily mathematics lesson only if it is the most efficient and effective way to meet your lesson's objectives. For example, an aimless exploration of an 'adventure game', or repetitive practice of number bonds already mastered, is not good use of lesson time. And it is time-consuming for children to develop their understanding of addition and subtraction by taking turns to instruct a floor robot to move along a number track; a much quicker way of achieving the same mathematical objective is for as many children as possible to walk up and down the track, and to observe others doing so.

The supplements of examples that are part of the Framework include some references to ICT, where its use can be managed efficiently by a teacher working with a whole class or a large group, and the activity helps to deliver the National Curriculum for ICT. Specific programs are scarcely mentioned, since the focus in the supplements is on mathematical outcomes, not the resources that can be used to achieve them. But you could annotate the supplements of examples in suitable places with references to the software and other resources that you have in school.

ICT is, of course, more than a teaching tool. For many pupils with special educational needs it is an essential communication aid. The Internet offers teachers access to research articles and materials to download for classroom use, such as mathematical problems for children to solve with accompanying notes for teachers. The web-sites of the mathematical associations give useful information and can guide you to other useful sites. The development of the National Grid for Learning, which will include the Virtual Teacher's Centre, will also offer schools practical sources of advice and the opportunity to exchange ideas with others.

Assessment

Assessment, recording and reporting are important elements of teaching but they have to be manageable if the information they yield is to be useful to you, the pupils and others. Practice needs to be agreed across the school to ensure consistency and efficiency.

As with planning (see page 38), it is best to think of assessment at three connected levels: short-term, medium-term and long-term. Your assessments can then inform your teaching plans at each level, in a continuous cycle of planning, teaching and assessment.

Short-term assessments

Short-term assessments are an informal part of every lesson. Their purposes are to:

- check that children have grasped the main teaching points in a particular lesson or unit of work, whether they have any misunderstandings that you need to put right, and whether they are ready to move on to the next activity;
- check that children are remembering number facts and can use mental calculation strategies;
- give you information which will help you to adjust day-to-day lesson plans and brief any support staff or adult helpers about which children to assist, and how to assist them.

For these short-term assessments what you assess will be closely matched to your teaching objectives. There are two main ways to make them.

- **During every lesson** you will absorb and react to children's responses, see whether they are confident or hesitant with new work, decide whether they need extension work or more help, or if groups need to be adjusted, and so on. With four groups in a class you might, for example, aim to keep a special eye on one of them on a different day each week, perhaps questioning the children informally to check specific knowledge, skills and understanding. If you notice any difficulties or misunderstandings, try to adjust your lesson and address them straight away, if necessary continuing in the next lesson or two. Use the plenary part of the lesson to acknowledge individual and collective achievement and effort.
- **At intervals** you can supplement your daily observations. For example, with older children, an out-of-class or homework exercise or activity at the end of a unit of work can give you useful information on who has learned what and who needs extra support. Or you might occasionally give the class a short, informal test of rapid recall of number facts and mental calculation skills. In a mixed-age class, older pupils could answer written questions, while the younger ones write answers to questions which you give to them orally. Homework and informal tests of this kind should be followed immediately by marking and discussion with the whole class to give pupils feedback on their performance and what they need to do to improve. At the same time you can make sure that any errors are put right and the merits of different methods discussed.

Short-term assessments don't need to be recorded, since they are for your immediate action and attention. But you may decide to keep your own informal jottings when a child surprises you, perhaps with his or her knowledge, or with something that is unexpectedly difficult. These informal, personal recordings can help you to clarify patterns in performance over time or responses to specific teaching or support.

Medium-term assessments

The purposes of medium-term assessments are different. Their focus should be on what you are unsure about, not on what you already know. They are mainly to:

- review and record the **progress** children are making over time in relation to the key objectives, what they know and can do, whether they can apply their skills in a new context, and whether any weaknesses remain;
- identify children's progress against specific individual targets, including those in IEPs, so you can give them and their parents feedback and set new targets;
- help you to plan work over the next half term;
- provide you with information to feed into end-of-year assessments.

It is not necessary or even feasible to check and record each pupil's individual progress against every single teaching objective in mathematics. Most children should be living up to expectations for their age group; what they know, understand and can do in general is already recorded as a class record of progress when you evaluate your medium-term teaching plan (see page 42).

Your medium-term assessments should centre on the most important aspects of mathematics and help you to identify children's particular strengths and weaknesses. They should relate to the **key objectives** that you have included in the half term's work (for details of the key objectives, see the separate section). These objectives are central to all children's progress in relation to the National Curriculum level descriptions, and hence to their performance in tests and teacher assessments.

Medium-term assessments should be timed to influence planning. For example, on two days in each half term you could plan **group and individual assessment activities and written tasks**. These might involve several different ideas and skills linked to one or more of the key objectives. You should tell the class the particular focus of your assessment: for example, accuracy, working shown clearly for written calculations, clear and concise explanations of the methods used to solve problems... When you plan 'assess and review' days, try to choose activities and tasks that children can largely tackle independently so that you can concentrate on observing how they set about their work as well as its quality. For example, in Year 4, you could make use of the Assessment Units published by the QCA.

As you assess the work and review progress, bear in mind your planned expectations for what pupils should be achieving in relation to the key objectives. Refer to the QCA exemplification of children's work which accompanies this Framework, and to the Framework's supplements of examples. Aim to judge how well your pupils can use and apply what they know, understand and can do, and what difficulties remain. Try to rectify any difficulties as soon as possible and take account of them in your next phase of medium-term planning.

You will need to mark any written task that is part of medium-term assessment to give feedback to children on what they have achieved and how to improve. You will probably want children to make corrections to their work, so constructive written comments are more helpful than mere ticks and crosses, or scores 'out of 10'. The marking, feedback and corrections should be done as soon as possible while children can still remember how they approached the task.

Children's progress towards the key objectives needs to be recorded. Since there are relatively few key objectives for each year, records will not be too onerous to maintain. To update them every six weeks or so after your 'assess and review' days is sufficient. If you have kept any personal jottings on your short-term assessments you can use these to help you.

The easiest system to use is a **class record of the key objectives**: a summary sheet for the whole class, with the key objectives appropriate for the class down one side and children's names across the top. For example:

Key objectives: Year 4											
Use symbols correctly, including <, >, =											
Round any positive integer less than 1000 to the nearest 10 or 100											
Recognise simple fractions that are several parts of a whole, and mixed numbers; recognise the equivalence of simple fractions											
Use known number facts and place value to add or subtract mentally, including any pair of two-digit whole numbers											
Carry out column addition and subtraction of two integers less than 1000, and column addition of more than two such integers											
Know by heart facts for the 2, 3, 4, 5 and 10 multiplication tables											
Derive quickly division facts corresponding to the 2, 3, 4, 5 and 10 multiplication tables											
Find remainders after division											
Know and use the relationships between familiar units of length, mass and capacity											
Classify polygons, using criteria such as number of right angles, whether or not they are regular, symmetry properties											
Choose and use appropriate number operations and ways of calculating (mental, mental with jottings, pencil and paper) to solve problems											
Other											

Your class record can be dated when you feel confident that a child has achieved a key objective. This is a sufficient record of most children's progress but you will need some **supplementary notes** for the few individual pupils whose progress towards the key objectives differs markedly from the majority of the class. Your notes should give the reasons for the difference, perhaps referring to a sample of work that you decide to retain.

Your class record can be kept in a folder with your supplementary notes. You will need to pass your folder to the next teacher at the end of the year.

Individual targets for pupils

Setting individual targets for pupils is another way in which you can help children to achieve the key objectives over the medium term.

Try to have a discussion of 5 to 10 minutes with each pupil during the course of each term to set his or her personal targets. Although you may want to arrange your discussion with some pupils on an individual basis – for example, pupils with special needs whose IEPs need updating, or pupils who would benefit from a degree of privacy – for other pupils you can organise the discussion in small groups. For example, on one of your 'assess and review' days you could use group time to circulate and ask pupils to name two or three simple improvements to work on over the next term. You could also use registration time to talk to three or so pupils each week, either individually or as a small group.

The aim is to discuss each pupil's individual progress in meeting their targets and praise success, then set a couple of new or amended targets for the pupil to aim for. You could also offer children and their parents some practical advice on the steps they might take to achieve their targets.

The targets will usually be linked to those key objectives that you will focus your teaching on over the next few weeks. They may be very specific: for example, to learn by heart multiplication facts in the 3 and 4 times-tables, or to become accurate at subtracting a pair of four-digit numbers using a pencil and paper method. For some pupils a target may need to be broken down into stages: for example, to learn by heart the 3 times-table up to 5×3. For others, it may be appropriate to choose a target linked to the key objectives for the year group below or above. Whatever the targets, they need to be straightforward and not too many at one time so that everyone understands them. You can then readily monitor and discuss them with children during mathematics lessons.

You need to note the targets you set so that you can refer to them in subsequent discussions with the children or their parents. In most cases you could highlight boxes on your class record of key objectives to indicate which of them have been given to children as targets. Exceptionally, there may be some pupils whose personal targets need to be recorded in your supplementary notes or IEP.

Keeping parents informed and involved

Your class record of key objectives and your supplementary notes will help you to keep parents informed and involved in their child's progress. When opportunities occur, use the record and notes as a point of discussion at a meeting with parents, emphasising what their child has already achieved as well as what she or he needs to work towards next. Try to gain parents' active support for helping their children to achieve the targets. For example, you could give parents a copy of their child's targets, with some suggestions for how families can help. You could also include work related to the targets in the homework activities you give your class to do.

Long-term assessments

Towards the end of the school year you will need to assess and review pupils' progress and attainment against school and national targets, drawing on your class record of key objectives and supplementary notes.

Long-term assessments are important in each year group, not just at the end of Key Stage 1 and Key Stage 2. Their purposes are to:

- assess pupils' work against the key objectives for the year;
- at the end of a key stage, assess pupils' work against national standards;
- give you supplementary information about individual children's attainment and progress so that you can report to parents and the child's next teacher;
- help the school to set targets for the National Curriculum tests in future years;
- allow the headteacher to brief the governing body, the staff and others on overall progress and attainment in the school as a whole, including progress towards school, LEA and national targets.

The main ways in which these long-term assessments are made are through end-of-year tests for children from Year 2 onwards, and teacher assessments.

- The compulsory **National Curriculum mathematics tests** for pupils in Years 2 and 6 can be supplemented by the **optional tests for Years 3, 4 and 5** provided by QCA. The age-standardised scores which result from these tests will help you to monitor whether pupils individually and collectively are attaining at, below or above the 'national average' score of 100, and how their attainment compares with their attainment in the previous year. Results expressed as National Curriculum levels will help you to judge overall standards and progress towards school, LEA and national targets.

  Each year QCA publishes for each Key Stage a *Standards Report* analysing pupils' performance on the National Curriculum test questions. These reports can help you to identify particular weaknesses which you may need to tackle in your next phase of teaching.
- You will also need to make a **teacher assessment** to sum up your judgement of children's attainment. For Year 2 and Year 6 your end-of-year assessment will need to be made against the National Curriculum level descriptions. The cumulative picture which you carry in your head of the progress of each child in your class can be extended and secured by looking through samples of children's work. You will then need to update and complete your class record of key objectives, and any supplementary notes you have made on individual pupils.

Before you make your end-of-key-stage teacher assessment, it is helpful if all staff across a key stage can examine together a sample of pupils' work from each class. This moderation exercise helps to make sure that judgements against the National Curriculum level descriptions are consistent through the school. Exemplifications of children's work published by QCA are particularly helpful at this time.

Passing on information about pupils' attainment and progress

You will be able to base your end-of-year reports to parents on your long-term assessments, making sure that they are free of jargon so that parents understand them easily.

For the next teacher, your class record of key objectives ought to give a good indication of how children have responded during the year and any difficulties that remain. Passing on a recent example of each child's written work to show, in particular, the stage reached in recording calculations is also helpful.

Planning

How the Framework is set out

The Framework consists of a set of **yearly teaching programmes** or 'programmes of study' summarising teaching objectives for each year from Reception to Year 6. From Year 1 each double-page programme covers the full range of the National Curriculum for mathematics that is relevant to the year group. The **key objectives** to which you should give priority are set out in a separate section and are also highlighted in bold in the yearly teaching programmes.

With each year's programme are two **planning grids** which, if you wish, you can use to help plan a term's lessons: a common one for use in the autumn and summer terms and one for the spring term (for Reception there is one for each term). Each grid indicates the topics to be taught in units of work, and the **recommended** number of days of lessons for each unit, except in Reception, where the length of units of work needs to be determined once children have settled in to school. The first and last units in each term are always shorter – just two or three days – to allow for the start and end of term. Two days are set aside in each half term for you to assess and review progress.

The units may be taught in any order but if you increase the number of days allocated to a particular unit you will need to decrease the number of days allocated to another. Overall, the units of work for each of Years 1 to 6 require 175 days of the school year, leaving about one week in each term for extra reinforcement or revision, making cross-curricular links or more extended problem solving. The grids for Reception allow time for settling in and for new children to join the class.

The grids for Years 1 and 2, for Years 3 and 4, and for Years 5 and 6 correspond very closely. This is to help teachers of mixed-age classes.

After the teaching programmes and grids come **supplements of examples**, for Reception, Years 1–3 and Years 4–6. The examples illustrate outcomes – a selection of what pupils should know and be able to do by the end of the year. For Reception, the examples illustrate Early Learning Goals for a child who becomes 5 in the autumn term, and who spends a full year in the class.

In each set of examples, the broad topics of counting, properties of numbers, place value and ordering, and so on, are printed in the top right corner of the relevant pages. Teaching objectives for the topic are listed in the left-hand column. Examples to illustrate each objective are shown in the columns alongside, set out so that you can recognise progression from one year to the next.

The examples are a selection, not a full set, and are not intended to be taught as a 'scheme of work' or used on a series of worksheets. Their main purpose is to help you first to interpret the level of the work and then to plan, pace and assess it so that there is steady progression throughout the school. The yearly teaching programmes and the termly planning grids both include cross-references to relevant pages in the example supplements.

The Framework's five strands

The Framework has five strands. The first three have direct links to the National Curriculum programme of study for number. The fourth strand is linked to measures, shape and space, while the fifth incorporates handling data. Using and applying mathematics is integrated throughout. The strands, and the topics they cover, are:

Numbers and the number system

- counting
- properties of numbers and number sequences, including negative numbers
- place value and ordering, including reading and writing numbers
- estimating and rounding
- fractions, decimals and percentages, and their equivalence; ratio and proportion

Calculations

- understanding number operations and relationships
- rapid mental recall of number facts
- mental calculation, including strategies for deriving new facts from known facts
- pencil and paper methods
- using a calculator
- checking that results of calculations are reasonable

Solving problems

- making decisions: deciding which operation and method of calculation to use (mental, mental with jottings, pencil and paper, calculator…)
- reasoning about numbers or shapes and making general statements about them
- solving problems involving numbers in context: 'real life', money, measures

Measures, shape and space

- measures, including choosing units and reading scales
- properties of 2-D and 3-D shapes, position, direction and movement

Handling data

- collecting, presenting and interpreting numerical data

Although the strands are described separately, mathematics has many connections within and across topics. For example, when pupils are being taught to multiply by multiples of 10, they will make connections within a topic by drawing on their knowledge of multiplication table facts and understanding of place value. Using counters to form rectangles to introduce factors and division of numbers helps to link different topics such as properties of shapes, numbers and calculation. The statement $3 + 2 = 5$ represents and summarises a range of situations which appear different but which are equivalent, such as making three whole turns followed by two whole turns, or starting with £3 and being given £2 more. Showing pupils how to multiply using partitioning, so that 12×3 becomes $(10 + 2) \times 3$, prepares the way for later connections such as long multiplication or work in algebra.

You need to be clear about what can be connected within and across topics, to make these connections visible for pupils and to help them to make some of their own. Providing different examples and activities and expecting pupils to make the links is not enough; pupils need to be shown them and reminded about their work in earlier lessons. Explanations, demonstrations and illustrations of connections should all be part of the direct teaching pupils receive during the main teaching activity.

The diagram below illustrates the five strands. **Using and applying mathematics is integrated throughout**: for example, in making and justifying decisions about which method, equipment or unit of measurement to use; in describing properties of numbers or shapes and in reasoning about them; in explaining methods of calculation; in devising and refining methods of recording calculations; in checking results...

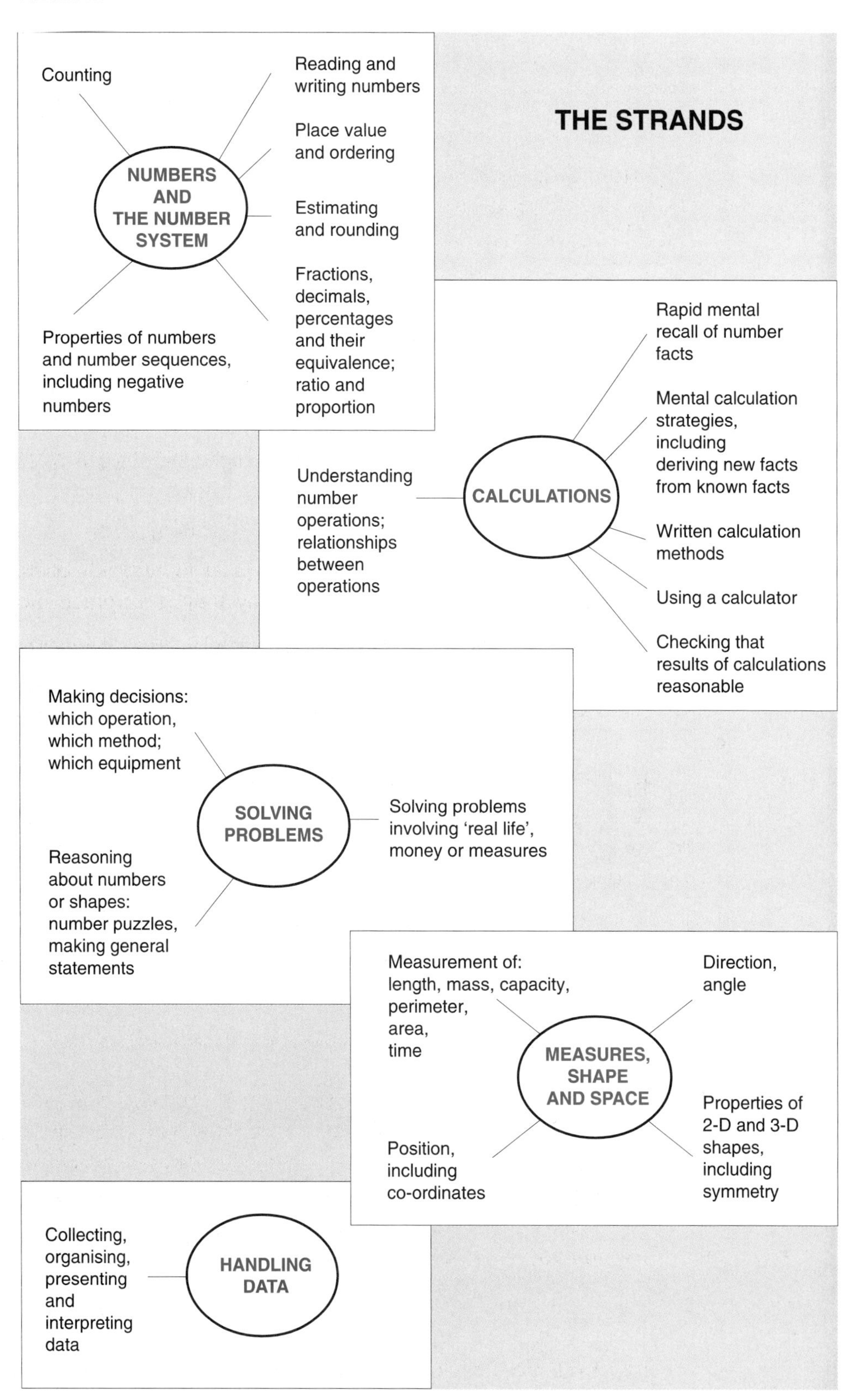

Principles of good planning

To put the Framework into practice you need three connected levels of planning:

- the Framework: what you should teach long term;
- medium-term plans: termly outlines of units of work and their main teaching objectives, and when you will teach them;
- short-term plans: weekly or fortnightly notes on tasks, activities, exercises, key questions and teaching points for 5 to 10 lessons, including how pupils will be grouped, which of them you will work with, and how you will use any support.

Your medium-term plan is the basis for your more detailed short-term plans. It identifies **what** you will teach across the term and when it should be happening. Your short-term plans can focus on **how** you will teach – in particular, what you will do and what the children will do.

Whether or not you choose to use the termly planning grids your school's planning procedures for mathematics should meet these criteria. There should be:

- common formats for planning a balanced programme of objectives for each term, and common formats for planning one or two weeks of lessons;
- arrangements to support planning: for example, through planning in teams with the help of the co-ordinator, SENCO or deputy;
- agreed procedures and deadlines for producing plans;
- monitoring arrangements to evaluate planning and progression throughout the school, and the impact of plans as they are put into practice in classrooms.

When you are planning lessons you should give some thought to what pupils have already been taught so that you can build on the concepts, knowledge and skills they have already acquired. You will need to keep these questions in mind.

- What mathematics have these pupils been taught before?
- How will my lessons build on what they already know, understand and can do?
- How can I use previous lessons to help pupils establish links between topics: for example, can I use similar examples, common vocabulary and earlier examples to illustrate and demonstrate connections?
- Can I use opportunities in other subjects to introduce or reinforce mathematical ideas? (See 'Making links between mathematics and other subjects', page 16.)

Developing medium-term plans and a scheme of work

If you choose to use the termly planning grids, copy the relevant grid before the start of term, enlarging it to A3 size. Identify the particular objectives that will be the main focus in each unit of work, choosing from the objectives in the relevant yearly teaching programme. Every objective should be included and covered at least once by the end of the year. For Years 1 to 6, choose and then record objectives for oral and mental mathematics sessions in the box for each half term.

The purpose of the units is to make sure that the balance and distribution of work across each term is appropriate, but they may be taught in any order. Since you will need to identify time in other subjects to supplement mathematics, particularly for practical work using measures and properties of shapes, this may have implications for the order of the units.

The page references on the termly planning grids should help you to refer to the examples in the supplement when you plan day-to-day lessons in detail.

Evaluating your medium-term plan

At the end of each unit of work you should evaluate it, based on your short-term assessments of the pupils. For example, you could highlight or code your termly plan to show whether in general:

- pupils responded well and met the objective in full;
- pupils were responsive but the objective still needs more attention;
- an objective was not covered, or pupils did not meet it.

You can then see at a glance what pupils in general can do and what still needs more work. You should develop next term's plan in the light of these evaluations, taking account of your assessments of children's progress towards the key objectives.

Creating a scheme of work

By keeping the termly and weekly plans for the whole school in a folder and replacing them with modified updates when you develop them next time round, you can create a developmental scheme of work for mathematics for your school that is never out of date.

Relationship to National Curriculum level descriptions

The overall target is for at least 75% of 11-year-olds, by 2002, to achieve level 4 in the National Curriculum tests for mathematics. The year-by-year programmes are designed with this target in mind.

The programmes also take account of the need in mathematics to revisit topics regularly to revise and consolidate skills and then extend them. They may, at first, seem ambitious. But if 11-year-olds are to achieve a secure level 4 when tested in the summer of Year 6, the teaching programme needs to be pitched at a level which is a little beyond this.

The expectations in the yearly teaching programmes correspond to these levels.

- **Year 1** level 1, and start on level 2
- **Year 2** consolidation of level 2, and start on level 3
- **Year 3** revision of level 2, but mainly level 3
- **Year 4** consolidation of level 3, and start on level 4
- **Year 5** revision of level 3, but mainly level 4
- **Year 6** consolidation of level 4, and start on level 5

Where to begin

The Framework is a guide to what to teach each class. However, there are schools where at present relatively few Year 6 pupils attain level 4 in the National Curriculum tests. These schools will need to look carefully at the teaching programmes for Years 5 and 6 and judge the extent to which they are appropriate.

For example, in the first year of using the Framework it may be more appropriate for a Year 5 class to work on the Year 4 programme for a couple of terms, before moving on to the Year 5 programme. This decision would need to be reviewed at the start of the next school year when a new group of pupils who have had some teaching based on the Framework enters the Year 5 class.

The Government has given schools greater flexibility to plan their curriculum provision in ways that give greater emphasis to literacy and numeracy. Where necessary, schools should use this flexibility to bring pupils up to the appropriate standard as soon as possible.

2

Key *objectives*

2
Key
objectives

Key objectives

Reception

- ◆ Say and use the number names in order in familiar contexts.
- ◆ Count reliably up to 10 everyday objects.
- ◆ Recognise numerals 1 to 9.
- ◆ Use language such as more or less, greater or smaller, heavier or lighter, to compare two numbers or quantities.
- ◆ In practical activities and discussion, begin to use the vocabulary involved in adding and subtracting.
- ◆ Find one more or one less than a number from 1 to 10.
- ◆ Begin to relate addition to combining two groups of objects, and subtraction to 'taking away'.
- ◆ Talk about, recognise and recreate simple patterns.
- ◆ Use language such as circle or bigger to describe the shape and size of solids and flat shapes.
- ◆ Use everyday words to describe position.
- ◆ Use developing mathematical ideas and methods to solve practical problems.

Year 1

- ◆ Count reliably at least 20 objects.
- ◆ Count on and back in ones from any small number, and in tens from and back to zero.
- ◆ Read, write and order numbers from 0 to at least 20; understand and use the vocabulary of comparing and ordering these numbers.
- ◆ Within the range 0 to 30, say the number that is 1 or 10 more or less than any given number.
- ◆ Understand the operation of addition, and of subtraction (as 'take away' or 'difference'), and use the related vocabulary.
- ◆ Know by heart all pairs of numbers with a total of 10.
- ◆ Use mental strategies to solve simple problems using counting, addition, subtraction, doubling and halving, explaining methods and reasoning orally.
- ◆ Compare two lengths, masses or capacities by direct comparison.
- ◆ Suggest suitable standard or uniform non-standard units and measuring equipment to estimate, then measure, a length, mass or capacity.
- ◆ Use everyday language to describe features of familiar 3-D and 2-D shapes.

Year 2

- Count, read, write and order whole numbers to at least 100; know what each digit represents (including 0 as a place holder).
- Describe and extend simple number sequences (including odd/even numbers, counting on or back in ones or tens from any two-digit number, and so on).
- Understand that subtraction is the inverse of addition; state the subtraction corresponding to a given addition and vice versa.
- Know by heart all addition and subtraction facts for each number to at least 10.
- Use knowledge that addition can be done in any order to do mental calculations more efficiently.
- Understand the operation of multiplication as repeated addition or as describing an array.
- Know and use halving as the inverse of doubling.
- Know by heart facts for the 2 and 10 multiplication tables.
- Estimate, measure and compare lengths, masses and capacities, using standard units; suggest suitable units and equipment for such measurements.
- Read a simple scale to the nearest labelled division, including using a ruler to draw and measure lines to the nearest centimetre.
- Use the mathematical names for common 2-D and 3-D shapes; sort shapes and describe some of their features.
- Use mathematical vocabulary to describe position, direction and movement.
- Choose and use appropriate operations and efficient calculation strategies to solve problems, explaining how the problem was solved.

Year 3

- Read, write and order whole numbers to at least 1000; know what each digit represents.
- Count on or back in tens or hundreds from any two- or three-digit number.
- Recognise unit fractions such as $\frac{1}{2}$, $\frac{1}{3}$, $\frac{1}{4}$, $\frac{1}{5}$, $\frac{1}{10}$, and use them to find fractions of shapes and numbers.
- Know by heart all addition and subtraction facts for each number to 20.
- Add and subtract mentally a 'near multiple of 10' to or from a two-digit number.
- Know by heart facts for the 2, 5 and 10 multiplication tables.
- Understand division and recognise that division is the inverse of multiplication.
- Use units of time and know the relationships between them (second, minute, hour, day, week, month, year).
- Understand and use £.p notation.
- Choose and use appropriate operations (including multiplication and division) to solve word problems, explaining methods and reasoning.
- Identify right angles.
- Identify lines of symmetry in simple shapes and recognise shapes with no lines of symmetry.
- Solve a given problem by organising and interpreting numerical data in simple lists, tables and graphs.

Year 4

- Use symbols correctly, including less than (<), greater than (>), equals (=).
- Round any positive integer less than 1000 to the nearest 10 or 100.
- Recognise simple fractions that are several parts of a whole, and mixed numbers; recognise the equivalence of simple fractions.
- Use known number facts and place value to add or subtract mentally, including any pair of two-digit whole numbers.
- Carry out column addition and subtraction of two integers less than 1000, and column addition of more than two such integers.
- Know by heart facts for the 2, 3, 4, 5 and 10 multiplication tables.
- Derive quickly division facts corresponding to the 2, 3, 4, 5 and 10 multiplication tables.
- Find remainders after division.
- Know and use the relationships between familiar units of length, mass and capacity.
- Classify polygons, using criteria such as number of right angles, whether or not they are regular, symmetry properties.
- Choose and use appropriate number operations and ways of calculating (mental, mental with jottings, pencil and paper) to solve problems.

Year 5

- Multiply and divide any positive integer up to 10 000 by 10 or 100 and understand the effect.
- Order a given set of positive and negative integers.
- Use decimal notation for tenths and hundredths.
- Round a number with one or two decimal places to the nearest integer.
- Relate fractions to division and to their decimal representations.
- Calculate mentally a difference such as 8006 – 2993.
- Carry out column addition and subtraction of positive integers less than 10 000.
- Know by heart all multiplication facts up to 10×10.
- Carry out short multiplication and division of a three-digit by a single-digit integer.
- Carry out long multiplication of a two-digit by a two-digit integer.
- Understand area measured in square centimetres (cm^2); understand and use the formula in words 'length $\times$ breadth' for the area of a rectangle.
- Recognise parallel and perpendicular lines, and properties of rectangles.
- Use all four operations to solve simple word problems involving numbers and quantities, including time, explaining methods and reasoning.

Year 6

- ◆ Multiply and divide decimals mentally by 10 or 100, and integers by 1000, and explain the effect.
- ◆ Order a mixed set of numbers with up to three decimal places.
- ◆ Reduce a fraction to its simplest form by cancelling common factors.
- ◆ Use a fraction as an operator to find fractions of numbers or quantities (e.g. $\frac{5}{8}$ of 32, $\frac{7}{10}$ of 40, $\frac{9}{100}$ of 400 centimetres).
- ◆ Understand percentage as the number of parts in every 100, and find simple percentages of small whole-number quantities.
- ◆ Solve simple problems involving ratio and proportion.
- ◆ Carry out column addition and subtraction of numbers involving decimals.
- ◆ Derive quickly division facts corresponding to multiplication tables up to 10×10.
- ◆ Carry out short multiplication and division of numbers involving decimals.
- ◆ Carry out long multiplication of a three-digit by a two-digit integer.
- ◆ Use a protractor to measure acute and obtuse angles to the nearest degree.
- ◆ Calculate the perimeter and area of simple compound shapes that can be split into rectangles.
- ◆ Read and plot co-ordinates in all four quadrants.
- ◆ Identify and use the appropriate operations (including combinations of operations) to solve word problems involving numbers and quantities, and explain methods and reasoning.
- ◆ Solve a problem by extracting and interpreting information presented in tables, graphs and charts.

3

Yearly teaching **programmes** *and planning grids*

3

Yearly teaching
programmes
and planning grids

Teaching programme: Reception

Counting and recognising numbers

2–8 Counting
- 2 • **Say and use the number names in order In familiar contexts** such as number rhymes, songs, stories, counting games and activities (first to five, then ten, then twenty and beyond).
- 2, 3 • Recite the number names in order, continuing the count forwards or backwards from a given number.
- 4, 5 • **Count reliably up to 10 everyday objects** (first to 5, then 10, then beyond), giving just one number name to each object. Recognise small numbers without counting.
- 5 • Begin to recognise 'none' and 'zero' in stories, rhymes and when counting.
- 6 • Count reliably in other contexts, such as clapping sounds or hopping movements.
- 7 • Count in tens.
- 7 • Count in twos.
- 8 • Estimate a number in the range that can be counted reliably, then check by counting.

9–10 Reading and writing numbers
- 9 • **Recognise numerals 1 to 9**, then 0 and 10, then beyond 10.
- 10 • Begin to record numbers, initially by making marks, progressing to simple tallying and writing numerals.

11–13 Comparing and ordering numbers
- 11, 12 • **Use language such as more or less, greater or smaller, to compare two numbers** and say which is more or less, and say a number which lies between two given numbers.
- 12 • Order a given set of numbers: for example, the set of numbers 1 to 6 given in random order.
- 12 • Order a given set of selected numbers: for example, the set 2, 5, 1, 8, 4.
- 13 • Begin to understand and use ordinal numbers in different contexts.

Adding and subtracting

14–17 Adding and subtracting
In practical activities and discussion:
- 14 • **Begin to use the vocabulary involved in adding and subtracting.**
- 14 • **Find one more or one less than a number from 1 to 10.**
- 14 • **Begin to relate addition to combining two groups of objects,** counting all the objects; extend to three groups of objects.
- 15 • Begin to relate addition to counting on.
- 15 • Begin to relate the addition of doubles to counting on.
- 15 • Find a total by counting on when one group of objects is hidden.
- 16 • Separate (partition) a given number of objects into two groups.
- 16 • Select two groups of objects to make a given total.
- 16 • **Begin to relate subtraction to 'taking away'** and counting how many are left.
- 17 • Remove a smaller number from a larger and find how many are left by counting back from the larger number.
- 17 • Begin to find out how many have been removed from a larger group of objects by counting up from a number.
- 17 • Work out by counting how many more are needed to make a larger number.

Solving problems

18–19 Reasoning about numbers or shapes
- 18 • **Talk about, recognise and recreate simple patterns**: for example, simple repeating or symmetrical patterns from different cultures.
- 18 • Solve simple problems or puzzles in a practical context, and respond to 'What could we try next?'
- 19 • Make simple estimates and predictions: for example, of the number of cubes that will fit in a box or strides across the room.
- 19 • Sort and match objects, pictures or children themselves, justifying the decisions made.

20–21 Problems involving 'real life' or money
- 20 • **Use developing mathematical ideas and methods to solve practical problems** involving counting and comparing in a real or role play context.
- 21 • Begin to understand and use the vocabulary related to money. Sort coins, including the £1 and £2 coins, and use them in role play to pay and give change.

Measures, shape and space

22–23 Comparing and ordering measures
- 22 • **Use language such as more or less, longer or shorter, heavier or lighter... to compare two quantities**, then more than two, by making direct comparisons of lengths or masses, and by filling and emptying containers.
- 23 • Begin to understand and use the vocabulary of time. Sequence familiar events. Begin to know the days of the week in order. Begin to read o'clock time.

24–27 Exploring pattern, shape and space
- 24, 25 • **Use language such as circle or bigger to describe the shape and size of solids and flat shapes.** Begin to name solids such as a cube, cone, sphere... and flat shapes such as a circle, triangle, square, rectangle... Use a variety of shapes to make models, pictures and patterns, and describe them.
- 26 • Put sets of objects in order of size.
- 26 • Talk about, recognise and recreate patterns: for example, simple repeating or symmetrical patterns in the environment (see also Reasoning).
- 27 • **Use everyday words to describe position**, direction and movement: for example, follow and give instructions about positions, directions and movements in PE and other activities.

NOTES
- Key objectives are highlighted in **bold type**.
- Page references are to the supplement of examples for Reception.

Unit	Days	Pages	Topic	Objectives: children will be taught to...
1		2–8	Counting	
2		2–8	Counting	
3		24–27	Shape and space	
4		2–8 22–23	Counting Measures	
5		2–8 14–15	Counting Adding (one more)	
6			**Assess and review**	
7		2–8 11–13	Counting Comparing and ordering numbers	
8		2–8 14–15	Counting Adding and subtracting (one more, one less)	
9		24–27 18–19	Shape and space Reasoning	
10		2–8 22–23	Counting Measures, including time	
11		2–8 20–21	Counting Money and 'real life' problems	
12			**Assess and review**	

NOTE For Reception, the number of teaching days for each unit can be determined once children have settled into school.

Unit	Days	Pages	Topic	Objectives: children will be taught to...
1		2–8 11–13	Counting Comparing and ordering numbers	
2		2–8 14–17	Counting Adding and subtracting	
3		24–27 18–19	Shape and space Reasoning	
4		2–8 22–23	Counting Measures	
5		2–8 14–17 19–20	Counting Adding and subtracting Money and 'real life' problems	
6			**Assess and review**	
7		2–9 11–13	Counting and reading numbers Comparing and ordering numbers	
8		2–9 14–17	Counting and reading numbers Adding and subtracting	
9		24–27 18–19	Shape and space Reasoning	
10		2–9 22–23	Counting and reading numbers Measures, including time	
11		2–9 14–17 20–21	Counting and reading numbers Adding and subtracting Money and 'real life' problems	
12			**Assess and review**	

Unit	Days	Pages	Topic	Objectives: children will be taught to...
1		2–10 11–13	Counting, reading and writing numbers Comparing and ordering numbers	
2		2–10 14–17	Counting, reading and writing numbers Adding and subtracting	
3		24–27 18–19	Shape and space Reasoning	
4		2–10 22–23	Counting, reading and writing numbers Measures	
5		2–10 14–17 20–21	Counting, reading and writing numbers Adding and subtracting Money and 'real life' problems	
6			**Assess and review**	
7		2–10 11–13	Counting, reading and writing numbers Comparing and ordering numbers	
8		2–10 14–17	Counting, reading and writing numbers Adding and subtracting	
9		24–27 18–19	Shape and space Reasoning	
10		2–10 22–23	Counting, reading and writing numbers Measures, including time	
11		2–10 14–17 20–21	Counting, reading and writing numbers Adding and subtracting Money and 'real life' problems	
12			**Assess and review**	

Teaching programme: Year 1

Numbers and the number system

2–7 Counting, properties of numbers and number sequences

- 2 • Know the number names and recite them in order to at least 20, from and back to zero.
- 2 • **Count reliably at least 20 objects.**
- 2, 4, 6 • Describe and extend number sequences:
  count on and back in ones from any small number, and in tens from and back to zero;
  count on in twos from zero, then one, and begin to recognise odd or even numbers to about 20 as 'every other number';
  count in steps of 5 from zero to 20 or more, then back again;
  begin to count on in steps of 3 from zero.

8–15 Place value and ordering

- 8 • **Read and write numerals from 0 to at least 20.**
- 8 • Begin to know what each digit in a two-digit number represents. Partition a 'teens' number and begin to partition larger two-digit numbers into a multiple of 10 and ones (TU).
- 10 • **Understand and use the vocabulary of comparing and ordering numbers**, including ordinal numbers to at least 20.
  Use the = sign to represent equality.
  Compare two familiar numbers, say which is more or less, and give a number which lies between them.
- 12 • **Within the range 0 to 30, say the number that is 1 or 10 more or less than any given number.**
- 14 • **Order numbers to at least 20**, and position them on a number track.

16–19 Estimating

- 16 • Understand and use the vocabulary of estimation.
  Give a sensible estimate of a number of objects that can be checked by counting (e.g. up to about 30 objects).

Calculations

24–29 Understanding addition and subtraction

- 24, 28 • **Understand the operation of addition, and of subtraction (as 'take away', 'difference'**, and 'how many more to make'), **and use the related vocabulary.**
  Begin to recognise that addition can be done in any order.
  Begin to use the +, – and = signs to record mental calculations in a number sentence, and to recognise the use of symbols such as □ or △ to stand for an unknown number.
- 26 • Begin to recognise that more than two numbers can be added together.

30–31 Rapid recall of addition and subtraction facts

- 30 • **Know by heart:**
  all pairs of numbers with a total of 10 (e.g. 3 + 7);
  addition facts for all pairs of numbers with a total up to at least 5, and the corresponding subtraction facts;
  addition doubles of all numbers to at least 5 (e.g. 4 + 4).
  Begin to know:
  addition facts for all pairs of numbers with a total up to at least 10, and the corresponding subtraction facts.

32–41 Mental calculation strategies (+ and –)

- 32 • Use knowledge that addition can be done in any order to do mental calculations more efficiently. For example:
  put the larger number first and count on in ones, including beyond 10 (e.g. 7 + 5);
  begin to partition into '5 and a bit' when adding 6, 7, 8 or 9, then recombine (e.g. 6 + 8 = 5 + 1 + 5 + 3 = 10 + 4 = 14).
- 32 • Identify near doubles, using doubles already known (e.g. 6 + 5).
- 34 • Add 9 to single-digit numbers by adding 10 then subtracting 1.
- 34 • Use patterns of similar calculations (e.g. 10 – 0 = 10, 10 – 1 = 9, 10 – 2 = 8...).
- 36, 38 • Use known number facts and place value to add or subtract a pair of numbers mentally within the range 0 to at least 10, then 0 to at least 20.
- 40 • Begin to bridge through 10, and later 20, when adding a single-digit number.

NOTES • Key objectives are highlighted in **bold type**.
• Page references are to the supplement of examples for Years 1, 2 and 3.

Solving problems

60–61 Making decisions

60 • Choose and use appropriate number operations and mental strategies to solve problems.
(For examples, see pages 62–71.)

62–65 Reasoning about numbers or shapes

62 • Solve simple mathematical problems or puzzles; recognise and predict from simple patterns and relationships. Suggest extensions by asking 'What if...?' or 'What could I try next?'

64 • Investigate a general statement about familiar numbers or shapes by finding examples that satisfy it.

64 • Explain methods and reasoning orally.

66–71 Problems involving 'real life', money or measures

66, 68, 70 • **Use mental strategies to solve simple problems** set in 'real life', money or measurement contexts, **using counting, addition, subtraction, doubling and halving, explaining methods and reasoning orally.**

68 • Recognise coins of different values.
Find totals and change from up to 20p.
Work out how to pay an exact sum using smaller coins

90–93 Organising and using data

90, 92 • Solve a given problem by sorting, classifying and organising information in simple ways, such as:
using objects or pictures;
in a list or simple table.
Discuss and explain results.

Measures, shape and space

72–79 Measures

72 • Understand and use the vocabulary related to length, mass and capacity.
Compare two lengths, masses or capacities by direct comparison; extend to more than two.
Measure using uniform non-standard units (e.g. straws, wooden cubes, plastic weights, yogurt pots), or standard units (e.g. metre sticks, litre jugs).

74, 76 • **Suggest suitable standard or uniform non-standard units and measuring equipment to estimate, then measure, a length, mass or capacity**, recording estimates and measurements as 'about 3 beakers full' or 'about as heavy as 20 cubes'.

78 • Understand and use the vocabulary related to time.
Order familiar events in time.
Know the days of the week and the seasons of the year.
Read the time to the hour or half hour on analogue clocks.

80–89 Shape and space

80 • **Use everyday language to describe features of familiar 3-D and 2-D shapes**, including the cube, cuboid, sphere, cylinder, cone..., circle, triangle, square, rectangle..., referring to properties such as the shapes of flat faces, or the number of faces or corners... or the number and types of sides.

82 • Make and describe models, patterns and pictures using construction kits, everyday materials, Plasticine...
Fold shapes in half, then make them into symmetrical patterns.
Begin to relate solid shapes to pictures of them.

86, 88 • Use everyday language to describe position, direction and movement.

88 • Talk about things that turn.
Make whole turns and half turns.
Use one or more shapes to make, describe and continue repeating patterns...

Oral and mental: eg counting, mental strategies, rapid recall

Unit	Days	Pages	Topic	Objectives: children will be taught to...
1	3	2–7	Counting and properties of numbers	
2–4	15	8–15 24–29 32–41 66–69 60–61	Place value and ordering Understanding + and – Mental calculation strategies (+ and –) Money and 'real life' problems Making decisions	
5–6	8	70–77 80–83 62–65	Measures, including problems Shape and space Reasoning about shapes	
7	2		**Assess and review**	

Oral and mental: eg counting, mental strategies, rapid recall

Unit	Days	Pages	Topic	Objectives
8	5	2–7 62–65	Counting and properties of numbers Reasoning about numbers	
9–11	15	8–17 24–29 32–41 66–69 60–61	Place value, ordering, estimating Understanding + and – Mental calculation strategies (+ and –) Money and 'real life' problems Making decisions	
12–13	10	70–79 90–93	Measures, and time, including problems Handling data	
14	2		**Assess and review**	
Total	60			

Oral and mental: eg counting, mental strategies, rapid recall

Unit	Days	Pages	Topic	Objectives: children will be taught to...
1	3	2–7	Counting and properties of numbers	
2–4	15	8–15 24–29 32–41 66–69 60–61	Place value and ordering Understanding + and – Mental calculation strategies (+ and –) Money and 'real life' problems Making decisions	
5–6	8	70–77 80–89 62–65	Measures, including problems Shape and space Reasoning about shapes	
7	2		**Assess and review**	

Oral and mental: eg counting, mental strategies, rapid recall

Unit	Days	Pages	Topic	Objectives
8	5	2–7 62–65	Counting and properties of numbers Reasoning about numbers	
9–10	10	8–17 24–29 32–41 66–69 60–61	Place value, ordering, estimating Understanding + and – Mental calculation strategies (+ and –) Money and 'real life' problems Making decisions	
11–12	10	70–79 90–93	Measures, and time, including problems Handling data	
13	2		**Assess and review**	
Total	55			

Teaching programme: Year 2

Numbers and the number system

2–7 Counting, properties of numbers and number sequences

3 • Say the number names in order to at least 100, from and back to zero.

3 • Count reliably up to 100 objects by grouping them: for example, in tens, then in fives or twos.

3, 5, 7 • **Describe and extend simple number sequences: count on or back in ones or tens, starting from any two-digit number;**
count in hundreds from and back to zero;
count on in twos from and back to zero or any small number, and **recognise odd and even numbers** to at least 30;
count on in steps of 3, 4 or 5 to at least 30, from and back to zero, then from and back to any given small number.

7 • Begin to recognise two-digit multiples of 2, 5 or 10.

8–15 Place value and ordering

9 • **Read and write whole numbers to at least 100** in figures and words.

9 • **Know what each digit in a two-digit number represents, including 0 as a place holder**, and partition two-digit numbers into a multiple of ten and ones (TU).

11 • Use and begin to read the vocabulary of comparing and ordering numbers, including ordinal numbers to 100.
Use the = sign to represent equality.
Compare two given two-digit numbers, say which is more or less, and give a number which lies between them.

13 • Say the number that is 1 or 10 more or less than any given two-digit number.

15 • **Order whole numbers to at least 100**, and position them on a number line and 100 square.

16–19 Estimating and rounding

17 • Use and begin to read the vocabulary of estimation and approximation; give a sensible estimate of at least 50 objects.

19 • Round numbers less than 100 to the nearest 10.

20–23 Fractions

21, 23 • Begin to recognise and find one half and one quarter of shapes and small numbers of objects.
Begin to recognise that two halves or four quarters make one whole and that two quarters and one half are equivalent.

Calculations

24–29 Understanding addition and subtraction

25, 29 • Extend understanding of the operations of addition and subtraction.
Use and begin to read the related vocabulary.
Use the +, – and = signs to record mental additions and subtractions in a number sentence, and recognise the use of a symbol such as □ or △ to stand for an unknown number.
Recognise that addition can be done in any order, but not subtraction: for example, 3 + 21 = 21 + 3, but 21 – 3 3 – 21.

27 • Understand that more than two numbers can be added.
Begin to add three single-digit numbers mentally (totals up to about 20) or three two-digit numbers with the help of apparatus (totals up to 100).

25, 29 • **Understand that subtraction is the inverse of addition** (subtraction reverses addition).

30–31 Rapid recall of addition and subtraction facts

31 • **Know by heart:**
all addition and subtraction facts for each number to at least 10;
all pairs of numbers with a total of 20 (e.g. 13 + 7, 6 + 14);
all pairs of multiples of 10 with a total of 100 (e.g. 30 + 70).

32–41 Mental calculation strategies (+ and –)

33 • **Use knowledge that addition can be done in any order to do mental calculations more efficiently.** For example:
put the larger number first and count on in tens or ones;
add three small numbers by putting the largest number first and/or find a pair totalling 10;
partition into '5 and a bit' when adding 6, 7, 8 or 9, then recombine (e.g. 16 + 8 = 15 + 1 + 5 + 3 = 20 + 4 = 24);
partition additions into tens and units, then recombine.

33 • Find a small difference by counting up from the smaller to the larger number (e.g. 42 – 39).

33 • Identify near doubles, using doubles already known (e.g. 8 + 9, 40 + 41).

35 • Add/subtract 9 or 11: add/subtract 10 and adjust by 1.
Begin to add/subtract 19 or 21: add/subtract 20 and adjust by 1.

35 • Use patterns of similar calculations.

35 • **State the subtraction corresponding to a given addition, and vice versa.**

37, 39 • Use known number facts and place value to add/subtract mentally.

41 • Bridge through 10 or 20, then adjust.

46–51 Understanding multiplication and division

47, 49 • **Understand the operation of multiplication as repeated addition or as describing an array**, and begin to understand division as grouping (repeated subtraction) or sharing.
Use and begin to read the related vocabulary.
Use the ×, ÷ and = signs to record mental calculations in a number sentence, and recognise the use of a symbol such as □ or △ to stand for an unknown number.

47, 49 • **Know and use halving as the inverse of doubling.**

52–53 Rapid recall of multiplication and division facts

53 • **Know by heart:**
multiplication facts for the 2 and 10 times-tables;
doubles of all number to 10 and the corresponding halves.
Begin to know:
multiplication facts for the 5 times-table.

53 • Derive quickly:
division facts corresponding to the 2 and 10 times-tables;
doubles of all numbers to at least 15 (e.g. 11 + 11 or 11 × 2);
doubles of multiples of 5 to 50 (e.g. 20 × 2 or 35 × 2);
halves of multiples of 10 to 100 (e.g. half of 70).

54–57 Mental calculation strategies (× and ÷)

57 • Use known number facts and place value to carry out mentally simple multiplications and divisions.

58–59 Checking results of calculations

59 • Repeat addition in a different order.

59 • Check with an equivalent calculation.

NOTES
- Key objectives are highlighted in **bold type**.
- Page references are to the supplement of examples for Years 1, 2 and 3.

Solving problems

60–61 Making decisions

61 • **Choose and use appropriate operations and efficient calculation strategies** (e.g. mental, mental with jottings) **to solve problems.**
(For examples see pages 62–71.)

62–65 Reasoning about numbers or shapes

63 • Solve mathematical problems or puzzles, recognise simple patterns and relationships, generalise and predict. Suggest extensions by asking 'What if...?' or 'What could I try next?'

65 • Investigate a general statement about familiar numbers or shapes by finding examples that satisfy it.

65 • **Explain how a problem was solved** orally and, where appropriate, in writing.

66–71 Problems involving 'real life', money or measures

67, 69, 71 • Use mental addition and subtraction, simple multiplication and division, to solve simple word problems involving numbers in 'real life', money or measures, using one or two steps.
Explain how the problem was solved.

69 • Recognise all coins and begin to use £.p notation for money (for example, know that £4.65 indicates £4 and 65p).
Find totals, give change, and work out which coins to pay.

90–93 Organising and using data

91, 93 • Solve a given problem by sorting, classifying and organising information in simple ways, such as:
in a list or simple table;
in a pictogram;
in a block graph.
Discuss and explain results.

Measures, shape and space

72–79 Measures

73 • Use and begin to read the vocabulary related to length, mass and capacity.

73, 75 • **Estimate, measure and compare lengths, masses and capacities, using standard units** (m, cm, kg, litre); **suggest suitable units and equipment for such measurements.**

77 • **Read a simple scale to the nearest labelled division, including using a ruler to draw and measure lines to the nearest centimetre,** recording estimates and measurements as '3 and a bit metres long' or 'about 8 centimetres' or 'nearly 3 kilograms heavy'.

79 • Use and begin to read the vocabulary related to time.
Use units of time and know the relationships between them (second, minute, hour, day, week).
Suggest suitable units to estimate or measure time.
Order the months of the year.
Read the time to the hour, half hour or quarter hour on an analogue clock and a 12-hour digital clock, and understand the notation 7:30.

80–89 Shape and space

81 • **Use the mathematical names for common 3-D and 2-D shapes**, including the pyramid, cylinder, pentagon, hexagon, octagon...
Sort shapes and describe some of their features, such as the number of sides and corners, symmetry (2-D shapes), or the shapes of faces and number of faces, edges and corners (3-D shapes).

83 • Make and describe shapes, pictures and patterns using, for example, solid shapes, templates, pinboard and elastic bands, squared paper, a programmable robot...
Relate solid shapes to pictures of them.

85 • Begin to recognise line symmetry.

87, 89 • **Use mathematical vocabulary to describe position, direction and movement**: for example, describe, place, tick, draw or visualise objects in given positions.

87, 89 • Recognise whole, half and quarter turns, to the left or right, clockwise or anti-clockwise.
Know that a right angle is a measure of a quarter turn, and recognise right angles in squares and rectangles.
Give instructions for moving along a route in straight lines and round right-angled corners: for example, to pass through a simple maze...

Oral and mental: eg counting, mental strategies, rapid recall

Unit	Days	Pages	Topic	Objectives: children will be taught to...
1	3	2–7	Counting and properties of numbers	
2–4	15	8–19 24–29 32–41 66–69 58–61	Place value, ordering, estimating, rounding Understanding + and – Mental calculation strategies (+ and –) Money and 'real life' problems Making decisions and checking results	
5–6	8	70–77 80–89 62–65	Measures, including problems Shape and space Reasoning about shapes	
7	2		**Assess and review**	

Oral and mental: eg counting, mental strategies, rapid recall

Unit	Days	Pages	Topic	Objectives
8	5	2–7 62–65	Counting and properties of numbers Reasoning about numbers	
9	5	8–19 24–29 32–41 66–69 58–61	Place value, ordering, estimating, rounding Understanding + and – Mental calculation strategies (+ and –) Money and 'real life' problems Making decisions and checking results	
10–11	10	46–51 54–57 66–69 58–61 20–23	Understanding × and ÷ Mental calculation strategies (× and ÷) Money and 'real life' problems Making decisions and checking results Fractions	
12–13	10	70–79 90–93	Measures, and time, including problems Handling data	
14	2		**Assess and review**	
Total	60			

Oral and mental: eg counting, mental strategies, rapid recall

Unit	Days	Pages	Topic	Objectives: children will be taught to...
1	3	2–7	Counting and properties of numbers	
2–4	15	8–19 24–29 32–41 66–69 58–61	Place value, ordering, estimating, rounding Understanding + and – Mental calculation strategies (+ and –) Money and 'real life' problems Making decisions and checking results	
5–6	8	70–77 80–89 62–65	Measures, including problems Shape and space Reasoning about shapes	
7	2		**Assess and review**	

Oral and mental: eg counting, mental strategies, rapid recall

Unit	Days	Pages	Topic	Objectives
8	5	2–7 62–65	Counting and properties of numbers Reasoning about numbers	
9	5	8–19 24–29 32–41 66–69 58–61	Place value, ordering, estimating, rounding Understanding + and – Mental calculation strategies (+ and –) Money and 'real life' problems Making decisions and checking results	
10	5	46–51 54–57 66–69 58–61 20–23	Understanding × and ÷ Mental calculation strategies (× and ÷) Money and 'real life' problems Making decisions and checking results Fractions	
11–12	10	70–79 90–93	Measures, and time, including problems Handling data	
13	2		**Assess and review**	
Total	55			

Numbers and the number system

2–7 Counting, properties of numbers and number sequences

- 3 • Count larger collections by grouping them: for example, in tens, then other numbers.
- 3, 5, 7 • Describe and extend number sequences:
  count on or back in tens or hundreds, starting from any two- or three-digit number.
  count on or back in twos starting from any two-digit number, and recognise odd and even numbers to at least 100;
  count on in steps of 3, 4 or 5 from any small number to at least 50, then back again.
- 7 • Recognise two-digit and three-digit multiples of 2, 5 or 10, and three-digit multiples of 50 and 100.

8–15 Place value and ordering

- 9 • **Read and write whole numbers to at least 1000** in figures and words.
- 9 • **Know what each digit represents**, and partition three-digit numbers into a multiple of 100, a multiple of ten and ones (HTU).
- 11 • Read and begin to write the vocabulary of comparing and ordering numbers, including ordinal numbers to at least 100. Compare two given three-digit numbers, say which is more or less, and give a number which lies between them.
- 13 • Say the number that is 1, 10 or 100 more or less than any given two- or three-digit number.
- 15 • **Order whole numbers to at least 1000**, and position them on a number line.

16–19 Estimating and rounding

- 17 • Read and begin to write the vocabulary of estimation and approximation.
  Give a sensible estimate of up to about 100 objects.
- 19 • Round any two-digit number to the nearest 10 and any three-digit number to the nearest 100.

20–23 Fractions

- 21, 23 • **Recognise unit fractions such as ½, ⅓, ¼, ⅕, ⅒... and use them to find fractions of shapes and numbers.**
  Begin to recognise simple fractions that are several parts of a whole, such as ¾, ⅔ or $\frac{3}{10}$.
  Begin to recognise simple equivalent fractions: for example, five tenths and one half, five fifths and one whole.
  Compare familiar fractions: for example, know that on the number line one half lies between one quarter and three quarters.
  Estimate a simple fraction.

NOTES • Key objectives are highlighted in **bold type**.
• Page references are to the supplement of examples for Years 1, 2 and 3.

Calculations

24–29 Understanding addition and subtraction

- 25, 29 • Extend understanding of the operations of addition and subtraction, read and begin to write the related vocabulary, and continue to recognise that addition can be done in any order. Use the +, – and = signs.
- 27 • Extend understanding that more than two numbers can be added; add three or four single-digit numbers mentally, or three or four two-digit numbers with the help of apparatus or pencil and paper.
- 25, 29 • Extend understanding that subtraction is the inverse of addition.

30–31 Rapid recall of addition and subtraction facts

- 31 • **Know by heart:**
  all addition and subtraction facts for each number to 20;
  all pairs of multiples of 100 with a total of 1000 (e.g. 300 + 700).
  Derive quickly:
  all pairs of multiples of 5 with a total of 100 (e.g. 35 + 65).

32–41 Mental calculation strategies (+ and –)

- 33 • Use knowledge that addition can be done in any order to do mental calculations more efficiently. For example:
  put the larger number first and count on;
  add three or four small numbers by putting the largest number first and/or by finding pairs totalling 9, 10 or 11;
  partition into '5 and a bit' when adding 6, 7, 8 or 9 (e.g. 47 + 8 = 45 + 2 + 5 + 3 = 50 + 5 = 55);
  partition into tens and units, then recombine (e.g. 34 + 53 = 30 + 50 + 4 + 3).
- 33 • Find a small difference by counting up from the smaller to the larger number (e.g. 102 – 97).
- 33 • Identify near doubles, using doubles already known (e.g. 80 + 81).
- 35 • **Add and subtract mentally a 'near multiple of 10' to or from a two-digit number**... by adding or subtracting 10, 20, 30... and adjusting.
- 35 • Use patterns of similar calculations.
- 35 • Say or write a subtraction statement corresponding to a given addition statement, and vice versa.
- 37, 39 • Use known number facts and place value to add/subtract mentally.
- 41 • Bridge through a multiple of 10, then adjust.

42–45 Pencil and paper procedures (+ and –)

- 43, 45 • Use informal pencil and paper methods to support, record or explain HTU ± TU, HTU ± HTU.
  Begin to use column addition and subtraction for HTU ± TU where the calculation cannot easily be done mentally.

46–51 Understanding multiplication and division

- 47 • Understand multiplication as repeated addition.
  Read and begin to write the related vocabulary.
  Extend understanding that multiplication can be done in any order.
- 49 • **Understand division** as grouping (repeated subtraction) or sharing. Read and begin to write the related vocabulary.
  Recognise that division is the inverse of multiplication, and that halving is the inverse of doubling.
- 51 • Begin to find remainders after simple division.
- 51 • Round up or down after division, depending on the context.

52–53 Rapid recall of multiplication and division facts

- 53 • **Know by heart:**
  multiplication facts for the 2, 5 and 10 times-tables.
  Begin to know the 3 and 4 times-tables.
- 53 • Derive quickly:
  division facts corresponding to the 2, 5 and 10 times-tables;
  doubles of all whole numbers to at least 20 (e.g. 17 + 17 or 17 × 2);
  doubles of multiples of 5 to 100 (e.g. 75 × 2, 90 × 2);
  doubles of multiples of 50 to 500 (e.g. 450 × 2);
  and all the corresponding halves (e.g. 36 ÷ 2, half of 130, 900 ÷ 2).

54–57 Mental calculation strategies (× and ÷)

- 55 • To multiply by 10/100, shift the digits one/two places to the left.
- 55 • Use doubling or halving, starting from known facts (e.g. 8 × 4 is double 4 × 4).
- 55 • Say or write a division statement corresponding to a given multiplication statement.
- 57 • Use known number facts and place value to carry out mentally simple multiplications and divisions.

58–59 Checking results of calculations

- 59 • Check subtraction with addition, halving with doubling and division with multiplication.
- 59 • Repeat addition or multiplication in a different order.
- 59 • Check with an equivalent calculation.

Solving problems

60–61 Making decisions

61 • **Choose and use appropriate operations (including multiplication and division) to solve word problems,** and appropriate ways of calculating: mental, mental with jottings, pencil and paper.
(For examples, see pages 62–71.)

62–65 Reasoning about numbers or shapes

63 • Solve mathematical problems or puzzles, recognise simple patterns and relationships, generalise and predict. Suggest extensions by asking 'What if...?'

65 • Investigate a general statement about familiar numbers or shapes by finding examples that satisfy it.

65 • **Explain methods and reasoning** orally and, where appropriate, in writing.

66–71 Problems involving 'real life', money and measures

67, 69, 71 • Solve word problems involving numbers in 'real life', money and measures, using one or more steps, including finding totals and giving change, and working out which coins to pay. Explain how the problem was solved.

69 • Recognise all coins and notes. **Understand and use £.p notation** (for example, know that £3.06 is £3 and 6p).

Handling data

90–93 Organising and using data

91, 93 • **Solve a given problem by organising and interpreting numerical data in simple lists, tables and graphs,** for example:
simple frequency tables;
pictograms – symbol representing two units;
bar charts – intervals labelled in ones then twos;
Venn and Carroll diagrams (one criterion).

Measures, shape and space

72–79 Measures

73 • Read and begin to write the vocabulary related to length, mass and capacity.
Measure and compare using standard units (km, m, cm, kg, g, l, ml), including using a ruler to draw and measure lines to the nearest half centimetre (see page 77).
Know the relationships between kilometres and metres, metres and centimetres, kilograms and grams, litres and millilitres.
Begin to use decimal notation for metres and centimetres.

75 • Suggest suitable units and measuring equipment to estimate or measure length, mass or capacity.

77 • Read scales to the nearest division (labelled or unlabelled).
Record estimates and measurements to the nearest whole or half unit (e.g. 'about 3.5 kg'), or in mixed units (e.g. '3 m and 20 cm').

79 • Read and begin to write the vocabulary related to time.
Use units of time and know the relationships between them (second, minute, hour, day, week, month, year). Suggest suitable units to estimate or measure time.
Use a calendar. Read the time to 5 minutes on an analogue clock and a 12-hour digital clock, and use the notation 9:40.

80–89 Shape and space

81 • Classify and describe 3-D and 2-D shapes, including the hemi-sphere, prism, semi-circle, quadrilateral...
referring to properties such as reflective symmetry (2-D), the number or shapes of faces, the number of sides/edges and vertices, whether sides/edges are the same length, whether or not angles are right angles...

83 • Make and describe shapes and patterns: for example, explore the different shapes that can be made from four cubes.
Relate solid shapes to pictures of them.

85 • **Identify** and sketch **lines of symmetry in simple shapes, and recognise shapes with no lines of symmetry.**
Sketch the reflection of a simple shape in a mirror line along one edge.

87 • Read and begin to write the vocabulary related to position, direction and movement: for example, describe and find the position of a square on a grid of squares with the rows and columns labelled.
Recognise and use the four compass directions N, S, E, W.

89 • Make and describe right-angled turns, including turns between the four compass points.
Identify right angles in 2-D shapes and the environment.
Recognise that a straight line is equivalent to two right angles.
Compare angles with a right angle.

Oral and mental: eg counting, mental strategies, rapid recall

Unit	Days	Pages	Topic	Objectives: children will be taught to...
1	3	8–19 76–77	Place value, ordering, estimating, rounding Reading numbers from scales	
2–3	10	24–29 32–41 66–69 58–61 42–45	Understanding + and – Mental calculation strategies (+ and –) Money and 'real life' problems Making decisions and checking results and in Term 3 Pencil and paper procedures	
4–6	13	70–77 80–89 62–65	Measures, including problems Shape and space Reasoning about shapes	
7	2		**Assess and review**	

Oral and mental: eg counting, mental strategies, rapid recall

Unit	Days	Pages	Topic	Objectives: children will be taught to...
8	5	2–7 62–65	Counting and properties of numbers Reasoning about numbers	
9–10	10	46–51 54–57 66–69 58–61	Understanding × and ÷ Mental calculation strategies (× and ÷) Money and 'real life' problems Making decisions and checking results	
11	5	20–23	Fractions	
12	5	24–29 32–41 42–45 71, 79 58–61	Understanding + and – Mental calculation strategies (+ and –) and in Term 3 Pencil and paper procedures Time, including problems Making decisions and checking results	
13	5	90–93	Handling data	
14	2		**Assess and review**	
Total	60			

Oral and mental: eg counting, mental strategies, rapid recall

Unit	Days	Pages	Topic	Objectives: children will be taught to...
1	3	8–19 76–77	Place value, ordering, estimating, rounding Reading numbers from scales	
2–3	10	24–29 32–41 66–69 58–61 42–45	Understanding + and – Mental calculation strategies (+ and –) Money and 'real life' problems Making decisions and checking results and in Term 3 Pencil and paper procedures	
4–6	13	80–89 62–65 70–79	Shape and space Reasoning about shapes Measures, and time, including problems	
7	2		**Assess and review**	

Oral and mental: eg counting, mental strategies, rapid recall

Unit	Days	Pages	Topic	Objectives: children will be taught to...
8	5	2–7 62–65	Counting and properties of numbers Reasoning about numbers	
9–10	10	24–29 32–41 46–51 54–57 66–69 58–61	Understanding + and – Mental calculation strategies (+ and –) Understanding × and ÷ Mental calculation strategies (× and ÷) Money and 'real life' problems Making decisions and checking results	
11	5	20–23	Fractions	
12	5	90–93	Handling data	
13	2		**Assess and review**	
Total	55			

Teaching programme: Year 4

Numbers and the number system

2–15 Place value, ordering and rounding (whole numbers)

2 • Read and write whole numbers to at least 10 000 in figures and words, and know what each digit represents.
Partition numbers into thousands, hundreds, tens and ones.

4 • Add/subtract 1, 10, 100 or 1000 to/from any integer, and count on or back in tens, hundreds or thousands from any whole number up to 10 000.

6 • Multiply or divide any integer up to 1000 by 10 (whole-number answers), and understand the effect.
Begin to multiply by 100.

8 • Read and write the vocabulary of comparing and ordering numbers. **Use symbols correctly, including less than (<), greater than (>), equals (=).**
Give one or more numbers lying between two given numbers and order a set of whole numbers less than 10 000.

10, 12 • Read and write the vocabulary of estimation and approximation. Make and justify estimates up to about 250, and estimate a proportion. **Round any positive integer less than 1000 to the nearest 10 or 100.**

14 • Recognise negative numbers in context (e.g. on a number line, on a temperature scale).

16–21 Properties of numbers and number sequences

16 • Recognise and extend number sequences formed by counting from any number in steps of constant size, extending beyond zero when counting back: for example, count on in steps of 25 to 500, and then back to, say, –100.

18 • Recognise odd and even numbers up to 1000, and some of their properties, including the outcome of sums or differences of pairs of odd/even numbers.

18 • Recognise multiples of 2, 3, 4, 5 and 10, up to the tenth multiple.

22–31 Fractions and decimals

22 • Use fraction notation. **Recognise simple fractions that are several parts of a whole,** such as $\frac{2}{3}$ or $\frac{5}{8}$, **and mixed numbers**, such as $5\frac{3}{4}$; **recognise the equivalence of simple fractions** (e.g. fractions equivalent to $\frac{1}{2}$, $\frac{1}{4}$ or $\frac{3}{4}$).
Identify two simple fractions with a total of 1 (e.g. $\frac{3}{10}$ and $\frac{7}{10}$).

22 • Order simple fractions: for example, decide whether fractions such as $\frac{3}{8}$ or $\frac{7}{10}$ are greater or less than one half.

24 • Begin to relate fractions to division and find simple fractions such as $\frac{1}{2}$, $\frac{1}{3}$, $\frac{1}{4}$, $\frac{1}{5}$, $\frac{1}{10}$... of numbers or quantities.
Find fractions such as $\frac{2}{3}$, $\frac{3}{4}$, $\frac{3}{5}$, $\frac{7}{10}$ ... of shapes.

26 • Begin to use ideas of simple proportion: for example, 'one for every...' and 'one in every...'

28 • Understand decimal notation and place value for tenths and hundredths, and use it in context. For example:
order amounts of money;
convert a sum of money such as £13.25 to pence, or a length such as 125 cm to metres;
round a sum of money to the nearest pound.

30 • Recognise the equivalence between the decimal and fraction forms of one half and one quarter, and tenths such as 0.3.

Calculations

34–37 Understanding addition and subtraction

34, 36 • Consolidate understanding of relationship between + and –.
Understand the principles (not the names) of the commutative and associative laws as they apply or not to addition and subtraction.

38–39 Rapid recall of addition and subtraction facts

38 • Consolidate knowing by heart:
addition and subtraction facts for all numbers to 20.
Derive quickly:
all number pairs that total 100 (e.g. 62 + 38, 75 + 25, 40 + 60);
all pairs of multiples of 50 with a total of 1000 (e.g. 850 + 150).

40–47 Mental calculation strategies (+ and –)

40 • Find a small difference by counting up (e.g. 5003 – 4996).

40 • Count on or back in repeated steps of 1, 10 or 100.

40 • Partition into tens and units, adding the tens first.

40 • Identify near doubles, using known doubles (e.g. 150 + 160).

40 • Add or subtract the nearest multiple of 10, then adjust.

42 • Continue to use the relationship between addition and subtraction.

42 • Add 3 or 4 small numbers, finding pairs totalling 10, or 9 or 11.
Add three two-digit multiples of 10, such as 40 + 70 + 50.

44, 46 • **Use known number facts and place value to add or subtract mentally, including any pair of two-digit whole numbers.**

48–51 Pencil and paper procedures (+ and –)

48, 50 • Use informal pencil and paper methods to support, record or explain additions/subtractions.
Develop and refine written methods for:
column addition and subtraction of two whole numbers less than 1000, and addition of more than two such numbers;
money calculations (for example, £7.85 ± £3.49).

52–57 Understanding multiplication and division

52, 54 • Extend understanding of the operations of × and ÷, and their relationship to each other and to + and –.
Understand the principles (not the names) of the commutative, associative and distributive laws as they apply to multiplication.

56 • **Find remainders after division.**
Divide a whole number of pounds by 2, 4, 5 or 10 to give £.p.
Round up or down after division, depending on the context.

58–59 Rapid recall of multiplication and division facts

58 • **Know by heart:**
multiplication facts for 2, 3, 4, 5 and 10 times-tables.

58 • Begin to know:
multiplication facts for 6, 7, 8 and 9 times-tables.

58 • **Derive quickly:**
division facts corresponding to 2, 3, 4, 5 and 10 times-tables;
doubles of all whole numbers to 50 (e.g. 38 + 38, or 38 × 2);
doubles of multiples of 10 to 500 (e.g. 460 × 2);
doubles of multiples of 100 to 5000 (e.g. 3400 × 2);
and the corresponding halves (e.g. 74 ÷ 2, $\frac{1}{2}$ of 420, half of 3800).

60–65 Mental calculation strategies (× and ÷)

60 • Use doubling or halving, starting from known facts. For example:
double/halve two-digit numbers by doubling/halving the tens first;
to multiply by 4, double, then double again;
to multiply by 5, multiply by 10 then halve;
to multiply by 20, multiply by 10 then double;
find the 8 times-table facts by doubling the 4 times-table;
find quarters by halving halves.

62 • Use closely related facts (e.g. to multiply by 9 or 11, multiply by 10 and adjust; develop the ×6 table from the ×4 and ×2 tables).

62 • Partition (e.g. 23 × 4 = (20 × 4) + (3 × 4)).

62 • Use the relationship between multiplication and division.

64 • Use known number facts and place value to multiply and divide integers, including by 10 and then 100 (whole-number answers).

66–69 Pencil and paper procedures (× and ÷)

66, 68 • Approximate first. Use informal pencil and paper methods to support, record or explain multiplications and divisions.
Develop and refine written methods for TU × U, TU ÷ U.

72–73 Checking results of calculations

72 • Check with the inverse operation.

72 • Check the sum of several numbers by adding in reverse order.

72 • Check with an equivalent calculation.

72 • Estimate and check by approximating (round to nearest 10 or 100).

72 • Use knowledge of sums or differences of odd/even numbers.

NOTES • Key objectives are highlighted in **bold type**.
• Page references are to the supplement of examples for Years 4, 5 and 6

Solving problems

74–75 Making decisions

74 • **Choose and use appropriate number operations and appropriate ways of calculating (mental, mental with jottings, pencil and paper) to solve problems.**
(For examples of problems see pages 78, 82–89, 100.)

76–81 Reasoning about numbers and shapes

76 • Explain methods and reasoning about numbers orally and in writing.

78 • Solve mathematical problems or puzzles, recognise and explain patterns and relationships, generalise and predict. Suggest extensions by asking 'What if...?'

80 • Make and investigate a general statement about familiar numbers or shapes by finding examples that satisfy it.

82–89 Problems involving 'real life', money and measures

82–89 • Use all four operations to solve word problems involving numbers in 'real life', money and measures (including time), using one or more steps, including converting pounds to pence and metres to centimetres and vice versa.

Handling data

114–117 Organising and interpreting data

114, 116 • Solve a problem by collecting quickly, organising, representing and interpreting data in tables, charts, graphs and diagrams, including those generated by a computer, for example:
tally charts and frequency tables;
pictograms – symbol representing 2, 5, 10 or 20 units;
bar charts – intervals labelled in 2s, 5s, 10s or 20s;
Venn and Carroll diagrams (two criteria).

Measures, shape and space

90–101 Measures

90 • Use, read and write standard metric units (km, m, cm, mm, kg, g, l, ml), including their abbreviations, and imperial units (mile, pint).

90 • **Know and use the relationships between familiar units of length, mass and capacity.**
Know the equivalent of one half, one quarter, three quarters and one tenth of 1 km, 1 m, 1 kg, 1 litre in m, cm, g, ml. Convert up to 1000 centimetres to metres, and vice versa.

92, 94 • Suggest suitable units and measuring equipment to estimate or measure length, mass or capacity.
Record estimates and readings from scales to a suitable degree of accuracy.

96 • Measure and calculate the perimeter and area of rectangles and other simple shapes, using counting methods and standard units (cm, cm^2).

98, 100 • Use, read and write the vocabulary related to time.
Estimate/check times using seconds, minutes, hours.
Read the time from an analogue clock to the nearest minute, and from a 12-hour digital clock.
Use am and pm and the notation 9:53.
Read simple timetables and use this year's calendar.

102–111 Shape and space

102 • Describe and visualise 3-D and 2-D shapes, including the tetrahedron and heptagon.
Recognise equilateral and isosceles triangles.
Classify polygons using criteria such as number of right angles, whether or not they are regular, symmetry properties.

104 • Make shapes: for example, construct polygons by paper folding or using pinboard, and discuss properties such as lines of symmetry.
Visualise 3-D shapes from 2-D drawings and identify simple nets of solid shapes.

106 • Sketch the reflection of a simple shape in a mirror line parallel to one side (all sides parallel or perpendicular to the mirror line).

108 • Recognise positions and directions: for example, describe and find the position of a point on a grid of squares where the lines are numbered.
Recognise simple examples of horizontal and vertical lines.
Use the eight compass directions N, S, E, W, NE, NW, SE, SW.

110 • Make and measure clockwise and anti-clockwise turns: for example, from SW to N, or from 4 to 10 on a clock face.
Begin to know that angles are measured in degrees and that:
one whole turn is 360° or 4 right angles;
a quarter turn is 90° or one right angle;
half a right angle is 45°.
Start to order a set of angles less than 180°.

Oral and mental: eg counting, mental strategies, rapid recall

Unit	Days	Pages	Topic	Objectives: children will be taught to...
1	3	2–15 94–95	Place value, ordering and rounding Reading numbers from scales	
2–3	10	34–37 40–47 48–51 82–85 72–75	Understanding + and – Mental calculation strategies (+ and –) Pencil and paper procedures (+ and –) Money and 'real life' problems Making decisions and checking results	
4–6	13	86–101 102–111 76–81	Measures, including problems Shape and space Reasoning about shapes	
7	2		**Assess and review**	

Oral and mental: eg counting, mental strategies, rapid recall

Unit	Days	Pages	Topic	Objectives: children will be taught to...
8	5	16–21 76–81	Properties of numbers Reasoning about numbers	
9–10	10	52–57 60–65 66–69 82–85 72–75	Understanding × and ÷ Mental calculation strategies (× and ÷) Pencil and paper procedures (× and ÷) Money and 'real life' problems Making decisions and checking results	
11	5	22–31	Fractions and decimals	
12	5	34–37 40–47 48–51 98–101 88	Understanding + and – Mental calculation strategies (+ and –) Pencil and paper procedures (+ and –) Time, including problems	
13	5	114–117	Handling data	
14	2		**Assess and review**	
Total	60			

Oral and mental: eg counting, mental strategies, rapid recall

Unit	Days	Pages	Topic	Objectives: children will be taught to...
1	3	2–15 94–95	Place value, ordering and rounding Reading numbers from scales	
2–3	10	34–37 40–47 48–51 82–85 72–75	Understanding + and – Mental calculation strategies (+ and –) Pencil and paper procedures (+ and –) Money and 'real life' problems Making decisions and checking results	
4–6	13	86–101 102–111 76–81	Measures, including problems Shape and space Reasoning about shapes	
7	2		**Assess and review**	

Oral and mental: eg counting, mental strategies, rapid recall

Unit	Days	Pages	Topic	Objectives: children will be taught to...
8	5	16–21 76–81	Properties of numbers Reasoning about numbers	
9–10	10	52–57 60–65 66–69 82–85 72–75	Understanding × and ÷ Mental calculation strategies (× and ÷) Pencil and paper procedures (× and ÷) Money and 'real life' problems Making decisions and checking results	
11	5	22–31	Fractions and decimals	
12	5	114–117	Handling data	
13	2		**Assess and review**	
Total	55			

Teaching programme: Year 5

Numbers and the number system

2–15 Place value, ordering and rounding

- 3 • Read and write whole numbers in figures and words, and know what each digit represents. (For decimals, see page 29.)
- 7 • **Multiply and divide any positive integer up to 10 000 by 10 or 100 and understand the effect** (e.g. 9900 ÷ 10, 737 ÷ 10, 2060 ÷ 100).
- 9 • Use the vocabulary of comparing and ordering numbers, including symbols such as $<$, $>$, , , =. Give one or more numbers lying between two given numbers. Order a set of integers less than 1 million. (For decimals, see page 29.)
- 11, 13 • Use the vocabulary of estimation and approximation. Make and justify estimates of large numbers, and estimate simple proportions such as one third, seven tenths. Round any integer up to 10 000 to the nearest 10, 100 or 1000. (For rounding decimals, see page 31.)
- 15 • **Order a given set of positive and negative integers** (e.g. on a number line, on a temperature scale). Calculate a temperature rise or fall across 0 °C.

16–21 Properties of numbers and number sequences

- 17 • Recognise and extend number sequences formed by counting from any number in steps of constant size, extending beyond zero when counting back. For example: count on in steps of 25 to 1000, and then back; count on or back in steps of 0.1, 0.2, 0.3…
- 19 • Make general statements about odd or even numbers, including the outcome of sums and differences.
- 19 • Recognise multiples of 6, 7, 8, 9, up to the 10th multiple. Know and apply tests of divisibility by 2, 4, 5, 10 or 100.
- 21 • Know squares of numbers to at least 10 × 10.
- 21 • Find all the pairs of factors of any number up to 100.

22–33 Fractions, decimals and percentages, ratio and proportion

- 23 • Use fraction notation, including mixed numbers, and the vocabulary numerator and denominator. Change an improper fraction to a mixed number (e.g. change $\frac{13}{10}$ to $1\frac{3}{10}$). Recognise when two simple fractions are equivalent, including relating hundredths to tenths (e.g. $\frac{70}{100} = \frac{7}{10}$).
- 23 • Order a set of fractions such as 2, $2\frac{3}{4}$, $1\frac{3}{4}$, $2\frac{1}{2}$, $1\frac{1}{2}$, and position them on a number line.
- 25 • **Relate fractions to division**, and use division to find simple fractions, including tenths and hundredths, of numbers and quantities (e.g. $\frac{3}{4}$ of 12, $\frac{1}{10}$ of 50, $\frac{1}{100}$ of £3).
- 27 • Solve simple problems using ideas of ratio and proportion ('one for every…' and 'one in every…').
- 29 • **Use decimal notation for tenths and hundredths.** Know what each digit represents in a number with up to two decimal places. Order a set of numbers or measurements with the same number of decimal places.
- 31 • **Round a number with one or two decimal places to the nearest integer.**
- 31 • **Relate fractions to their decimal representations**: that is, recognise the equivalence between the decimal and fraction forms of one half, one quarter, three quarters… and tenths and hundredths (e.g. $\frac{7}{10} = 0.7$, $\frac{27}{100} = 0.27$).
- 33 • Begin to understand percentage as the number of parts in every 100, and find simple percentages of small whole-number quantities (e.g. 25% of £8). Express one half, one quarter, three quarters, and tenths and hundredths, as percentages (e.g. know that $\frac{3}{4}$ = 75%).

Calculations

38–39 Rapid recall of addition and subtraction facts

- 39 • Derive quickly or continue to derive quickly: decimals that total 1 (e.g. 0.2 + 0.8) or 10 (e.g. 6.2 + 3.8); all two-digit pairs that total 100 (e.g. 43 + 57); all pairs of multiples of 50 with a total of 1000 (e.g. 350 + 650).

40–47 Mental calculation strategies (+ and –)

- 41 • Find differences by counting up through next multiple of 10, 100 or 1000, e.g. **calculate mentally a difference such as 8006 – 2993.**
- 41 • Partition into H, T and U, adding the most significant digits first.
- 41 • Identify near doubles, such as 1.5 + 1.6.
- 41 • Add or subtract the nearest multiple of 10 or 100, then adjust.
- 43 • Develop further the relationship between addition and subtraction.
- 43 • Add several numbers (e.g. four or five single digits, or multiples of 10 such as 40 + 50 + 80).
- 45, 47 • Use known number facts and place value for mental addition and subtraction (e.g. 470 + 380, 810 – 380, 7.4 + 9.8, 9.2 – 8.6).

48–51 Pencil and paper procedures (+ and –)

- 49, 51 • Use informal pencil and paper methods to support, record or explain additions and subtractions. **Extend written methods to: column addition/subtraction of two integers less than 10 000;** addition of more than two integers less than 10 000; addition or subtraction of a pair of decimal fractions, both with one or both with two decimal places (e.g. £29.78 + £53.34).

52–57 Understanding multiplication and division

- 53, 55 • Understand the effect of and relationships between the four operations, and the principles (not the names) of the arithmetic laws as they apply to multiplication. Begin to use brackets.
- 57 • Begin to express a quotient as a fraction, or as a decimal when dividing a whole number by 2, 4, 5 or 10, or when dividing £.p. Round up or down after division, depending on the context.

58–59 Rapid recall of multiplication and division facts

- 59 • **Know by heart all multiplication facts up to 10 × 10.**
- 59 • Derive quickly or continue to derive quickly: division facts corresponding to tables up to 10 × 10; doubles of all whole numbers 1 to 100 (e.g. 78 × 2); doubles of multiples of 10 to 1000 (e.g. 670 × 2); doubles of multiples of 100 to 10 000 (e.g. 6500 × 2); and the corresponding halves.

60–65 Mental calculation strategies (× and ÷)

- 61 • Use doubling or halving, starting from known facts. For example: double/halve any two-digit number by doubling/halving the tens first; double one number and halve the other; to multiply by 25, multiply by 100 then divide by 4; find the ×16 table facts by doubling the ×8 table; find sixths by halving thirds.
- 61 • Use factors (e.g. 8 × 12 = 8 × 4 × 3).
- 63 • Use closely related facts (e.g. multiply by 19 or 21 by multiplying by 20 and adjusting; develop the ×12 table from the ×10 and ×2 tables).
- 63 • Partition (e.g. 47 × 6 = (40 × 6) + (7 × 6)).
- 63 • Use the relationship between multiplication and division.
- 65 • Use known facts and place value to multiply and divide mentally.

66–69 Pencil and paper procedures (× and ÷)

- 67, 69 • Approximate first. Use informal pencil and paper methods to support, record or explain multiplications and divisions. **Extend written methods to: short multiplication of HTU** or U.t **by U; long multiplication of TU by TU; short division of HTU by U** (with integer remainder).

70–71 Using a calculator

- 71 • Develop calculator skills and use a calculator effectively.

72–73 Checking results of calculations

- 73 • Check with the inverse operation when using a calculator.
- 73 • Check the sum of several numbers by adding in the reverse order.
- 73 • Check with an equivalent calculation.
- 73 • Estimate by approximating (round to nearest 10 or 100), then check result.
- 73 • Use knowledge of sums and differences of odd/even numbers.

NOTES • Key objectives are highlighted in **bold type**.
• Page references are to the supplement of examples for Years 4, 5 and 6.

Solving problems

74–75 Making decisions

75 • Choose and use appropriate number operations to solve problems, and appropriate ways of calculating: mental, mental with jottings, written methods, calculator.
(For examples of problems see pages 34–37, 79, 82–89, 101.)

76–81 Reasoning and generalising about numbers or shapes

77 • Explain methods and reasoning, orally and in writing.

79 • Solve mathematical problems or puzzles, recognise and explain patterns and relationships, generalise and predict. Suggest extensions asking 'What if...?'

81 • Make and investigate a general statement about familiar numbers or shapes by finding examples that satisfy it. Explain a generalised relationship (formula) in words.

82–89 Problems involving 'real life', money and measures

82–89 • **Use all four operations to solve simple word problems involving numbers and quantities** based on 'real life', money and measures **(including time)**, using one or more steps, including making simple conversions of pounds to foreign currency and finding simple percentages.
Explain methods and reasoning.

Handling data

112–117 Organising and interpreting data

113 • Discuss the chance or likelihood of particular events.

115, 117 • Solve a problem by representing and interpreting data in tables, charts, graphs and diagrams, including those generated by a computer, for example:
bar line charts, vertical axis labelled in 2s, 5s, 10s, 20s or 100s, first where intermediate points have no meaning (e.g. scores on a dice rolled 50 times), then where they may have meaning (e.g. room temperature over time).

117 • Find the mode of a set of data.

Measures, shape and space

90–101 Measures

91 • Use, read and write standard metric units (km, m, cm, mm, kg, g, l, ml), including their abbreviations, and relationships between them. Convert larger to smaller units (e.g. km to m, m to cm or mm, kg to g, l to ml).
Know imperial units (mile, pint, gallon).

93, 95 • Suggest suitable units and measuring equipment to estimate or measure length, mass or capacity.
Measure and draw lines to the nearest millimetre.
Record estimates and readings from scales to a suitable degree of accuracy.

97 • **Understand area measured in square centimetres (cm^2). Understand and use the formula in words 'length $\times$ breadth' for the area of a rectangle.**
Understand, measure and calculate perimeters of rectangles and regular polygons.

99, 101 • Use units of time; read the time on a 24-hour digital clock and use 24-hour clock notation, such as 19:53. Use timetables.

102–111 Shape and space

103 • **Recognise properties of rectangles.**
Classify triangles (isosceles, equilateral, scalene), using criteria such as equal sides, equal angles, lines of symmetry.

105 • Make shapes with increasing accuracy.
Visualise 3-D shapes from 2-D drawings and identify different nets for an open cube.

107 • Recognise reflective symmetry in regular polygons: for example, know that a square has four axes of symmetry and an equilateral triangle has three.
Complete symmetrical patterns with two lines of symmetry at right angles (using squared paper or pegboard).
Recognise where a shape will be after reflection in a mirror line parallel to one side (sides not all parallel or perpendicular to the mirror line).
Recognise where a shape will be after a translation.

109 • Recognise positions and directions:
read and plot co-ordinates in the first quadrant;
recognise perpendicular and parallel lines.

111 • Understand and use angle measure in degrees.
Identify, estimate and order acute and obtuse angles.
Use a protractor to measure and draw acute and obtuse angles to the nearest 5°.
Calculate angles in a straight line.

Oral and mental: eg counting, mental strategies, rapid recall

Unit	Days	Pages	Topic	Objectives: children will be taught to...
1	3	2–15 70–71	Place value, ordering and rounding Using a calculator	
2–3	10	52–57 60–65 66–69 82–85 70–75	Understanding × and ÷ Mental calculation strategies (× and ÷) Pencil and paper procedures (× and ÷) Money and 'real life' problems Making decisions and checking results, including using a calculator	
4–5	10	22–33 26–27	Fractions, decimals and percentages Ratio and proportion	
6	8	112–117 70–71	Handling data Using a calculator	
7	2		**Assess and review**	

Oral and mental: eg counting, mental strategies, rapid recall

Unit	Days	Pages	Topic	Objectives: children will be taught to...
8–10	15	102–111 76–81 86–101	Shape and space Reasoning about shapes Measures, including problems	
11	5	40–47 48–51 82–85 70–75	Mental calculation strategies (+ and –) Pencil and paper procedures (+ and –) Money and 'real life' problems Making decisions and checking results, including using a calculator	
12	5	16–21 76–81	Properties of numbers Reasoning about numbers	
13	2		**Assess and review**	
Total	60			

Oral and mental: eg counting, mental strategies, rapid recall

Unit	Days	Pages	Topic	Objectives: children will be taught to...
1	3	2–15 70–71	Place value, ordering and rounding Using a calculator	
2–3	10	52–57 60–65 66–69 82–85 70–75	Understanding × and ÷ Mental calculation strategies (× and ÷) Pencil and paper procedures (× and ÷) Money and 'real life' problems Making decisions and checking results, including using a calculator	
4	5	22–33 70–71	Fractions, decimals and percentages Using a calculator	
5	8	102–111 76–81	Shape and space Reasoning about shapes	
6	2		**Assess and review**	

Oral and mental: eg counting, mental strategies, rapid recall

Unit	Days	Pages	Topic	Objectives: children will be taught to...
7–8	10	86–101 112–117	Measures, including problems Handling data	
9–10	10	40–47 48–51 82–85 70–75	Mental calculation strategies (+ and –) Pencil and paper procedures (+ and –) Money and 'real life' problems Making decisions and checking results, including using a calculator	
11	5	16–21 76–81	Properties of numbers Reasoning about numbers	
12	2		**Assess and review**	
Total	55			

Teaching programme: Year 6

Numbers and the number system

2–15 Place value, ordering and rounding

7 • **Multiply and divide decimals mentally by 10 or 100, and integers by 1000, and explain the effect.**
(For more on place value with decimals, see page 29.)

11, 13 • Use the vocabulary of estimation and approximation.
Consolidate rounding an integer to the nearest 10, 100 or 1000.
(For rounding decimals, see page 31.)

15 • Find the difference between a positive and a negative integer, or two negative integers, in a context such as temperature or the number line, and order a set of positive and negative integers.

16–21 Properties of numbers and number sequences

17 • Recognise and extend number sequences, such as the sequence of square numbers, or the sequence of triangular numbers 1, 3, 6, 10, 15...
Count on in steps of 0.1, 0.2, 0.25, 0.5..., and then back.

19 • Make general statements about odd or even numbers, including the outcome of products.

19 • Recognise multiples up to 10 × 10. Know and apply simple tests of divisibility. Find simple common multiples.

21 • Recognise squares of numbers to at least 12 × 12.

21 • Recognise prime numbers to at least 20.
Factorise numbers to 100 into prime factors.

22–33 Fractions, decimals, percentages, ratio and proportion

23 • Change a fraction such as $\frac{33}{8}$ to the equivalent mixed number $4\frac{1}{8}$, and vice versa.
Recognise relationships between fractions: for example, that $\frac{1}{10}$ is ten times $\frac{1}{100}$, and $\frac{1}{16}$ is half of $\frac{1}{8}$.
Reduce a fraction to its simplest form by cancelling common factors in the numerator and denominator.

23 • Order fractions such as $\frac{2}{3}$, $\frac{3}{4}$ and $\frac{5}{6}$ by converting them to fractions with a common denominator, and position them on a number line.

25 • **Use a fraction as an 'operator' to find fractions,** including tenths and hundredths, **of numbers or quantities (e.g. $\frac{5}{8}$ of 32, $\frac{7}{10}$ of 40, $\frac{9}{100}$ of 400 centimetres).**

27 • **Solve simple problems involving ratio and proportion.**

29 • Use decimal notation for tenths and hundredths in calculations, and tenths, hundredths and thousandths when recording measurements.
Know what each digit represents in a number with up to three decimal places.
Give a decimal fraction lying between two others (e.g. between 3.4 and 3.5).
Order a mixed set of numbers or measurements **with up to three decimal places.**

31 • Round a number with two decimal places to the nearest tenth or to the nearest whole number.

31 • Recognise the equivalence between the decimal and fraction forms of one half, one quarter, three quarters, one eighth... and tenths, hundredths and thousandths (e.g. $\frac{700}{1000} = \frac{70}{100} = \frac{7}{10} = 0.7$).
Begin to convert a fraction to a decimal using division.

33 • **Understand percentage as the number of parts in every 100.** Express simple fractions such as one half, one quarter, three quarters, one third, two thirds..., and tenths and hundredths, as percentages (e.g. know that $\frac{1}{3} = 33\frac{1}{3}\%$).
Find simple percentages of small whole-number quantities (e.g. find 10% of £500, then 20%, 40% and 80% by doubling).

NOTES • Key objectives are highlighted in **bold type**.
• Page references are to the supplement of examples for Years 4, 5 and 6.

Calculations

40–47 Mental calculation strategies (+ and −)

41, 43 • Consolidate all strategies from previous year, including:
find a difference by counting up;
add or subtract the nearest multiple of 10, 100 or 1000, then adjust;
use the relationship between addition and subtraction;
add several numbers.

45, 47 • Use known number facts and place value to consolidate mental addition/subtraction (e.g. 470 + 380, 810 − 380, 7.4 + 9.8, 9.2 − 8.6).

48–51 Pencil and paper procedures (+ and −)

49, 51 • Use informal pencil and paper methods to support, record or explain additions and subtractions.
Extend written methods to column addition and subtraction of numbers involving decimals.

52–57 Understanding multiplication and division

53, 55 • Understand and use the relationships between the four operations, and the principles (not the names) of the arithmetic laws.
Use brackets.

57 • Express a quotient as a fraction or as a decimal rounded to one decimal place. Divide £.p by a two-digit number to give £.p.
Round up or down after division, depending on the context.

58–59 Rapid recall of multiplication and division facts

59 • Consolidate knowing by heart:
multiplication facts up to 10 × 10.

59 • **Derive quickly:**
division facts corresponding to tables up to 10 × 10;
squares of multiples of 10 to 100 (e.g. 60 × 60);
doubles of two-digit numbers (e.g. 3.8 × 2, 0.76 × 2);
doubles of multiples of 10 to 1000 (e.g. 670 × 2);
doubles of multiples of 100 to 10 000 (e.g. 6500 × 2);
and the corresponding halves.

60–65 Mental calculation strategies (× and ÷)

61 • Use related facts and doubling or halving. For example:
double or halve the most significant digit first;
to multiply by 25, multiply by 100 then divide by 4;
double one number and halve the other;
find the ×24 table by doubling the ×6 table twice.

61 • Use factors (e.g. 35 × 18 = 35 × 6 × 3).

63 • Use closely related facts: for example, multiply by 49 or 51 by multiplying by 50 and adjusting.
Develop the ×17 table by adding facts from the ×10 and ×7 tables.

63 • Partition (e.g. 87 × 6 = (80 × 6) + (7 × 6);
3.4 × 3 = (3 × 3) + (0.4 × 3)).

63 • Use the relationship between multiplication and division.

65 • Use known number facts and place value to consolidate mental multiplication and division.

66–69 Pencil and paper procedures (× and ÷)

67, 69 • Approximate first. Use informal pencil and paper methods to support, record or explain multiplications and divisions.
Extend written methods to:
multiplication of ThHTU × U (short multiplication);
short multiplication of numbers involving decimals;
long multiplication of a three-digit by a two-digit integer;
short division of TU or HTU by U (mixed-number answer);
division of HTU by TU (long division, whole-number answer);
short division of numbers involving decimals.

70–71 Using a calculator

71 • Develop calculator skills and use a calculator effectively.

72–73 Checking results of calculations

73 • Check with the inverse operation when using a calculator.

73 • Check the sum of several numbers by adding in reverse order.

73 • Check with an equivalent calculation.

73 • Estimate by approximating (round to nearest 10, 100 or 1000), then check result.

73 • Use knowledge of sums, differences, products of odd/even numbers.

73 • Use tests of divisibility.

Solving problems

74–75 Making decisions

75 • Choose and use appropriate number operations to solve problems, and appropriate ways of calculating: mental, mental with jottings, written methods, calculator.
(For examples of problems see pages 34–37, 79, 82–89, 101.)

76–81 Reasoning and generalising about numbers or shapes

77 • Explain methods and reasoning, orally and in writing.

79 • Solve mathematical problems or puzzles, recognise and explain patterns and relationships, generalise and predict. Suggest extensions asking 'What if...?'

81 • Make and investigate a general statement about familiar numbers or shapes by finding examples that satisfy it.
Develop from explaining a generalised relationship in words to expressing it in a formula using letters as symbols (e.g. the cost of *n* articles at 15p each).

82–89 Problems involving 'real life', money or measures

82–89 • **Identify and use appropriate operations (including combinations of operations) to solve word problems involving numbers and quantities** based on 'real life', money or measures (including time), using one or more steps, including converting pounds to foreign currency, or vice versa, and calculating percentages such as VAT.
Explain methods and reasoning.

Handling data

112–117 Handling data

113 • Use the language associated with probability to discuss events, including those with equally likely outcomes.

115, 117 • **Solve a problem by** representing, **extracting and interpreting data in tables, graphs, charts** and diagrams, including those generated by a computer, for example:
line graphs (e.g. for distance/time, for a multiplication table, a conversion graph, a graph of pairs of numbers adding to 8);
frequency tables and bar charts with grouped discrete data (e.g. test marks 0–5, 6–10, 11–15...).

117 • Find the mode and range of a set of data.
Begin to find the median and mean of a set of data.

Measures, shape and space

90–101 Measures

91 • Use, read and write standard metric units (km, m, cm, mm, kg, g, l, ml, cl), including their abbreviations, and relationships between them. Convert smaller to larger units (e.g. m to km, cm or mm to m, g to kg, ml to l) and vice versa.
Know imperial units (mile, pint, gallon, lb, oz).
Know rough equivalents of lb and kg, oz and g, miles and km, litres and pints or gallons.

93, 95 • Suggest suitable units and measuring equipment to estimate or measure length, mass or capacity.
Record estimates and readings from scales to a suitable degree of accuracy.

97 • **Calculate the perimeter and area of simple compound shapes that can be split into rectangles.**

99, 101 • Appreciate different times around the world.

102–111 Shape and space

103, 109 • Describe and visualise properties of solid shapes such as parallel or perpendicular faces or edges.
Classify quadrilaterals, using criteria such as parallel sides, equal angles, equal sides...

105 • Make shapes with increasing accuracy.
Visualise 3-D shapes from 2-D drawings and identify different nets for a closed cube.

107 • Recognise where a shape will be after reflection:
in a mirror line touching the shape at a point (sides of shape not necessarily parallel or perpendicular to the mirror line);
in two mirror lines at right angles (sides of shape all parallel or perpendicular to the mirror line).
Recognise where a shape will be after two translations.

109 • **Read and plot co-ordinates in all four quadrants.**

111 • Recognise and estimate angles.
Use a protractor to measure and draw **acute and obtuse angles to the nearest degree.**
Check that the sum of the angles of a triangle is 180°: for example, by measuring or paper folding.
Calculate angles in a triangle or around a point.
Recognise where a shape will be after a rotation through 90° about one of its vertices.

Oral and mental: eg counting, mental strategies, rapid recall

Unit	Days	Pages	Topic	Objectives: children will be taught to...
1	3	2–15 70–71	Place value, ordering and rounding Using a calculator	
2–3	10	52–57 60–65 66–69 82–85 70–75	Understanding × and ÷ Mental calculation strategies (× and ÷) Pencil and paper procedures (× and ÷) Money and 'real life' problems Making decisions and checking results, including using a calculator	
4–5	10	22–33 26–27	Fractions, decimals and percentages Ratio and proportion	
6	8	112–117 70–71	Handling data Using a calculator	
7	2		**Assess and review**	

Oral and mental: eg counting, mental strategies, rapid recall

Unit	Days	Pages	Topic	Objectives
8–10	15	102–111 76–81 86–101	Shape and space Reasoning about shapes Measures, including problems	
11	5	40–47 48–51 82–85 70–75	Mental calculation strategies (+ and –) Pencil and paper procedures (+ and –) Money and 'real life' problems Making decisions and checking results, including using a calculator	
12	5	16–21 76–81	Properties of numbers Reasoning about numbers	
13	2		**Assess and review**	
Total	60			

Oral and mental: eg counting, mental strategies, rapid recall

Unit	Days	Pages	Topic	Objectives: children will be taught to...
1	3	2–15 70–71	Place value, ordering and rounding Using a calculator	
2–3	10	52–57 60–65 66–69 82–85 70–75	Understanding × and ÷ Mental calculation strategies (× and ÷) Pencil and paper procedures (× and ÷) Money and 'real life' problems Making decisions and checking results, including using a calculator	
4	5	22–33 70–71	Fractions, decimals and percentages Using a calculator	
5	8	102–111 76–81	Shape and space Reasoning about shapes	
6	2		**Assess and review**	

Oral and mental: eg counting, mental strategies, rapid recall

Unit	Days	Pages	Topic	Objectives: children will be taught to...
7–8	10	86–101 112–117	Measures, including problems Handling data	
9–10	10	40–47 48–51 82–85 70–75	Mental calculation strategies (+ and –) Pencil and paper procedures (+ and –) Money and 'real life' problems Making decisions and checking results, including using a calculator	
11	5	16–21 76–81	Properties of numbers Reasoning about numbers	
12	2		**Assess and review**	
Total	55			

Supplement of examples: **Reception**

4

Supplement of examples:
Reception

Children should be taught to:	As end-of-year outcomes, children should, for example:
Say and use the number names in familiar contexts	Say the number names in familiar contexts such as number rhymes, songs, stories, counting games and other activities. For example, join in rhymes or songs like: *One, two, three, four, five. Once I caught a fish alive...* *One potato, two potatoes, three potatoes, four...* *Higgledy, Piggledy, my fat hen...* *This old man, he played one...* Recite the sequence: *one, two, three...* • first to ten, progressing to twenty, counting consistently through the unorthodox teens; • then to beyond twenty, recognising that 'somethingty-nine' signals a change in the decade, so that 'twenty-nine' is not followed by 'twenty-ten'. Overcome difficulties and recognise recitation errors, perhaps by saying what is wrong when a puppet 'speaks'. For example, with numbers one to ten: *one, two, four, five...* — word omitted *one, two, four, three, five...* — words in the wrong order *one, two, three, three, four...* — repeating a word Then with numbers to twenty and beyond: *thirteen, fourteen, fiveteen...* — not changing the pattern *eighteen, nineteen, tenteen...* — error by analogy *thirty-nine, thirty-ten...* — error by analogy
Recite the number names in order, continuing the count from a given number	Recite starting from a given number name: • when the recitation is begun from one by someone else; • when it does not begin from one; • when given a specific number name to continue from. Say the number name that goes after a given number name. For example: • What number comes next after six when you count? After eight? After sixteen? Start from a given number name and stop at another. • Start with two. Hold it in your head. Count on to eight... *three, four, five, six, seven, eight.* Now start with seven. Count on to twelve... *eight, nine, ten, eleven, twelve.* • Count on round the circle of children. Start at Jo with five. Who do you think will say ten? Count on several numbers from a given number. Use your fingers to help. • Count on three numbers from four... *five, six, seven.* • Count on four, starting from eleven... *twelve, thirteen, fourteen, fifteen.* **See also counting on (page 15).**

Children should be taught to:	As end-of-year outcomes, children should, for example:

Recite the number names in order, counting back from a given number

Join in rhymes or sing songs such as:

Five little ducks went swimming one day…
Five little speckled frogs…
Five little monkeys jumping into bed…
Five currant buns in the baker's shop…
Alice the camel has ten humps…
Ten green bottles…
One man went to mow…

Say the number name that goes before a given number name. For example:

- What number comes one before six when you count? Before nine? Before fourteen?

Start to use *zero* as an extension of the counting sequence when counting backwards (the number name for 'none').
See also recognising zero (page 5).

Recite the number sequence consistently back to zero:

- starting from five… from ten… from twenty…
- from a number such as seven… or sixteen… or thirty-one…

Start from a given number name and stop at another.

- Start with nine. Hold it in your head. Count back to three…
  eight, seven, six, five, four, three.
  Now start with twelve. Count back to five…
  Now start with nineteen. Count back to ten…
- Count back round the circle of children, starting at Jo with ten. Who do you think will say six?

Count back several numbers from a given number.
Use your fingers to help.

- Count back three numbers from four…
  three, two, one.
- Count back four, starting from seventeen…
  sixteen, fifteen, fourteen, thirteen.

See also counting back (page 17).

Children should be taught to:	As end-of-year outcomes, children should, for example:

Count reliably a set of everyday objects

Begin to understand in practical contexts:
count, how many…?

Count a number of objects (first up to 5, progressing to up to 10, then beyond, using a wide variety of opportunities). Give one and only one number name in one-to-one correspondence with each object. For example, count the number of:
- sand pies made in the sand tray;
- tiny things you can pack in a matchbox;
- hats you can find in the set of dressing-up clothes;
- pieces in the jigsaw;
- children who are playing in the home corner… who are waiting in the queue… who have finished their painting…;
- peas that you find in different pods;
- penny coins in the till;
- letters in your name;
- times you can bounce or catch the ball… can throw a bean bag in the bucket… can hop while the tambourine shakes…

Count the same number of different objects. Begin to realise when counting that the number of objects is not affected by their size or position, or whether or not they are of the same type. For example:
- count six buttons, six pencils, six bricks, six tables, six children, six hoops, six £1 coins, six mixed coins, six random objects from the 'bits and pieces' box…
- count them in a different order…
- count them spread out, close together, in a line, stacked up…

Count out a specified number of things from a collection of objects. For example, count out or take a given number of:
- beans to plant in a pot from a packet;
- plates, cups and spoons… from the 'kitchen';
- farm animals for each 'field';
- penny coins from the till.

Recognise small numbers of objects without counting, then check by counting one by one, for example:
- collections of up to three objects;
- the numbers of fingers held up on one then two hands;
- dot patterns on a 1–6 dice, playing cards or dominoes.

Begin to realise through a variety of counting opportunities:
- that there is no need to count when the number can be recognised without counting;
- that the purpose of counting is to tell how many there are;
- that the last number name spoken is the answer to 'how many?' questions and tells you how many there are;
- that no matter in which order a collection is counted the number remains the same;
- that if two different counts of a collection of objects give different answers, then something is wrong.

Children should be taught to:	As end-of-year outcomes, children should, for example:

Count reliably a set of everyday objects (continued)

Count systematically to keep a track of the count
Count a collection of objects in different arrangements, organising the counting by using a strategy for keeping track of where the count begins and ends.

- Count objects in a line:
  first touching them one by one;
  then without touching them.

  For example,
  count these flags.

- Count objects arranged randomly:
  by moving them into a straight line;
  by moving them across one by one when counted;
  by leaving them in position but touching them;
  by counting systematically without touching them:
  for example, from top to bottom, left to right.

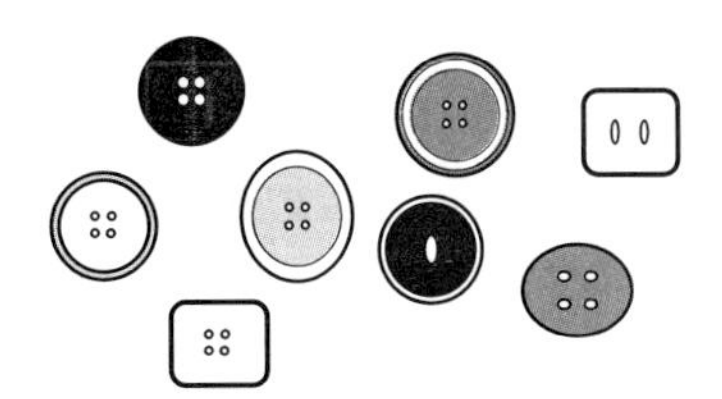

For example,
count these buttons.

Recognise counting errors, perhaps made by a puppet.
For example:

saying the number sequence correctly but:
- assigning two number names to one object (counting the same object twice);
- missing out an object completely;

pointing correctly to each object in turn but:
- making an error in saying the counting sequence;
- not giving a number name to one or more of the objects touched;

or alternatively:
- counting the correct number of objects but saying the wrong number: for example, counting five objects correctly but saying: 'There are six'.

Discuss ways of organising counting so that it is easier to count accurately.

Begin to recognise 'none' and 'zero'

Begin to recognise 'zero' as the cardinal number associated with 'none', through stories, rhymes and when counting back.

Children should be taught to:	As end-of-year outcomes, children should, for example:

Count reliably in other contexts

Realise that sounds, movements, hidden things... can be counted. For example:

- Count evenly spaced or regular claps or drum beats, first with eyes open to watch, then with eyes closed.
- Count pairs of claps or drum beats.
- Count the sounds in repeated rhythmic patterns such as: *tap, tap, pause, tap...*
- Count the number of times you skip with your skipping rope.
- Count the number of times that I jump.
- Count how many big strides you take across the room...

Count a collection of up to ten objects in more difficult formations, using a strategy for keeping track of where the count begins. For example:

- Count objects that are out of reach: for example, panes in windows, pictures on the wall, lights hanging from the ceiling...
- Count objects in a ring, such as different coloured beads on a necklace or a group of children in a circle, marking the starting point in some way.
- Count some mixed objects that vary markedly in size.
- Count some moving objects: for example, children playing, floating objects, fish in a fish tank, hatched chicks, the bubbles that I blow...
- Begin a count starting with a named object: for example, count the animals starting with the horse.

Count along and back a blank number track. For example, respond to situations such as:

- Put a cone on a blank number track on the floor.
  Stand at the beginning of the track.
  Hop on to the first space, and say 'one'.
  Continue to count aloud the hops you make until you get to the cone.

- Put a 'frog' on a blank number track on a table top.
  Watch the frog jump along to the blue counter.
  Count the jumps aloud as the frog makes them.
  How many jumps did the frog make?

  Count the jumps quietly using fingers.
  Count them in your head.

Children should be taught to:	As end-of-year outcomes, children should, for example:

Count in tens

Recite the sequence: *ten, twenty, thirty… one hundred.*
Say it backwards.

Count on or back in tens, starting from a given tens number.
- Count on in tens from fifty.
- Count back in tens from eighty.

Say the tens number that goes before or after a given one.
For example, when you count in tens:
- what number comes just after sixty;
- what number comes before ninety?

Count along a large number track numbered only in tens.

Count from a given tens number and stop at another.
- Count on in tens from twenty and stop at seventy…
- Count on in tens from thirty to ninety…
- Count back in tens from eighty and stop at thirty…
- Count back in tens from seventy to ten…
- Count round the circle of children, starting at Paul with thirty. Who do you think will say sixty?

Count in twos

Begin to understand and use in practical contexts:
odd, even, every other…

Join in rhymes like:
Two, four, six, eight, Mary at the cottage gate…
One, two, buckle my shoe…
Ten fat sausages sizzling in the pan…
Ten little squirrels sat on a tree…
I've got sixpence…
Make up your own rhymes involving counting in twos.

Count pairs: for example,
the pairs of children,
the pairs of socks on the line,
the pairs of animals,
the eggs in this egg box.

Count in ones, but say every other word in a whisper.
Count with the teacher saying every other number.

Look at and point to a number track.
- Say aloud every other number, starting at one.
- Say aloud every other number, starting at two.

Colour hops of two on a number track to 10 or more…
- Say aloud the coloured numbers as a sequence.
- Say aloud the numbers that are not coloured.

Children should be taught to:	As end-of-year outcomes, children should, for example:

Estimate a number in the range that can be counted reliably, then check by counting

Begin to understand and use in practical contexts:
guess how many, estimate...
nearly, close, about the same as, just over, just under...
too many, too few, enough, not enough...

For example, respond to:

- Guess the number of:
  books on the shelf, counters in a pile, penny coins in a purse, small toys in a transparent jar, dried beans in a matchbox, acorns I am holding in my hand...
  Are there more than 3? Are there about 5 or about 10?
  Now check by counting.
  Were you nearly right? How close were you?

- Estimate how many marbles, counters, dried peas, matchsticks, small balls of cotton wool, wooden cubes... there are in a lidded tin when you shake it.
  When everyone has guessed, look in and count.
  Why did you choose your number?

- Estimate the number of children present at registration, who have brought a packed lunch today, who wore a hat to school, who are five years old...
  Check by counting.

- Estimate whether there are enough pegs for the coats, knives for the forks, chairs for the children, cups for the saucers, eggs for the egg cups, spoons for the eggs...
  Now check.
  Are there too many or too few?
  Are there enough or not enough?

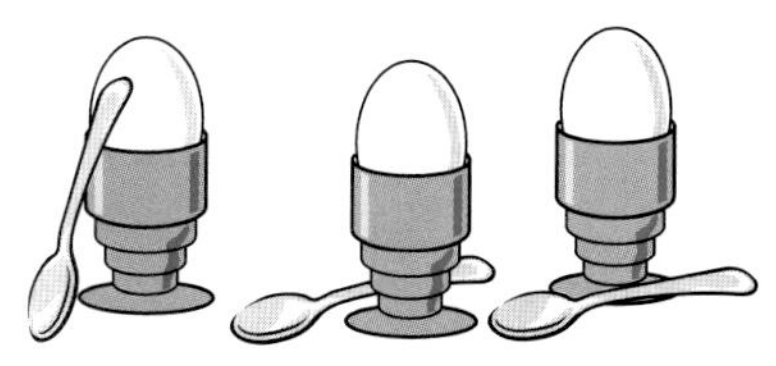

- Estimate the number of words on the story book page. Write your estimate on a Post-it note and stick it on the chart.

- Use a number track with all numbers 1 to 10 marked. Point to different numbers and say what they are.
  Next use a track with only 1 and 10 marked. Point to different places.
  What number do you think this is?
  Discuss your reasons.

  Extend to using a number track beyond 10.

  See also recognising and using numerals (page 9).

Children should be taught to:

Recognise and use numerals 1 to 9, extending to 0 and 10, then beyond 10

As end-of-year outcomes, children should, for example:

Recognise numerals familiar to them: for example, their age, house number, bus number…

Recognise numerals: first from 1 to 5, progressing to 10, then beyond. For example, respond to:

- Look at this number track.
  Count along it with me.
  Say each number as I point to it.
  Who can point to 7 on the number track?
- This card says 'five'.  What does this one say? 
- Take some individual number cards.
  Hold up your card if you have five… or eighteen… or fifty…
  Read this card to me.
  Which card is Eloise holding?
- Find the birthday card with 4 on it… with 6 on it…
- Find page 10 in your picture book.
- Match collections of real objects, then pictures of collections of things, to numbers.
- Match numbers to dot patterns: for example, in home-made dominoes, in jigsaw pieces, in pairs of dice, one with dots, one with numerals…
- Point to each number on individual grids of numbers to 30, and say them together.
- Point to 8 on a clock face, in this pack of shuffled cards, on a calculator key-pad, on the 'shop' till, on the telephone, on the computer keyboard, on a video recorder…
- Point to the numbers on this card in order.
  Say them aloud.

2	8	9
5	1	3
6	4	7

- Spot numbers around the school, out on a walk, going to a shop, and say what they are.

Begin to recognise 0 as the numeral associated with 'none', or the space before 1 on the number track.

- Use these number cards as labels.
  Show how many animals there are in each field…
  Show how many eggs there are in each nest…
- Stand on 6 on the floor number track.
  Hop back to 0. Say the numbers as you go.

Begin to read the first few number names, including zero. For example:

- Pick out number names on the pages of favourite rhymes or stories such as: *Three Billie Goats Gruff, Three Little Pigs, Goldilocks, Snow White…*
- Read these words: *zero, one, two, three, four, five…*

Children should be taught to:

Begin to record numbers

As end-of-year outcomes, children should, for example:

Make own marks or tallies to record numbers or quantities arising in or resulting from practical activities. For example:

- Bury several small things in sand. Record in own way how many are buried: for example, by drawing shapes or making tally marks.

Begin to write numerals correctly, tracing from top to bottom in a continuous line where possible, first 1, 2, 3… then 0 to 5, progressing to at least 10. For example:

- Trace with a finger cut-out numerals: made from sandpaper, rough fabric, smooth fabric, tin foil, corrugated paper, textured wallpaper…
- Write numerals 'in the air' following a teacher's directions. For example:
  half round, half round — for three
  across and down — for seven
- Make numerals by finger painting, using dough, Plasticine, clay…
- Watch me while I trace a numeral in the air (or on the table). Can you guess what it is?
- Guess what this number is when I trace it on your back.
- Write a number to go with these spots.

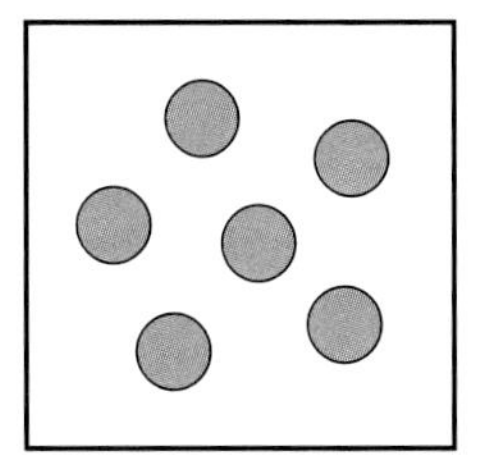

- Make number labels for the seats in an 'aeroplane', the spaces in the 'car park', pegs for coats, appointments for the 'doctor'…
- Make number labels for the number of pairs of scissors kept in the jar, the number of paint brushes kept in the pot, the number of pieces in the jigsaw box…
- Make price labels for things in the 'shop', for tickets for the 'bus', for things on the menu in the 'café', for raffle tickets…
- Write in the numbers on a blank number track, clock face…
- Make your own number frieze or board game.

Children should be taught to:

Understand and use language to compare two given numbers and say which is more or less

As end-of-year outcomes, children should, for example:

Begin to understand and use in practical contexts:
the same number as…
bigger, larger, smaller…
biggest, largest, smallest…
more, less, fewer…
most, least, fewest…
order, first, last, before, after, next, between…

Make a staircase pattern with bricks, or on pegboard…
Make each step one more, or two more…
Count how many on each step.
Predict what would come next.

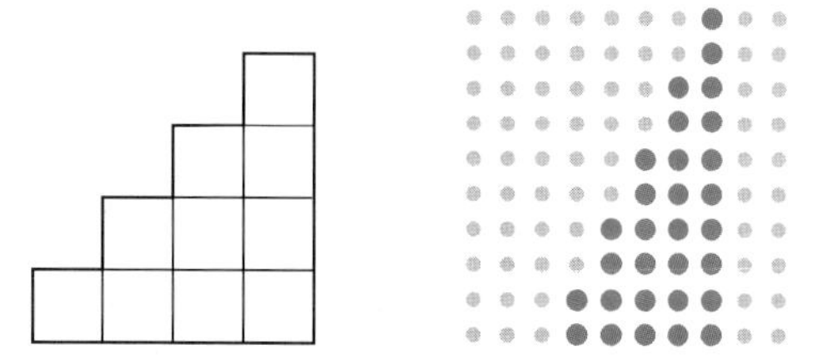

Find out **by counting** which of two collections has more/fewer objects. In each case, check if necessary by lining up and matching one-to-one. For example:

- Count the cups and saucers (e.g. 5 cups and 3 saucers).
  Are there more cups or more saucers, or the same number?
  (Say: 5 is more than 3.)
- Count the girls and boys (e.g. 4 girls and 3 boys).
  Are there fewer girls or fewer boys?
  (Say: 3 is less than 4.)
- Would you rather have five £1 coins, or four £1 coins? Why?

Know that a number following another number in the counting sequence is bigger. For example, look at a number track.

- Which is more: 3 or 6? *(Say: 6 is more than 3.)*
- Which is less: 4 or 7? *(Say: 4 is less than 7.)*

Say the number that is one more or one less than a given number. For example, respond to:

- What number comes before 10?
- What number comes after 3?
- What numbers are next to 12?
- What number is one more than 7? Than 14?
  (Say: 8 is one more than 7…)
- What number is one less than 5? Than 12?
  (Say: 4 is one less than 5…)

Discuss (unpriced, later priced) items in the classroom 'shop'. Say which might cost more, or which might cost less.
For example, respond to:

- An apple costs 4p.
  An orange costs 1p more.
  What does the orange cost?

See also adding/subtracting one to/from a number (page 14).

Children should be taught to:	As end-of-year outcomes, children should, for example:

Say a number lying between two given numbers

Say one or more numbers lying between two given small numbers. For example, respond to:

- In this line of nests with eggs in, one nest is missing. Which nest is it? How do you know?
- In this line of spotty cards, one card is missing. Which card is it? Where does it go?
- Here is part of a number track. Can you say what the missing numbers are?

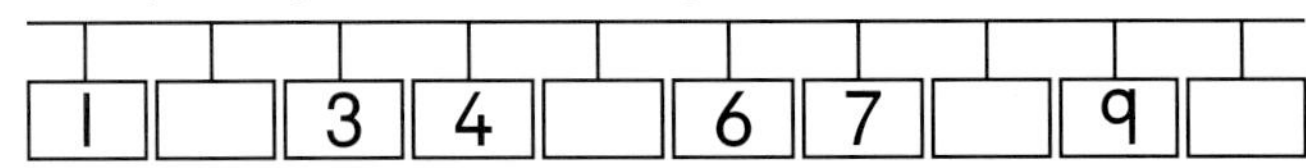

- Tell me all the numbers that lie between 4 and 9.

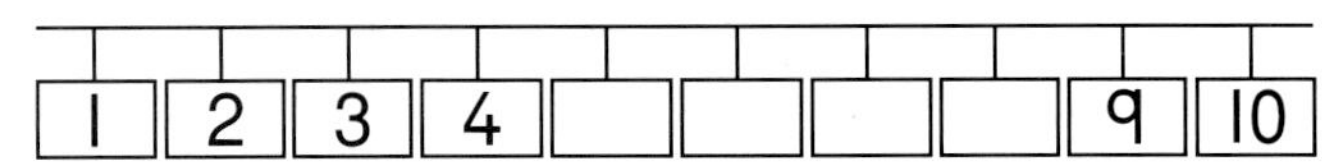

- Say all the numbers that lie between 5 and 10.
- If you are holding a number between 4 and 8, stand between Ian and Nadia.
- Playtime is between 9 o'clock and 12 o'clock. What time could it be?

Order a given set of numbers

Arrange in order a complete set of numbers (first objects, then dot patterns, then numerals): from 1 to about 5... progressing to 10 or more... Say together the complete sequence.
For example, respond to:

- Put in order these nests with eggs in... this set of cards with buttons on... these boxes with bricks in... these jars with walnuts in... these sticks of cubes... these pots with pens in...
- Peg these dotty cards in order to the washing line. Start with the smallest/biggest number.
- Put in order a set of shuffled cards... numbered carpet tiles... What number should go first? Next? What number should come after 7? Before 6? What numbers are next to 12?
- Each of you take a number card from this pile. Arrange yourselves in order. You have number 7. Which side of Ali should you stand?
- Which two numbers have been changed over on this track?

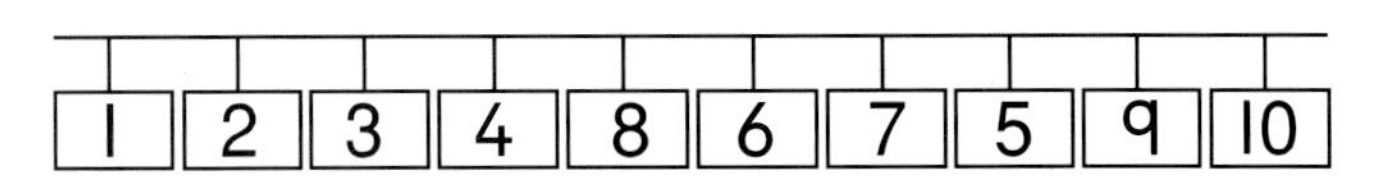

Order a given set of selected numbers

Arrange in order a selection of small numbers.
For example, respond to:

- Put in order, smallest first, a set of numbered carpet tiles 1 to 10, with three or four of the numbers removed. Which numbers are missing?

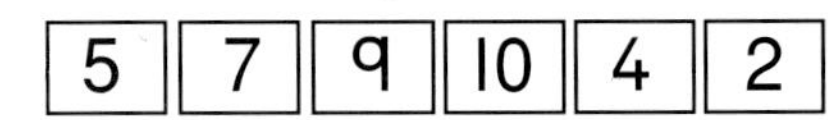

- Put in order these raffle tickets... peg labels... birthday cards. Start with the smallest number. Start with the largest number.

Children should be taught to:	As end-of-year outcomes, children should, for example:

Begin to understand and use ordinal numbers in different contexts

Begin to understand and use in practical contexts ordinal numbers to denote position:
first, second, third, fourth...
last, last but one...

For example, respond to:

- Who is the first, second, last, last but one... in this line of children?
- Make a string of beads.
  First thread a red one.
  Second thread a blue one...
  What colour is the first bead you threaded?
  And the sixth bead?
- Who was first, second, third... in the skipping race?
- In this line of farm animals, which animal is third?
  Which animal is between the fourth and the sixth?
- Find the fifth page of your story book.
- What is the first, second, last... letter of the alphabet?
- Point to your third finger... the fourth bead we threaded on this string... the second car in the car park...
- What date is your birthday?
- What is the date after the 7th of June?
- Make a line of plastic cars.
  Make the second car yellow.
  Make the fifth car red.
- Is the fifth car in the car park black or white?
  Point to the second blue car.

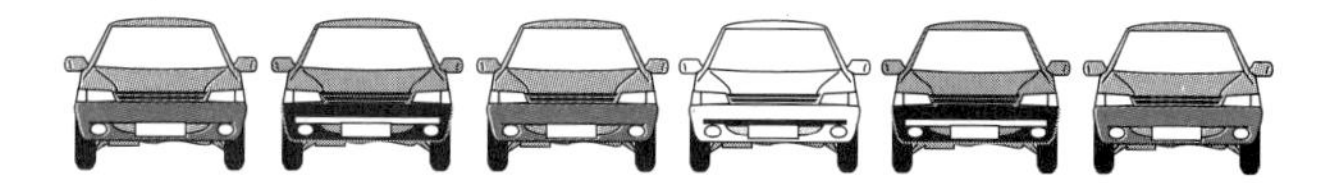

Begin to understand the relationship between cardinal and ordinal numbers up to 'tenth': that is, an object allocated 'six' in a count is the sixth object counted. For example, respond to questions such as:

- When you count, what is the third number?
  And the ninth number?

Begin to understand that if you are fifth in a running race, then four runners beat you, and that if you are the ninth out of ten runners, then you were 'next to last' or 'last but one'. For example, respond to questions such as:

- Make a queue of 7 children. Afzal is third in the queue.
  How many are in front of him?
  How many are behind him?

Children should be taught to:	As end-of-year outcomes, children should, for example:
Begin to use the vocabulary involved in adding and subtracting	Through practical activities and discussion, begin to understand and use the vocabulary of addition and subtraction: a. in practical contexts, using objects; b. by modelling with apparatus; c. by modelling with fingers. *more, and, add, make, sum, total, altogether, score...* *take away, leave, how many are left?... how many are gone?* *one more, two more... one less, two less...* *how many more to make ...?* *how many more is ... than ...?* *how many less is ... than ...?* *difference between...*
Find one more and one less than a given number	For example, respond to: • There are 3 people on the bus. 1 more gets on. How many are on the bus now? *(Say together: 4 is 1 more than 3. 3 add 1 is 4.)* • There are 4 children in the home corner. 1 more comes to join them. How many are there now? *(Say together: 5 is 1 more than 4. 4 add 1 is 5.)* • There are 10 children. 1 goes out. How many are left? *(Say together: 9 is 1 less than 10. 10 take away 1 is 9.)* • There were 5 baby birds in the nest. 1 flew off. How many are left? *(Say together: 4 is 1 less than 5. 5 take away 1 is 4.)*
Begin to relate addition to combining two groups of objects; extend to three groups	Say how many there are altogether by **counting all** the objects. For example, respond to: • Count out 4 cakes. Count out 3 cakes. How many cakes altogether? Count all the cakes. *(Count: 1, 2, 3, 4... 1, 2, 3...* *Altogether there are: 1, 2, 3, 4, 5, 6, 7.* *Say together: 4 add 3 is 7.)* • There are 2 cars in the garage. Let's count them. 3 more arrive. Let's count them. How many cars now? *(Count: 1, 2... 1, 2, 3... 1, 2, 3, 4, 5.* *Say together: 2 add 3 is 5.)* • Show me 3 fingers on your right hand. Show me 2 fingers on your left hand. How many fingers showing altogether? *(Count: 1, 2, 3... 1, 2... 1, 2, 3, 4, 5.* *Say together: 3 and 2 is 5.)* • Buy three things in the 'shop'. One costs 2p. One costs 3p. One costs 1p. How many pennies do you give the shopkeeper? *(Count: 1, 2... 1, 2, 3... 1... 1, 2, 3, 4, 5, 6.* *Say together: 2 add 3 add 1 is 6.)* Repeat activities with different numbers.

Children should be taught to:	As end-of-year outcomes, children should, for example:
Begin to relate addition to counting on	Say how many there are altogether by **counting on**. For example, respond to: • When a count is started by another child: *'one, two, three, four...'* continue: *'five, six, seven...'* • Count 5 objects into a cloth bag. How many objects in the bag? Count 2 more objects into the bag. How many objects in the bag now? • Sell 3 tickets for the 'bus'. Sell 5 more. How many tickets have you sold now? *(Count on 5 from 3: 4, 5, 6, 7, 8. Say together: 3 add 5 is 8.)* • Show me 5 fingers on one hand. Show me 2 fingers on the other hand. How many fingers altogether? *(Count on 2 from 5: 6, 7. Say together: 5 add 2 is 7.)* • Make a hop of three spaces on the number track. Now hop two more. Where are you now? *(Count on 2 from 3: 4, 5. Say together: 3 add 2 is 5.)*
Begin to relate the addition of doubles to counting on	Say how many altogether in a double by **counting on**. For example: • In a playground dice game with large dice, roll double 2. What's your total score? *(Count on 2: 3, 4. Say together: 2 add 2 is 4.)* • One child has 3 pennies. Another child has 3 pennies. How much do they have altogether? *(Count on 3: 4, 5, 6. Say together: 3 add 3 is 6.)* • There are 4 wheels on the car. How many wheels on two cars? *(Count on 4: 5, 6, 7, 8. Say together: 4 add 4 is 8.)* • How many toes on two feet? *(Count on 5: 6, 7, 8, 9, 10. Say together: 5 add 5 is 10.)* • How many eggs in each row of the box? How many eggs altogether? *(Count on 6: 7, 8, 9, 10, 11, 12. Say: 6 add 6 is 12.)* • Make two hops, each the same, on a number track. Where do you land? Sing, for example, *The animals went in two by two...*
Find a total by counting on when one group of objects is hidden	Say how many there are altogether by **counting on** when one of the groups of objects cannot be seen. For example: • Count 4 beans into a tin with a lid on. Emphasise that there are 4 beans in the tin. Label the lid with 4. Put 3 more beans on the table. How many beans altogether? *(Count on 3 from the hidden 4: 5, 6, 7. Say together: 4 add 3 is 7.)* • Count 5 pennies into a purse and shut it. Show 2 more pennies in a hand. How many pennies altogether? *(Count on 2 from the hidden 5: 6, 7. Say together: 5 add 2 is 7.)* • Show 2 fingers on one hand, then put it behind your back. Show 3 more fingers on the other hand. How many fingers altogether? *(Count on 3 from the hidden 2: 3, 4, 5. Say: 2 add 3 is 5.)*

Children should be taught to:	As end-of-year outcomes, children should, for example:
Separate (partition) a given number of objects into two groups	Say how up to 10 objects can be separated into two groups. Find different ways of doing it. Using 5 as an example, find different ways of: • planting 5 bulbs in two bowls; • putting out 5 biscuits on two plates; • bowling at 5 skittles and talking about how many are standing up and how many have fallen down each time; • throwing 5 bean bags one by one and talking about how many went in the bucket and how many missed; • choosing all the big dominoes with 5 spots altogether; • using up and down fingers on one hand to show 5 fingers; • making two jumps to land on 5 on the number track. Talk about outcomes, saying, for example, 2 bean bags outside the bucket and 3 inside, so 2 and 3 make 5. Find own way of recording: for example, by making marks or drawing, or by making domino patterns.
Select two groups of objects to make a given total	Choose two groups of objects to make a given total of up to 10 objects. Find different ways of doing it. Using 6 as an example, find different ways of: • putting two kinds of animals in a stable for 6 animals; • putting 6 eggs in a box, choosing from red eggs and yellow eggs; • making towers of 6 jumbo bricks in two different colours; • making bracelets of 6 beads in two different shapes; • using two large foam dice to try to score 6. Talk about outcomes, saying, for example, 4 red eggs and 2 yellow eggs, that's 6 eggs altogether. Find own way of recording: for example, by making marks or drawing.
Begin to relate subtraction to 'taking away', and counting how many are left	Say how many are left when some are taken away, by **counting how many are left**. For example, respond to: • We ate 2 of our 6 jellies. How many jellies are left? *(Count: 1, 2, 3, 4, 5, 6. Take away 1, 2… 1, 2, 3, 4 left.* *Say together: 6 take away 2 is 4.)* • You have 10 pennies. Spend 3 pennies. How much do you have left? *(Count: 1, 2, 3, 4, 5, 6, 7, 8, 9, 10.* *Take away 1, 2, 3… 1, 2, 3, 4, 5, 6, 7 left.* *Say together: 10 take away 3 is 7.)*

Children should be taught to:	As end-of-year outcomes, children should, for example:

Remove a smaller number from a larger and find how many are left by counting back from the larger number

Say how many are left when some are taken away, by **counting back** from the number. For example, respond to:

- We made 6 mince pies.
  We ate 2 of them.
  How many pies are left?
  (Count back 2 from 6: 5, 4.
  Say together: 6 take away 2 is 4.)
- You have 8 pennies.
  Spend 3 pennies.
  How much do you have left?
  (Count back 3 from 8: 7, 6, 5.
  Say together: 8 take away 3 is 5.)

Begin to find out how many have been removed from a larger group of objects by counting up from a number

Find out how many have been removed by **counting up** to the larger number. For example, respond to:

- There were 8 books on this shelf.
  There are only 5 books now.
  How many have gone?
  (Count up from 5 to 8: 6, 7, 8... and say 3.
  Say together: 5 add 3 is 8. 8 take away 3 is 5.)
- Count out 4 pennies.
  Secretly put some in one hand and some in the other.
  Show the pennies in one hand (say, 1 penny).
  How much is there in the other hand?
  (Count up from 1 to 4: 2, 3, 4... and say 3.
  Say together: 1 add 3 is 4. 4 take away 3 is 1.)
- Count 6 cotton reels into an open box.
  Take a few out (say 2) and put them on the table.
  Say (without peeping) how many are still in the box.
  (Count up from 2: 3, 4, 5, 6... and say 4.
  Say together: 2 add 4 is 6. 6 take away 4 is 2.)

Work out by counting how many more are needed to make a larger number

Find out by **counting up** how many more will make a given number. For example, respond to:

- We have 2 easels.
  There are 5 children who want to paint.
  How many more easels do we need?
  (Count up from 2: 3, 4, 5... and say 3 more.
  Say together: 2 add 3 is 5.)
- There are 9 cows and 6 sheep in the field.
  How many more cows than sheep are there?
  (Count up from 6: 7, 8, 9... and say 3 more.
  Say together: 6 add 3 is 9.)
- A lolly costs 6p.
  How much change do you get from 10p?
  (Count up from 6: 7, 8, 9, 10... and say 4p.
  Say together: 6 add 4 is 10.)

Children should be taught to:	As end-of-year outcomes, children should, for example:
Recognise and recreate simple patterns	Talk about and describe simple patterns, based on experience with patterns from different cultures: on ornaments, in necklaces and bracelets, on textiles, pottery, carpets... Use sets of shapes, printing, collage, weaving, bead threading, computer programs or other media to make own repeating patterns such as: *cotton reel, sponge, cotton reel, sponge...* *thumb print, palm, palm, thumb print, palm, palm...* Talk about, copy and continue repeating patterns of sounds or movements in music or dance, such as: *tap, tap, pause, tap...* on the tambourine; *hop, hop, jump...* in PE.
Solve simple problems or puzzles in a practical context, and respond to 'What could we try next?'	Solve simple problems or puzzles in a practical context. For example, explore different ways of: • distributing four play-people in and out of a house; • arranging five ladybirds on two leaves; • choosing three items from the classroom 'café' menu; • choosing a domino with a total of six spots; • distributing seven buttons between two boxes; • putting three cakes of different shapes in a line in a box; • breaking up four squares of chocolate; • building a tower of bricks as tall as the cupboard; • putting together the pieces of a cut-up birthday card; • making equal an unequal number of spots on each wing of a butterfly... Talk about and record in own way how the problem was solved. Suggest what to try in response to 'What could we try next?' For example, suggest distributing five play-people in and out of the house, or five ladybirds on three leaves...

Children should be taught to:	As end-of-year outcomes, children should, for example:

Make simple estimates and predictions

Make estimates and other predictions, giving reasons for them. For example:

- Play Kim's game to find matching pairs of shapes, patterns or numbers.
- Say what is hidden when an element in a pattern is covered up, or two elements are changed over.
- Predict who will say 8 when counting round a circle of children.
- Predict what will come next in a calculator display (in a teacher demonstration) when it is set to count in ones.
- Say which numeral or other shape (made of wood or plastic) is hidden in a feely bag.
- Estimate then check how many...
  cars will go in the garage, cakes will fit in this tin, strides it takes to cross the room, cups can be filled from this jug...

See also estimating numbers (page 8).

Sort and match objects, pictures or themselves

Begin to understand and use in practical contexts:
sort, match, count...

Sorting
Sort things as part of classroom routines, such as tidying up: for example, putting cutlery in the cutlery tray, coins in the cash till, books on shelves...

Respond to a given criterion for sorting, then suggest own criterion. For example:

- Sort and display objects according to their characteristics. For example, in science activities sort objects that are shiny or dull, hard or soft, rough or smooth...
- Sort and count the children themselves.
  Respond to a single criterion, such as all those who have brown eyes, are wearing trousers, are five years old...
- Sort, match or order flat or solid shapes and explain how they have been sorted, matched or ordered.

Children should be taught to:

Use developing mathematical ideas and methods to solve practical problems involving counting and comparing in a real or role play context

As end-of-year outcomes, children should, for example:

Solve problems in everyday life in the classroom, or in role play. Make decisions about what to do. Explain orally and, where appropriate, record the solution in own way. For example, respond in practical situations to questions such as:

Comparing

- Are there enough mugs on the table for us all to have a drink? How many more do we need?
- Are there enough cars for the play-people to drive?
- Are there more blue bricks or more red bricks in this pile? How can we find out?
- Are there enough stamps to give everyone two?

Counting: adding and subtracting

For examples, see adding and subtracting (pages 14–17).

Counting: doubling and halving

Use vocabulary such as:
double, half, halve, pair...

- How many shoelace holes are there?
- How many slices of bread do we need to make 4 whole sandwiches for the 'café'?
- How many eggs will fill this box?
- Can you cut the cake in half? How many pieces?
- Fill half the tarts with strawberry jam and half with lemon curd.
- How many cakes in the box? Take half of them out. How many did you take out? How many are left?
- Put half of: the sheep in the field... the cars in the garage... the dinosaurs in the forest... the animals in the ark...
- How many pairs of socks are in the 'launderette'? Are any left over?
- Find a partner. How many children are there? How many pairs?

Counting: repeated addition, grouping or sharing

Use vocabulary such as:
share, group, left over, how many times?...

- How many wheels do we need for these three Lego cars?
- How should we plant the daffodil bulbs in these three pots? Is there a way of doing it so that they all have the same number? Are any left over?
- Count out these stickers round the circle of children. How many times will they go round? Are any left over?
- Can we share out these cakes fairly? How shall we do it?

Solve problems based on stories such as:
The Giant Jam Sandwich... The Bad-Tempered Ladybird... The Very Hungry Caterpillar... New Clothes for Alex... Goldilocks and the Three Bears... The Little Gingerbread Boy...

See also solving simple problems or puzzles (page 18).

Children should be taught to:

Begin to understand and use the vocabulary related to money; begin to recognise coins and use them in role play to pay and give change

As end-of-year outcomes, children should, for example:

Begin to understand and use in practical contexts:
coin, penny, pence, pound, price, cost, costs more, costs less, total, pay, change, how much?... how many?

Use coins to pay for things or buy things in the class 'shop', tickets on the 'bus', at the 'funfair' or 'skittle alley'... recognising that coins are used to pay and give change.

Distinguish coins. For example:

- sort money into spaces in a shop till, e.g. 10p, 50p, £1, £2;
- feed 20p or 50p coins into a pretend drinks machine or car park ticket machine;
- buy 20p stamps, using 20p coins;
- in the 'pound shop', buy items costing £1, using £1 coins...

Play money games. For example, roll dice to collect £1 coins to the value of £10... or 1p coins to the value of 10p.

Choose and use the appropriate number operation to solve 'story' problems involving money. Explain orally and, where appropriate, record in own way how the problem was solved. For example, respond to:

Find how much altogether, or give change.

- Jim had £5. He spent £3. How much did he have left?
- Rosie had a 10p coin. She spent 1p.
  How much change did she get?
- How much altogether is 1p and 1p and 1p and 1p?

Begin to recognise that some coins have a greater value than others, and will buy more: for example, 2p is worth more than 1p; 5p is worth more than 2p; £2 is worth more than £1.
For example:

- Begin to count up how much this is altogether.

For example, respond to:

- Sunita spent 1p and 2p on toffees.
  What did she pay altogether?
- Chews cost 2p each. How much do 2 chews cost?
- In the 'pound shop', everything costs £1.
  Work out the total cost of a basket of items (up to about 6): for example, 2 tins of paint, 2 brushes and 1 roll of paper.

Work out what to buy and how to pay. For example:

- James paid 3p for chews. What coins could he use?
  What if he paid 4p?
- An apple costs 6p. Which two coins would pay for it?
- Which three coins make 5p? How else could you make 5p?

Begin to read and write prices such as 8p or £4.

- Count penny or pound coins. Watch while I write how much. Now find a price label to match how much.
- Make price labels on items in the class 'shop' (drawn, symbolic, written)... and match penny coins to them. Extend to using combinations of 2p and 1p coins.

Children should be taught to:

Use language such as more or less, longer or shorter, heavier or lighter… to compare directly two lengths, masses or capacities; extend to three or more quantities

As end-of-year outcomes, children should, for example:

Begin to understand and use in practical contexts: *size…*
length and distance: *long, short, tall, high, low, wide, narrow, deep, shallow, thick, thin, far, near, close…*
mass: *weight, weigh, heavy, light…*
capacity: *full, half full, empty…*
and words such as: *compare, more, less, longer, shorter…*

Length, mass, capacity: direct comparison
For example:
- Compare the heights of two, then three, children by standing back to back or lying on the floor.
- Compare the lengths of two, then three or more, doll's beds, pencils, paint brushes, ribbons, necklaces…
- Use a balance to find out which of two, then three, teddies, lunch boxes, shoes… is lighter, or whether a large packet of cotton wool is heavier or lighter than a small tin of tomatoes.

- Fill and empty containers, describing them as full, 'half' full, empty, or as having more/less in them after filling/emptying.

Find, pick out or make objects that are taller, shorter, wider, thinner or heavier, lighter… than a given one, for example:
- a ribbon in the 'ribbon shop' that is wider than this one…
- a shell that is lighter than this one…
- a bucket that holds more than this one…

Begin to understand and use in practical contexts:
estimate… enough, not enough… too much, too little…
nearly, close, about the same as, just over, just under…

For example, guess first then check:
- how far up the wall you can reach;
- how far you can throw the bean bag;
- how far you can jump from this line;
- if this teddy is too tall for this bed;
- if the red parcel is heavier than the blue one, or the banana is lighter than the orange, when they are held in the hands;
- how full this bottle will be when I pour in this jug of water;
- if all the water in the bowl will go into the bucket, or whether there is too much.

Children should be taught to:

Begin to understand and use the vocabulary related to time; sequence familiar events; begin to know the days of the week in order and read o'clock time

As end-of-year outcomes, children should, for example:

Begin to understand and use in practical contexts:
names of days of the week...
day, week... morning, afternoon, night...
today, yesterday, tomorrow... birthday, holiday...
o'clock...
bed time, dinner time, play time...
now, soon, before, after, next, last...
quickly, slowly ...

Begin to know the names of the days of the week.
Talk about days of the week in everyday activities like taking the register, keeping a weather chart...
Respond to questions like:

- What did you do yesterday?
- What will you do tomorrow?
- How old are you?
- Who has a birthday next week? Which day is it?

Begin to sequence events in their day, or in a well-known story.
For example:

- Tell me what you did on your birthday... on the journey...
- Make a zigzag book or arrange picture cards to tell a story: for instance, what you see when you walk home...

Listen to and discuss stories such as:
The Very Hungry Caterpillar by Eric Carle
The Bad-Tempered Ladybird by Eric Carle
Mr Wolf's Week by Colin Hawkins
Goodnight Owl by Pat Hutchins
Can't You Sleep Little Bear? by Martin Waddell
Monster Monday by Susanna Gretz
When I was a Little Girl by Susie Jenkin-Pearce
Hard Boiled Legs by Michael Rosen and Quentin Blake

Begin to be aware of the duration of time.
For example, estimate whether you can:

- change for PE before the sand runs through the timer;
- pack the bricks away before I count to 10...

Be aware of the language of clock time in rhymes and stories, such as *Hickory Dickory Dock...*

Begin to know key times of the day, such as:
we go to assembly at 9 o'clock;
we go home at 3 o'clock;
my bed time is at 7 o'clock.

Begin to read the time to the hour on a clock.

Children should be taught to:

Use language to describe the shape and size of solids and flat shapes, begin to name shapes and use them to make models, pictures and patterns

As end-of-year outcomes, children should, for example:

Understand and use in practical contexts the words:
shape, pattern... flat, curved, round, straight, solid, hollow, corner, face, side, end...
sort... make, build, draw...

Recognise, name and talk about 3-D and 2-D shapes such as:
cube, cone, sphere...
circle, triangle, square, rectangle...

3-D shapes

- Identify solid shapes that can be seen around the school and in the classroom: for example, on different display tables; in the home corner or classroom shop; on a 'shape walk' around the school...

- Start to become aware of some properties of solid shapes when looking at, talking about and comparing them: for example, shapes that are hollow... whose faces are all flat... that roll... that slide...

- Guess the name of a solid shape when it is covered with tin foil or wrapping paper, or placed in a cloth bag.

- Make models using shapes that vary in shape, size and texture, using, for example:
  big blocks, wooden or plastic, of different shape and size...
  reclaimed materials: packets, rolls, containers, boxes, tins...
  construction kits: Poleidoblocks, Lego, Duplo...

  Describe the model and say what shapes have been used to make it. For example:
  The garage for my car has been made from lots of blocks, and they have straight edges and flat sides and ends.

- Make shapes from modelling material such as: Playdough, Plasticine, sand...
  Describe the shape made. For example:
  My cube has eight corners.

- Make a copy of a simple model as accurately as possible.

- Fit solid shapes together. For example:
  investigate solid shapes to see which of them will stack;
  pack smaller boxes, packets, containers... inside a large cardboard box and talk about how they fit in...

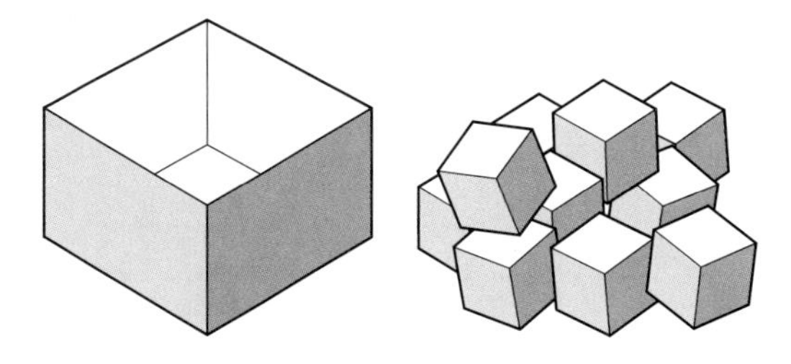

Children should be taught to:

Use language to describe the shape and size of solids and flat shapes, begin to name shapes and use them to make models, pictures and patterns (continued)

As end-of-year outcomes, children should, for example:

2-D shapes

- Find similar shapes on faces of objects. For example:
  find two circles, such as a drinks mat and the base of a jar;
  find two triangles, such as a silk scarf and a Logiblock;
  match lids to jars or boxes...

- Sort or match scraps of fabric, or buttons. Identify:
  Which scraps of fabric have the same pattern? Which have stripes? Which have dots? Which have square checks?
  Which scraps, or which buttons, are the same shape?
  Which are the same shape and size?

- Find solid shapes around the classroom with at least one face matching a 2-D outline or picture.

- Without using its name, describe a thin plastic shape hidden in a cloth bag. For example:
  My shape has three corners and three sides.
  My shape is curved all the way round.

- Sort into trays a collection of varied flat shapes, either thin plastic shapes, shapes made from paper, or drawn or stuck on card, and explain how they have been sorted:
  for example, shapes with corners, with three sides...

- Find shapes which are **not** square, round...

- Talk about and make shapes when playing in the sand pit or working at the sand tray. For example:
  trace a shape with a finger;
  draw round a shaped template;
  make impressions of solid and hollow shapes by pushing them into damp sand... or identify which shape has made a particular impression.

- Cut up a greetings card to make a jigsaw and reassemble it.

- Begin to sketch 2-D shapes. For example:
  draw two squares, draw three circles...
  make a rectangle by finger painting...

Children should be taught to:	As end-of-year outcomes, children should, for example:

Put sets of objects in order of size

Understand and use in practical contexts:
size, bigger, larger, smaller...

Listen to and talk about stories related to size, such as:
The Three Bears, Three Little Pigs, Jack and the Beanstalk...
You'll Soon Grow Into Them, Titch by Pat Hutchins
Jolly Tall by Jane Hussey
How Do I Put It On? by Shigeo Watanake
Hue Boy by Caroline Binch

Put in order of size a set of teddies, nesting boxes, Russian dolls, towers, saucepans, saucepan lids...
Discuss the fact that the shapes are the same although the sizes change.
Now place one more in the order. Where does it go?

Make 'families' of the same shape in different sizes:
- make a family of Plasticine worms...
- paint a family of monsters or giants...
- build houses for the three bears...

Talk about, recognise and recreate patterns

Talk about and recreate simple patterns made from people, beads, shapes, sounds... or by using computer programs...

For example:

- Use a mirror and mosaics to explore patterns.
- Find halves of paper shapes by folding them.
- Make a symmetrical model from bricks, or from reclaimed materials such as packets, rolls and containers. Point out matching pairs on each side of the middle, such as the two cones, the two pyramids...

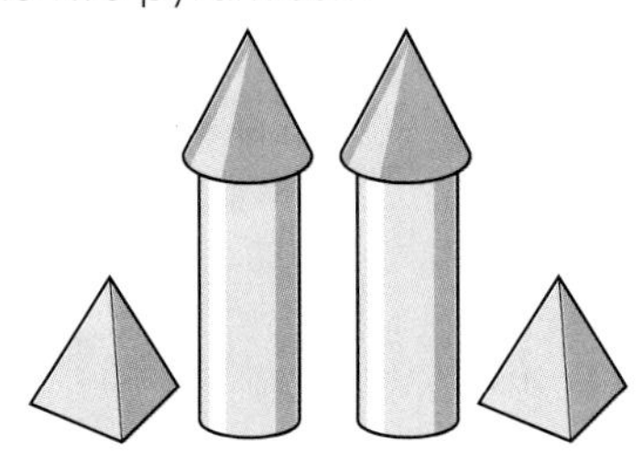

- Make repeating patterns from bricks or beads: for example, two cubes, one cone, two cubes, one cone...
  Describe the pattern and say what shapes have been used to make it. For example:
  My pattern has two circles, then two squares, then two more circles and two more squares.

- Make patterns from thin plastic shapes, gummed paper shapes, felt shapes, mosaic shapes, pegs and pegboard...
  by using a computer program...
  by printing on paper or fabric... with sponges or blocks...
  by painting blobs on paper and folding...
  by cutting out shapes from folded paper...

  Talk about the shapes that have been used, the way that they fit together, how one shape matches another...

For more examples, see reasoning about shapes (page 18).

Children should be taught to:

Use everyday words to describe position, direction and movement

As end-of-year outcomes, children should, for example:

Understand and use in practical contexts:
position, over, under, above, below, on, in, outside, inside, behind, beside, before, after, next to, opposite, between...
close, far, apart...
middle, corner, top, bottom, front, back, side...
direction, left, right, up, down, forwards, backwards, sideways, across, along, around, through, to, from, towards, away from...
movement, roll, slide, turn, stretch, bend...

Listen to and discuss stories such as *Rosie's Walk, Bear Hunt, Where's Spot?* Make own *Where's Spot?* book.

Talk about **positions**. For example:

- Describe where objects are in a picture. For example:
  The fish is above the weed in the pond...
  The frog is under the rock beside the pond...
- In PE, stand in front of, behind, beside, opposite a partner... or between two others... Follow instructions to get through an obstacle course or over climbing equipment.
- In class, answer questions such as:
  Who is sitting next to, beside, in front of... Ranjit?
- Describe how things are stored on shelves in the classroom or in a cupboard. For example, respond to:
  Are the felt pens on top of, under, next to... the books?
- Follow instructions to put play-people or models into a scene. For example: put the girl outside the shop; put the car inside the garage...

Talk about **movements and directions**. For example:

- In PE, follow instructions to run forwards, walk backwards, turn on the spot, turn to the left, turn to the right, face the front or side or back or corner of the room, move away from the bars, slide down the ramp, roll on the mat...
- Give instructions to other children: *Go around the stool, go in front of the beam, stop behind the swing...*
- Use a simple modelling program to explore the sequence of instructions to complete a task: for example, to load an elephant on to a lorry.
- Describe a walk round the school or its grounds:
  We went along the path, through the tunnel in the adventure playground and then across the field...
- Describe movements taken on a track or in a maze:
  I am moving forwards, turning left, going straight on, turning the corner...
- Explore and talk about things that turn, such as the hands of a clock, wheels, taps, keys in locks, screw top lids on jars... Try to fit nuts and bolts together when blindfolded...
- Collect and sort objects that will:
  roll (a wooden egg, a ball, an apple...);
  slide (a Lego brick, a story book...);
  both roll and slide (a baked bean tin, a coin...).

5

Supplement of examples: **Years 1, 2 & 3**

5

Supplement of examples: **Years 1, 2 & 3**

Pupils should be taught to:	As outcomes, Year 1 pupils should, for example:

Know the number names and recite them in order, from and back to zero

Join in rhymes like: *One, two, three, four, five, Once I caught a fish alive...* or: *Ten green bottles...*

Say the sequence: *one, two, three...* to 20 then beyond.
Say it backwards.
Respond to questions such as:
What number comes after 6? After 17? Before 9? Before 14?

Say the sequence: *ten, twenty, thirty... one hundred.*

Recognise *zero* and *none* in stories and other contexts, including the counting sequence.

Count reliably a set of objects

Understand and use in practical contexts: *count, how many?*

Count reliably at least 20 objects.
Recognise that the size of the set (how many) is given by the last number in the count.

Respond to questions such as:

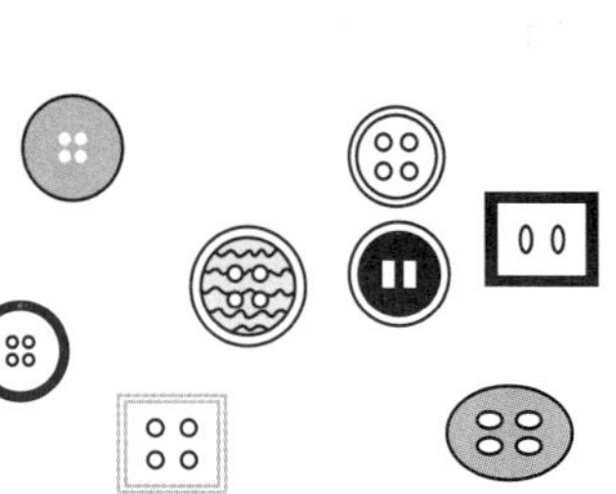

- Count 20 or more buttons, pencils, straws, bricks, children... spread out, close together, in a line, stacked up...
  Rearrange and count again.
  Is the number of buttons... still the same?
  Now count them without touching them.
- Put 5 bricks in a line, 5 cubes in a cup, 5 animals on top of a box, 5 beads in a bowl...
  Are there the same number of each?
- Lay a table for four people with knives, forks, cups, plates...
- Show me these numbers using your fingers.
- Clap or beat the drum five times.
  Count these regular claps or drum beats.
  Count the steps you take across the room.

Describe and extend number sequences: count on or back in steps of 1, 10 or 100 from any number

Counting in ones
Respond to questions such as:
- Start at any small number and count on in ones to 30 or more, then back in ones to zero.
- Write the next two numbers: 11, 10, 9, 8, ...
- Here is part of a number track. Where does 9 go? And 2?

			4	5	6				

- Count round the circle of children, starting at Mary with 5. Who will say 11?
- Count on four from 3... — *four, five, six, seven.*
  Count back four from 12... — *eleven, ten, nine, eight.*
- Count on from 7 to 10... — *eight, nine, ten.*
  How many did you count? — *I counted three.*
  Count back from 10 to 6. — *nine, eight, seven, six.*
  How many did you count? — *I counted four.*

As outcomes, Year 2 pupils should, for example:

Say forwards and backwards the sequences:
zero, ten, twenty, thirty... one hundred;
zero, one hundred, two hundred... one thousand.

Respond to questions such as:
Which tens number comes after 60? Before 30?
Which hundreds number comes after 400?
Before 900?

Use zero when counting and understand the function of 0 as a place holder in two-digit numbers
(see also page 9).

Understand, use and begin to read:
count, tally, how many?

Count reliably to at least 100.

Count larger collections by grouping in tens, then fives or twos.

Respond to questions such as:

- Can you count these 47 things by grouping them in tens?
- If we count in ones, or count in tens, will the total number be the same?
- Keep a tally as you count: in twos, fives, tens...
  If Mary keeps a tally in twos and David keeps a tally in fives, will they finish with the same total number?
- Count these pairs of claps or drum beats.
  Make a tally while I clap.
- What would be the best way to count:
  all the children in the class, birds coming to the bird table, sugar cubes in a box...?

Counting in ones
Respond to questions such as:
- Start at any two-digit number and count on in ones to 100, or back in ones to zero.

- Here is part of a number track.
  Where would 42 be? Where would 33 be?

				36	37	38	39				

- Count on six from 63...
  Count back six from 78...
- Count on from 33 to 37.
  Count back from 76 to 71.
  How many did you count each time?

As outcomes, Year 3 pupils should, for example:

Use, read and begin to write:
count, tally, how many?

Count larger collections by grouping them.

Respond to questions such as:

- Can you count 47 things by grouping them in fives?
- Count these irregular claps or drum beats.
  Make a tally while I clap.
- What would be the best way to count:
  all the children in school, all the pasta shapes in this jar...?

Counting in ones
Respond to questions such as:
- Start counting at 80, 200, 452... and count on or back in ones.

- Here is part of a number track.
  Where would 142 be? Where would 132 be?

				136	137	138	139				

- Count on six from 169...
  Count back six from 172...
  Count on/back 15 from 110. Where are you?
- Count on from 141 to 147.
  Count back from 176 to 171.
  How many did you count each time?

Pupils should be taught to:	As outcomes, Year 1 pupils should, for example:
Describe and extend number sequences: count on or back in steps of 1, 10 or 100 from any number (continued)	*Counting in tens* Using a 100 square, respond to questions such as: • Count on in tens from zero... from 30... from 3... Count back in tens from 100... from 80... from 63... • Count in tens from zero until I say stop. I will keep a count of the tens on my fingers. How many tens did you count? • Count on or back several tens, starting from a given number. Show me the tens with your fingers as you count. For example: Count on three tens from 50... from 20... from 70... Count back five tens from 80... from 50... • Count round the circle in tens, starting at Mary with 50. Who will say 90? • Describe this pattern: 80, 70, 60, 50... Say the next three numbers.
Describe and extend number sequences: count on or back in twos, and recognise odd and even numbers	Understand and use in practical contexts: *odd, even, every other...* Count rhythmically in twos to 20 or more. Count back again. Now start at 1. Count in steps of two to 20 or more. Count back again. Join in rhymes like: *Two, four, six, eight, Mary at the cottage gate...* *One, two, buckle my shoe...* Colour every other number on a number track to 20. Say every other number, first starting with 0, then with 1. Respond to questions such as: • What numbers come next? 2, 4, 6, 8... 15, 13, 11, 9... Describe the pattern.

As outcomes, Year 2 pupils should, for example:

Counting in tens

First with and then without a 100 square, respond to questions such as:

- Count on in tens from 30... from 26...
  Count back in tens from 80... from 72...
- Count on 40 in tens:
  from 30... from 27...
  Count back 40 in tens:
  from 80... from 72...
- Count on in tens from 30 to 70. How many tens did you count?
  Count back in tens from 90 to 40. How many tens did you count?
- Count round the circle in tens, starting at Ram with 52. Who will say 92?
- Describe this sequence:
  43, 53, 63, 73...
  Write the next three numbers.

Understand, use and begin to read:
odd, even, sequence, predict, continue, rule...

Count from 0 or 1 in steps of two to 40 or more. Count back again.

Respond to questions such as:

- Ring every other number on a number line.
  What do you notice about the ringed numbers?
  Is 18 odd or even? How do you know?
- Take a handful of (interlocking) cubes.
  Which numbers will make two equal sticks?
- Ring the even numbers:
  5 8 18 21 29 34
- Continue these sequences:
  13, 15, 17, 19... 26, 24, 22, 20...
  Describe each pattern.
- What odd number comes after 13? After 7?

Make general statements about odd or even numbers such as:
- an even number divides exactly by 2;
- there is 1 left over when an odd number is divided by 2.

As outcomes, Year 3 pupils should, for example:

Counting in tens

Respond to questions such as:

- Count on and back in tens, crossing 100.
- Count on 40 in tens:
  from 30, from 27, from 480, from 652...
  Count back 40 in tens:
  from 80, from 72, from 590, from 724...
- Count on in tens from 36 to 76. How many tens did you count?
  Count back in tens from 84 to 34. How many tens did you count?

Counting in hundreds

Respond to questions such as:

- Count on or back 400 in hundreds:
  from 500, from 520, from 570...
- Count on in hundreds from 460 to 960.
  How many hundreds did you count?
- Count back in hundreds round the circle of children, starting at Jo with 970. Who will say 370?
- Describe these sequences:
  256, 356, 456, 556... 421, 431, 441, 451...
  Write the next three numbers in each sequence.

Use, read and begin to write:
odd, even, sequence, predict, continue, rule, relationship...

Count from 0 or 1 in steps of two to about 50. Count back again.

Respond to questions such as:

- Is 74 odd or even? How do you know?
- Test whether 75 is odd or even.
  Now try all the numbers from 75 to 95. What do you notice?
- Ring the odd numbers:
  65 70 77 88 91 94
- Continue these sequences:
  35, 37, 39, 41... 68, 66, 64...
  Describe each pattern.
- What odd number comes before 91? After 69?

Make general statements about odd or even numbers such as:
- an even number ends in 0, 2, 4, 6 or 8;
- an odd number ends in 1, 3, 5, 7 or 9;
- if you add two even numbers the answer is even;
- if you add two odd numbers the answer is even.

Pupils should be taught to:	As outcomes, Year 1 pupils should, for example:
Describe and extend number sequences: count on or back in steps of any size	Respond to questions such as: • Mark hops of 2 or 3 or 5... on a number track to at least 20. Say the numbers you land on. • What number comes next? 16, 14, 12... 5, 10, 15... 3, 6, 9... Describe each pattern. • Fill in the missing numbers: 2, 4, □, 8, 10, □ 25, 20, 15, □, □ Create number patterns with a given constraint: for example, make a number pattern which has the number 6 in it.
Recognise familiar multiples	

As outcomes, Year 2 pupils should, for example:

Respond to questions such as:

- From zero and then from any small number, count on in 2s, 3s, 4s or 5s to 30 or more.
  Can you go past 100?
  Now count back.

- Take a 4 × 4 number grid.
  Count on in twos from 1.
  Colour numbers you land on.
  Describe the pattern you get.

1	2	3	4
5	6	7	8
9	10	11	12
13	14	15	16

  Try a 5 × 5 number grid.

  Predict what would happen with a 6 × 6 number grid.

- 3, 6, 9, 12... 16, 14, 12, 10...
  Describe each pattern. What is the rule?
  What are the next three numbers in each sequence?

- Fill in the missing number in this sequence:
  3, 6, □, 12, 15

Create sequences with a given constraint: for example, make a sequence which has the numbers 6 and 12 in it.

Understand, use and begin to read: *multiple*.

Recognise that multiples of:
10 end in 0;
5 end in 0 or 5.
Begin to recognise that multiples of:
2 end in 0, 2, 4, 6, 8.

Begin to recognise two-digit multiples of 10, 5 or 2: for example, that 65 is a multiple of 5, or that 32 is a multiple of 2.

Respond to questions such as:

- Ring the numbers which are multiples of 10:
  70 45 12 80 10 27

As outcomes, Year 3 pupils should, for example:

Respond to questions such as:

- Count on from any small number in steps of 2, 3, 4, 5, 10 or 100, and then back.

- Use a number grid computer program to display multiples of 2, 5, 10... on a 10 × 10 grid, and describe the patterns made.

- Take a 5 × 5 number grid.
  Count on in threes from 1.
  Colour numbers you land on.
  What do you notice?

1	2	3	4	5
6	7	8	9	10
11	12	13	14	15
16	17	18	19	20
21	22	23	24	25

  If you went on, would 28 be in your sequence? Or 40?
  How do you know?

  What would happen if you started at 2?
  Would the pattern be the same?
  Now try a 6 × 6 number grid. Try steps of 4 and 5.

- 2, 7, 12, 17... 78, 76, 74, 72...
  Describe each pattern. What is the rule?
  What are the next three numbers in each sequence?

- Fill in the missing numbers in this sequence:
  5, 9, □, 17, 21, □, □

Create sequences with a given constraint: for example, make a sequence which has the numbers 7 and 16 in it.

Use, read and begin to write: *multiple*.

Recognise that multiples of:
100 end in 00;
50 end in 00 or 50;
10 end in 0;
5 end in 0 or 5;
2 end in 0, 2, 4, 6, 8.

Respond to questions such as:

- Ring the numbers which are multiples of 5:
  15 35 52 55 59 95

- Count in 50s to 1000, then back to zero.
  Write three different multiples of 50.

- What is the multiple of 10 before 140?
  What is the multiple of 100 after 500?
  What is the next multiple of 5 after 195?

Pupils should be taught to:	As outcomes, Year 1 pupils should, for example:

Read and write numbers in figures and words

Read and write numbers to at least 20.
Respond to questions such as:

- This card says 'fifteen'. 15 What does this one say? 18
- Find the card with '12' or 'twelve', with '0' or 'zero' on it...

- Point to 9 on the number line, on the clock face, in this pack of shuffled cards... on a telephone, computer keyboard...
- Read numbers such as: 3, 5, 9... 14, 20, 26...
- Write numerals from 0 to 9 correctly, tracing from top to bottom.

  For example, write a numeral to go with each of these dot patterns.

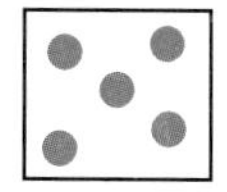
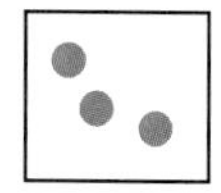

- Write numerals on a blank number line, clock face...
- Write in figures, then words:
  eight... seventeen... zero...

Know what each digit in a number represents, and partition a number into a multiple of 10 and ones (TU), or a multiple of 100, a multiple of 10 and ones (HTU)

Understand and use in practical contexts:
units or ones, tens, digit...

Know what each digit represents in numbers from 10 to 20.

Know, for example, that 14 is 10 and 4, and 14 – 4 = 10,

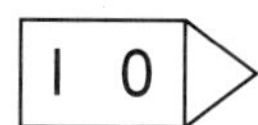
4

and represent 14 on an abacus.

Exchange up to 20 pennies for 10p and 1p coins:
for example, give 14p in 10p and 1p coins.

Respond to questions such as:

- Say what the digit 1 in 14 stands for. And the 4?
  (They represent 10 and 4.)
- Say which number is the same as:
  one ten and seven ones (units);
  two tens (and no ones or units).
- In one step:
  make 6 into 16;
  make 14 into 4.
- What number needs to go in each box?
  14 = □ + 4
  12 = 10 + □

Begin to partition larger numbers. For example:
34 = □ + 4
42 = 40 + □

As outcomes, Year 2 pupils should, for example:

Read and write numbers to at least 100.
Respond to questions such as:

- What number is on this card? 
- Find the card with '70' or 'seventy' on it...
- Point to 63 on the number line, on the 100 square, in this pack of shuffled cards...
- Read these numbers:
  3, 5, 11, 19, 32, 50, 94, 700...
- Read these words:
  one, two, three... nineteen, twenty...
  thirty, forty...
  hundred, thousand...
- Write in figures, then words:
  seventy...
  forty-nine...

Understand, use and begin to read:
units or ones, tens, hundreds, digit, one-digit number, two-digit number, three-digit number... place value...

Know what each digit in a two-digit number represents.

Recognise 0 as a place holder in two-digit multiples of 10 such as 50, 90, 10...

Know, for example, that 68 is 60 + 8,

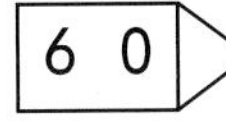 8 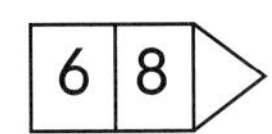

and represent 68 on an abacus.

Exchange up to 100 pennies for 10p and 1p coins: for example, give 68p in 10p and 1p coins.

Respond to questions such as:

- Say what the digit 6 in 64 represents.
  And the 4? *(They represent 60 and 4.)*
- Say which number is equivalent to:
  six tens and four ones (units);
  nine tens and no ones (units).
- In one step (operation):
  make 5 into 75;
  change 49 to 9.
- Explain what number needs to go in each box.
  64 = □ + 4
  53 = 50 + □

As outcomes, Year 3 pupils should, for example:

Read and write numbers to at least 1000.
Respond to questions such as:

- What number is on this card? 428
- Find the card with '260' or 'two hundred and sixty' on it, with '206' or 'two hundred and six' on it...
- Read these numbers:
  14, 32, 50, 117, 461, 302, 875...
- Read these words:
  forty-two...
  one hundred and two...
  three hundred and sixty-four
- Write in figures, then words:
  one hundred and sixty-seven...
  four hundred and nine...
  three hundred and fifty...

Use, read and begin to write:
units or ones, tens, hundreds, digit, one-digit number, two-digit number, three-digit number... place value...

Know what each digit in a three-digit number represents.

Recognise 0 as a place holder in three-digit numbers such as 430, 506...

Know, for example, that 537 is 500 + 30 + 7,

5 0 0 | 3 0 | 7 | 5 3 7

and represent 537 on an abacus.

Exchange pennies for £1, 10p and 1p coins: for example, give 364p in £1, 10p and 1p coins.

Respond to questions such as:

- Say what the digit 3 in 364 represents. And the 6? And the 4? *(They represent 300 and 60 and 4.)*
- Say which number is equivalent to:
  four hundreds, five tens and six ones (units);
  nine hundreds and two ones (units).
- In one step (operation):
  make 478 into 978; make 326 into 396;
  change 707 to 507; change 263 to 203.
- Explain what number needs to go in each box.
  364 = □ + 60 + 4   472 = 400 + □ + 2
- Make the biggest/smallest number you can with these digits: 2, 5, 3. Now read the numbers.

Pupils should be taught to:

Understand and use the vocabulary of comparing and ordering numbers, including ordinal numbers; use the = sign to represent equality; compare two given numbers, say which is more or less, and give a number lying between them

As outcomes, Year 1 pupils should, for example:

Understand and use in practical contexts:
ordinal numbers: *first, second, third, fourth...*
how many...
as many as, the same number as...
equal to, more than, less than, fewer than, greater than, smaller than, larger than...
most, least, smallest, largest...
order, first, last, before, after, next, between, half way between...
Use the = sign to represent equality.

Respond to questions such as:

- Who is the first, last, third... in this queue?
- What is on the fifth page of this book?
- Point to the seventh bead in this line.
- What is the twelfth letter of the alphabet?

Respond to questions such as:

- Which is less: 15 or 19?
- Which is more: 12p or 21p?
- Are there enough cups for these saucers?

- Pat has 6 pens. Alice has 8 pens.
  Who has fewer pens?
  How many more pens has Alice than Pat?

- Find page 16 in this book of 24 pages.

- Tell me a number between 14 and 19.

- Write the numbers between 3 and 9 on the number track.

1	2	3						9	10

- Write a number in the box so the three numbers are in order.

  2 □ 7

- The time is between 3 o'clock and 8 o'clock.
  What time could it be?

- The classroom is between 10 and 15 strides wide.
  How many strides across could it be?

As outcomes, Year 2 pupils should, for example:

Understand, use and begin to read:
ordinal numbers: *first, second, third, fourth...*
how many...
as many as, the same number as...
equal to, more than, less than, fewer than,
greater than, smaller than, larger than...
most, least, smallest, largest...
order, first, last, before, after, next, between,
half way between...
Use the = sign to represent equality.

Respond to questions such as:

- Write today's date.
- What date is your birthday?
- What is the third month of the year?

- What position is the fourth black bead?

Respond to questions such as:

- Which is less: 36 or 63?
- Which is shorter: 18 metres or 15 metres?
- Which is more: 31 kg or 37 kg?
- Which is less: 67p or 76p?

- Ali has 16 pens. Ben has 28 pens.
  Who has fewer pens?
  How many more pens has Ben than Ali?

- Find page 67 in this book of 112 pages.

- What even numbers lie between 15 and 20?

- Write a number in the box so the three numbers are in order.

  25 ☐ 31

- What number is half way between 10 and 20?

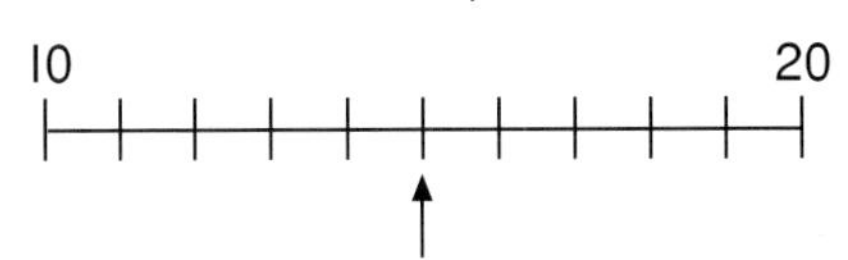

- What number is half way between 9 and 13?

- A number lies between 38 and 42.
  What could it be?

- This ribbon is between 30 cm and 40 cm long.
  How long could it be?

- My cake cost between 90p and £1.
  What could it have cost?

As outcomes, Year 3 pupils should, for example:

Use, read and begin to write:
ordinal numbers: *first, second, third, fourth...*
and abbreviations: *1st, 2nd, 3rd, 4th...*
how many... as many as, the same number as...
equal to, more than, less than, fewer than,
greater than, smaller than, larger than...
most, least, smallest, largest...
order, first, last, before, after, next, between,
half way between...
Use the = sign to represent equality.

Respond to questions such as:

- What position is the sixth black bead?

- What colour would the 19th bead be in this pattern of beads?

Respond to questions such as:

- Which is more: 216 or 261?
- Which is longer: 157 cm or 517 cm?
- Which is lighter: 3.5 kg or 5.5 kg?
- Which is less: £4.63 or £3.46?

- Jo has 47 stamps. Ny has 92 stamps.
  Who has fewer stamps?
  How many more stamps has Ny than Jo?

- Find page 167 in this book of 320 pages.

- What even numbers lie between 415 and 420?

- What number is half way between 40 and 60?

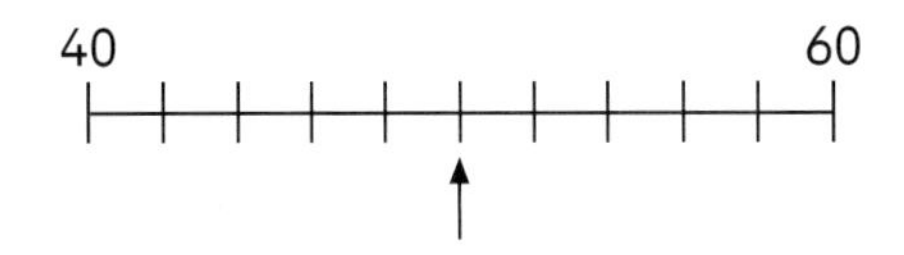

- What number is half way between 40 and 50?
  Between 300 and 400? Between 7 and 8?

- This string is between 90 cm and 140 cm long.
  How long could it be?

- This watch cost between £6 and £7.
  What could it have cost?

Pupils should be taught to:

Say the number that is 1, 10 or 100 more or less than any given number

As outcomes, Year 1 pupils should, for example:

Use and apply knowledge of adding and subtracting 1 or 10 in a variety of contexts.

Respond to questions such as:

- What is 1 more than 6? Than 9? Than 19? Than 24?
  What is 1 less than 8? Than 20? Than 25?
- What number is one before 7? After 6?
- What number is 10 more than 6? 10 less than 17?
  What is 10 more than 17? 10 less than 30?
- An apple costs 7p.
  An orange costs 10p more.
  What does the orange cost?
- Fill in the missing numbers on this number track.

	2	3	4		6		8	9	10		12	13		15

- Write the correct numbers in the boxes.

7 = □ + 7
= □ + 6
= □ + 5
= □ + 4
= □ + 3
= □ + 2
= □ + 1
= □ + 0

As outcomes, Year 2 pupils should, for example:

Use and apply knowledge of adding and subtracting 1 or 10 in a variety of contexts.

Respond to questions such as:

- What is 1 more than 53? Than 89? Than 112?
  What is 1 less than 82? Than 60? Than 120?

- What number is 10 after 43? 10 before 78?
  What is 10 more than 96? 10 less than 102?

- Aziz has saved 10p more than me.
  I have saved 65p.
  How much has Aziz saved?

- Pick up a card from a pack of two-digit numbers.
  Write the number in the correct place on this 0 to 99 square.

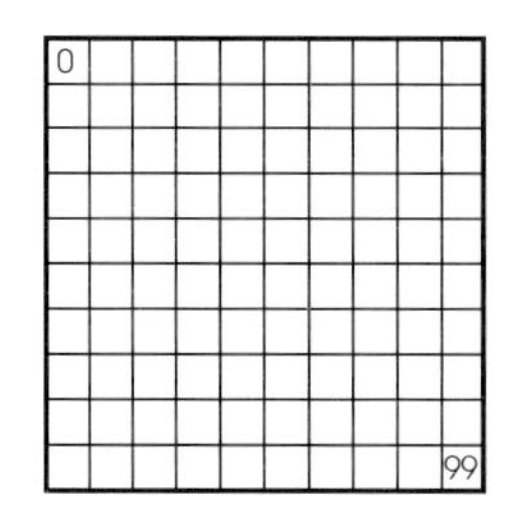

- This is part of a 100 square.
  Fill in the missing numbers.

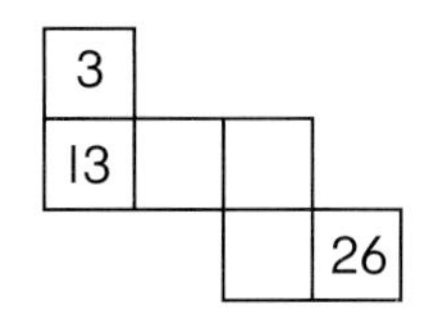

- Write the correct numbers in the boxes.

64	=	□	+	4
	=	□	+	14
	=	□	+	24
	=	□	+	34
	=	□	+	44
	=	□	+	54

- Write the correct number in each box.

As outcomes, Year 3 pupils should, for example:

Use and apply knowledge of adding and subtracting 1 or 10 or 100 in a variety of contexts.

Respond to questions such as:

- What is 1 more than 485? Than 569? Than 299?
  What is 1 less than 756? Than 340? Than 500?

- What number is 10 after 437? 10 less?
  100 more? 100 less? 1 more? 1 less?

- Jack walks 645 metres to school.
  Suzy walks 100 metres less.
  How far does Suzy walk?

- These are parts of a 100 square.
  Fill in the missing numbers.

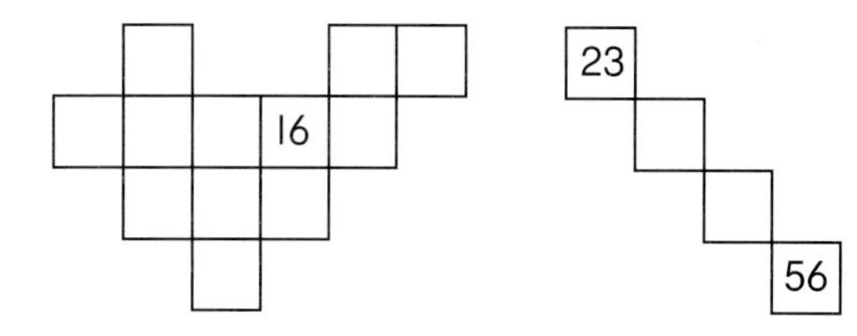

- Write the correct number in each box.

500 —100 more is→ □   □ —100 less is→ 7

Pupils should be taught to:

Order a set of familiar numbers and position them on a number line and, where appropriate, a 100 square

As outcomes, Year 1 pupils should, for example:

Order numbers in real contexts in science, design and technology, geography, history, physical education...

Put in order sets of walnuts in jars, sticks of cubes, pens in pots...

Respond to questions such as:

- Put these shuffled cards in order:
  from 1 to about 12;
  from 1 to 30.

- Write a number on each blank card so that the numbers are in order.

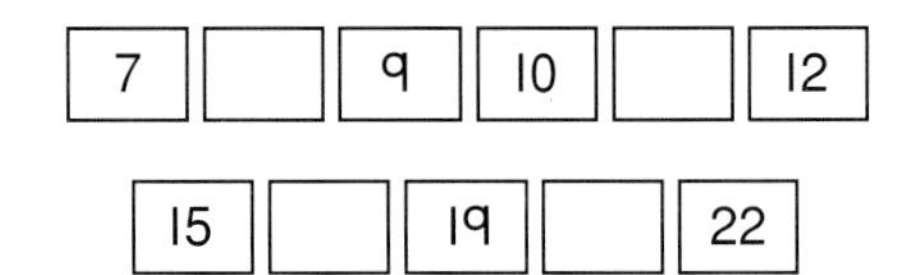

- Which two numbers have been changed over?

3	4	8	6	7	5

- Put these in order, largest/smallest first:

  7, 2, 9, 4;

  17, 6, 15, 7, 12, 22;

  12p, 9p, 2p, 15p.

- I have ten cards. I want them to be in order.
  Write where these numbers go:
  7, 5, 9, 3...

As outcomes, Year 2 pupils should, for example:

Order numbers in real contexts in science, design and technology, geography, history, physical education…

Respond to questions such as:

- Put these shuffled cards in order:
  from 35 to about 45;
  from 0 to 100.

- Fill in the missing numbers on this number line.

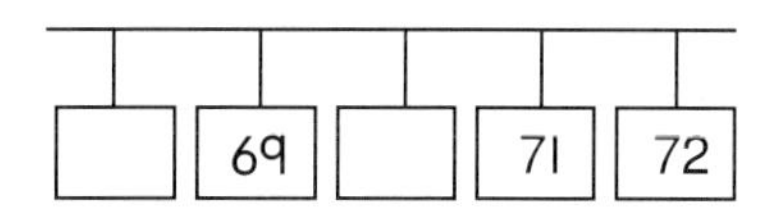

- Write a number on each blank card so that the five numbers are in order.

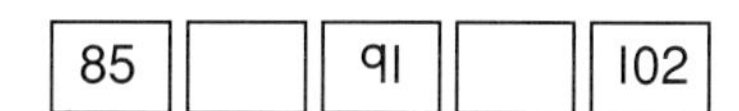

- My cards from 10 to 30 were in order.
  Two have been changed over.
  Which two are they?

- Put these in order, largest/smallest first:

  27, 16, 85, 72, 52;

  50p, 45p, 54p, 40p, 55p.

- This is a 0 to 100 line marked in tens.
  Write where these numbers go on the line:
  20, 60, 90…

  0 100

Position one- and two-digit numbers on a 100 square **(see page 13)**.

As outcomes, Year 3 pupils should, for example:

Order numbers in real contexts in science, design and technology, geography, history, physical education…

Respond to questions such as:

- Put these shuffled cards in order:
  from 95 to about 105;
  from –10 to 10.

- Fill in the missing numbers on this number line.

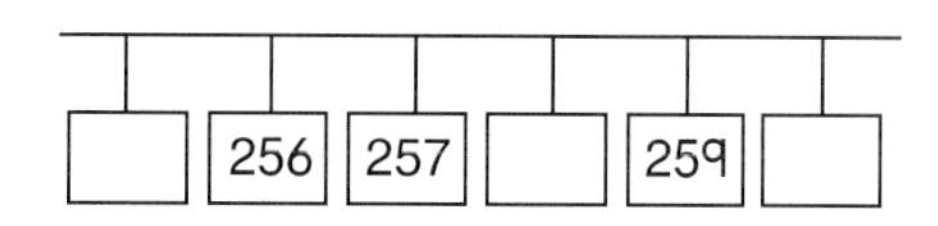

- Write a number on each blank card so that the five numbers are in order.

- My cards from 90 to 120 were in order.
  Two have been changed over.
  Which two are they?

- Put these in order, largest/smallest first:

  136, 258, 285, 163, 208;

  £1.50, £5.50, £2.30, £3.20, £5.30;

  67 cm, 121 cm, 107 cm, 70 cm, 160 cm.

- This is a 0 to 100 line marked in tens.
  Mark where these numbers go on the line:
  28, 65, 92… Label each number.

  0 100

Position one- and two-digit numbers on a 100 square **(see page 13)**.

Pupils should be taught to:

Understand and use the vocabulary of estimation and approximation, and give a sensible estimate for a number of objects

As outcomes, Year 1 pupils should, for example:

Understand and use in practical contexts:
guess how many, estimate...
roughly, nearly, close to, about the same as...
too many, too few, enough, not enough...

Make estimates of numbers and measurements in a range of practical contexts, including those arising in other subjects. For example:

- Estimate a number of objects up to about 30. Guess, for example, the number of: counters in a pile, penny coins in a purse, small toys in a jar, shells in a collection...

- Estimate whether there are enough: pegs for these coats, cups for these saucers, knives for these forks, chairs for these children, pencils for these notebooks...

  Now check. Are there too many or too few?

See also estimating measurements (page 74).

As outcomes, Year 2 pupils should, for example:

Understand, use and begin to read:
guess how many, estimate...
round, nearest...
roughly, nearly, close to, about the same as...
too many, too few, enough, not enough...

Make estimates of numbers and measurements in a range of practical contexts, including those arising in other subjects. For example:

- Estimate a number up to about 50, then more. Estimate, for example, the number of: potatoes in a bag, buttons in a box, mixed coins in a purse, spots on a card...

  Explain how the estimate was made. For example: *I can see two groups of about five.*

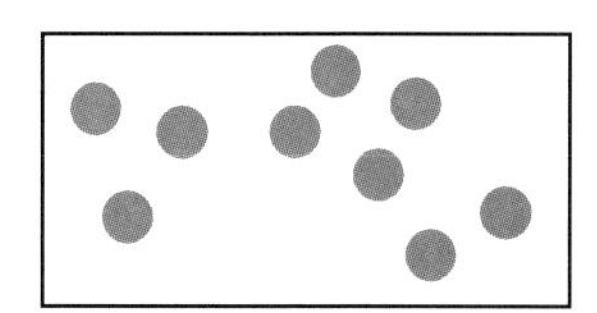

- Record estimates on a number line and find the difference between the estimate and the actual number.
- Estimate the position of a point on a line. For example, estimate the whole number marked by the arrow. How did you decide?

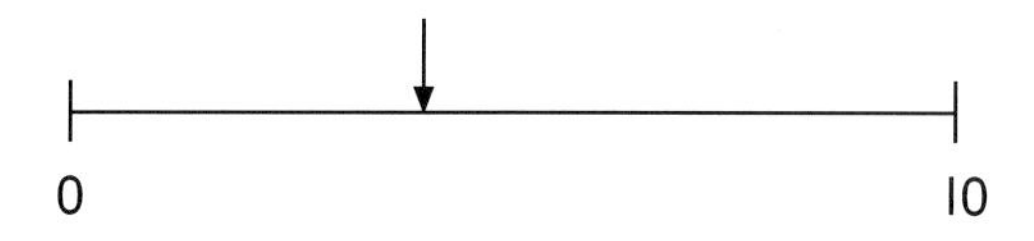

See also estimating measurements (page 75).

As outcomes, Year 3 pupils should, for example:

Use, read and begin to write:
guess how many, estimate...
round, nearest...
roughly, nearly, close to, approximately...
too many, too few, enough, not enough...

Make estimates of numbers and measurements in a range of practical contexts, including those arising in other subjects. For example:

- Estimate a number up to about 100. Estimate, for example, the number of: red sweets and green sweets in a jar, lines on the left page and the right page of a book, leaves on a twig...

  Explain how the estimate was made and justify why it is reasonable.

  Talk about different strategies for getting estimates.

- Record estimates on a number line and find the difference between the estimate and the actual number.
- Estimate the position of a point on a line. For example, estimate the whole numbers marked by the arrows. How did you decide?

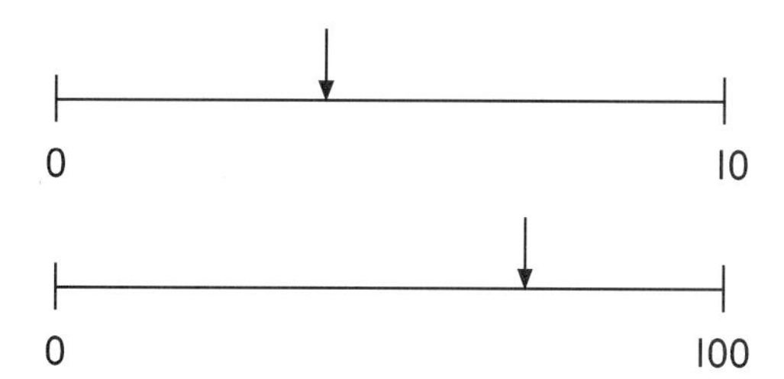

See also estimating a simple fraction (page 23) and estimating measurements (page 75).

Pupils should be taught to:	As outcomes, Year 1 pupils should, for example:
Round a number to the nearest 10 or 100	

As outcomes, Year 2 pupils should, for example:

Begin to round numbers less than 100 to the nearest ten. For example:

- 33 is closer to 30 than 40.
  The nearest ten to 33 is 30.
- 37 is closer to 40 than to 30.
  The nearest ten to 37 is 40.
- 35 is half way between 30 and 40.
  We say that the nearest ten to 35 is 40, because we round up when the number is half way between two tens.

When finding information in a book, say, for example, whether page 34 in a book is closer to page 30 or closer to page 40, and why.

As outcomes, Year 3 pupils should, for example:

Round numbers less than 100 to the nearest ten. For example:

- 33 is 30 rounded to the nearest ten.
- 37 is 40 rounded to the nearest ten.
- 35 is 40 rounded to the nearest ten.

Begin to approximate by rounding any three-digit number to the nearest hundred. For example:

- 433 is closer to 400 than to 500.
  433 is 400 rounded to the nearest hundred.
- 856 is closer to 900 than to 800.
  856 is 900 rounded to the nearest hundred.
- 650 is half way between 600 and 700.
  We say that the nearest hundred to 650 is 700, because we round up when the number is half way between two hundreds.

Round measurements made in other subjects, or found in information books, to the nearest 10 units, and begin to round them to the nearest 100 units. For example:

- Peter's ice melted in 28 minutes, which is 30 minutes to the nearest 10 minutes.
- London to Glasgow is 418 miles, or 400 miles to the nearest hundred miles.

See also rounding up or down after division (page 51).

Pupils should be taught to:

Recognise and find simple fractions; recognise the equivalence between them; compare two simple fractions in practical contexts

As outcomes, Year 1 pupils should, for example:

As outcomes, Year 2 pupils should, for example:

Understand, use and begin to read:
part, fraction…
one whole, one half, one quarter…

Recognise and write ½, ¼, as one half, one quarter.

Respond to questions such as:

- What fraction is shaded?

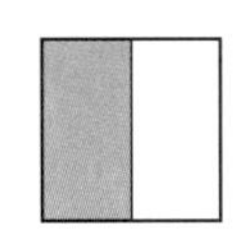
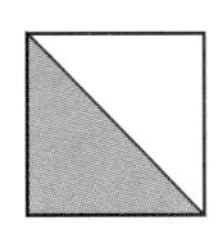
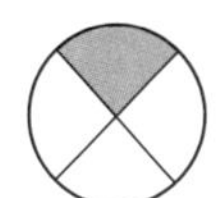

- Ring one half of this set of 10 buttons.

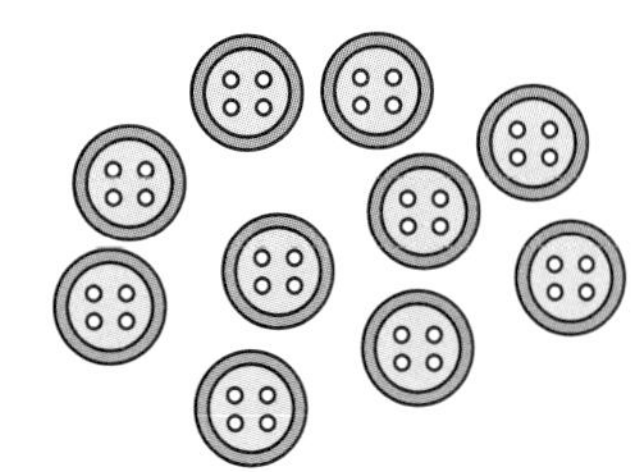

- Say half of any even whole number to 20.
- Find one quarter of 12 biscuits, of 8 pencils…
- Find half of: this bar of chocolate squares, these 14 pennies, these nine biscuits… half of the 30 children in the class…

- Say what fraction of a cake each person will get when it is divided equally between two or four people.

See also making whole, half and quarter turns (page 89), and telling the time (page 79).

Recognise what is not one half or one quarter. For example, explain why:

- these shapes are not divided into halves;

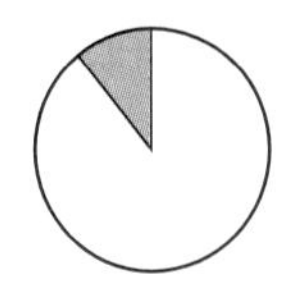

- this jar is not half full.

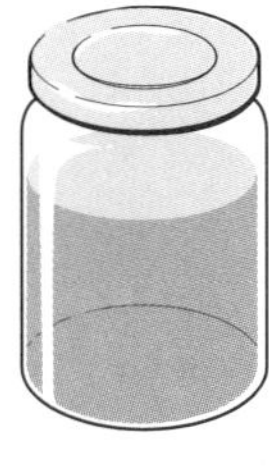

As outcomes, Year 3 pupils should, for example:

Use, read and begin to write:
part, fraction, one whole, one half, one quarter, three quarters, one third, two thirds, one tenth…

Recognise ⅒ as one tenth, and know that it means one whole divided into 10 equal parts.

Respond to questions such as:

- Shade one half.
Shade one tenth.

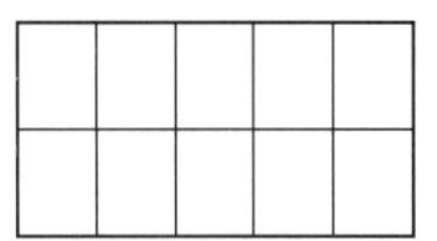

- What fraction of the set of buttons is ringed?

Say what fraction of the set of buttons is not in the ring.

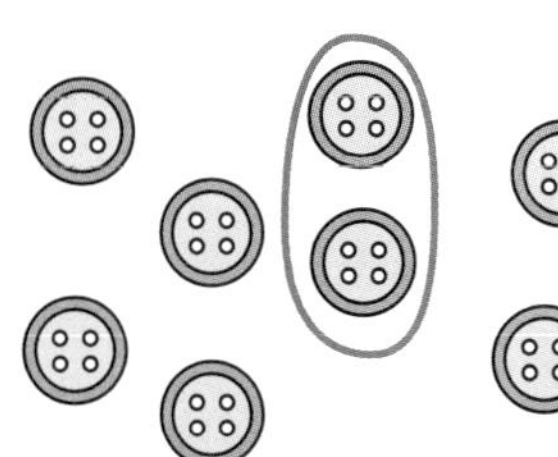

- Find half of each of the numbers to 30.
What is ⅒ of 20?
What is three quarters of 20?

- Complete the shading on this diagram so that one half of it is shaded.

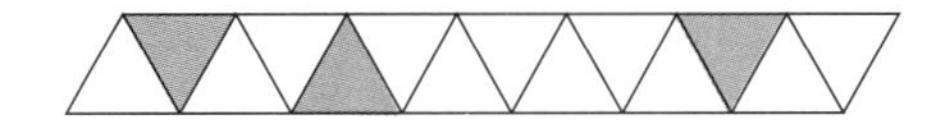

- Write a fraction to show how much each person gets when:
1 cake is divided equally among 10 people;
5 cakes are divided equally between 2 people.

- Take 20 cubes.
Make a shape which is ½ red and ⅒ blue.

Recognise what is not ½, ¼, ⅓, ⅒. For example, explain why this shape is not divided into thirds.

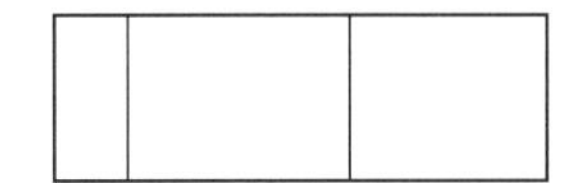

Pupils should be taught to:

Recognise and find simple fractions; recognise the equivalence between them; compare two simple fractions in practical contexts (continued)

As outcomes, Year 1 pupils should, for example:

As outcomes, Year 2 pupils should, for example:

Recognise that one whole can be broken into two identical halves or four identical quarters, and that two halves or four quarters will make one whole.
For example:

- Fold this piece of paper in half. Now unfold it. How many parts are there?
  Now fold the same piece of paper into quarters. How many parts are there?

Recognise that:

- two quarters are the same as one half;
- three quarters and one quarter make one whole.

For example, recognise that:

- this whole shape consists of four equal quarters;
- two quarters or one half of the shape is shaded.

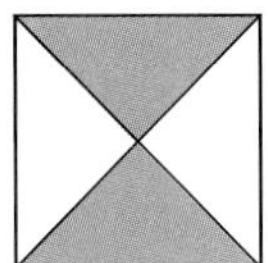

Begin to position halves on a number line. For example, place 5½ on a number line, and recognise that it lies mid-way between 5 and 6.

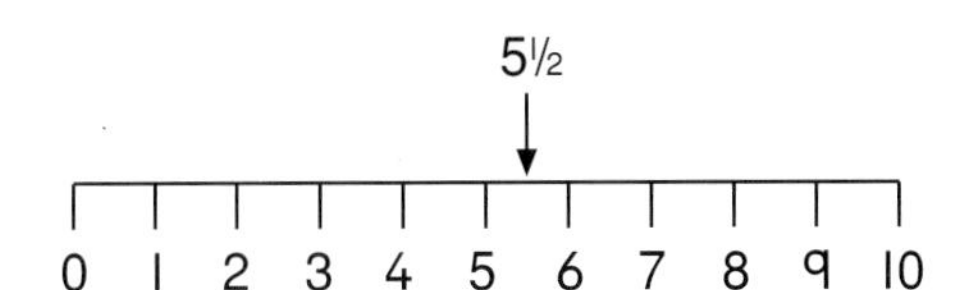

As outcomes, Year 3 pupils should, for example:

Know that:

- two quarters are the same as one half;
- one half is equivalent to five tenths;
- ten tenths make one whole;
- one whole is three quarters plus one quarter, three tenths plus seven tenths...;
- one quarter is half of one half.

For example, recognise that:

- this whole shape consists of ten tenths;
- five tenths or one half is shaded.

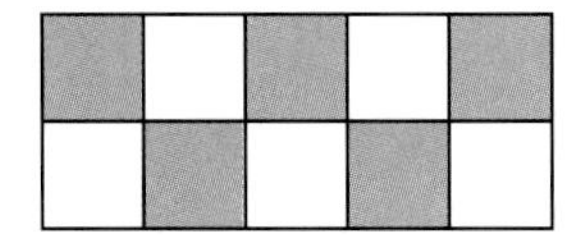

Position simple fractions on a number line.
For example, make a line to 10 showing whole, half and quarter numbers. Count on or back along sections of the line in steps of one half, one quarter.
Answer questions such as:

- What number is half way between 3 and 4? Between 2½ and 3?
- Tell me any number between 6 and 7.

Recognise that on a number line:

- one half is greater than one quarter;
- one half is less than three quarters;
- three quarters lies between one half and one whole.

Estimate a fraction. Respond to questions such as:

- Roughly how much of this cake has been eaten?

- About what time is it?

- This jar holds 100 sweets when it is full. Some have been eaten. About how many are left?

- Choose any number on a number line to 100. Estimate where half that number is.

Pupils should be taught to:	As outcomes, Year 1 pupils should, for example:
Understand the operation of addition and the related vocabulary, and recognise that addition can be done in any order	Understand and use in practical contexts: *more, add, sum, total, altogether, equals, sign...* and read and write the plus (+) and equals (=) signs.
	Understand addition as: • combining sets to make a total; • steps along a number track (counting on).
	Begin to understand that adding zero leaves a number unchanged.
	Respond rapidly to oral questions phrased in a variety of ways, such as: • 3 add 1. • Add 2 to 4. • 6 plus 3. • What is the sum/total of 2 and 8? • How many are 3 and 5 altogether? • Which two/three numbers could make 9 altogether? • What must I add to 4 to make 10? • I think of a number. I add 3. The answer is 7. What is my number?
	Record simple mental additions in a number sentence using the + and = signs.
	Recognise the use of symbols such as □ or △ to stand for unknown numbers, and complete, for example: • with rapid recall, based on facts to 5: 2 + 3 = □ □ + △ = 4 • using counters or a number line, or 10p and 1p coins, then mental strategies, explaining method: 11 + 4 = □ △ + □ = 13 17 + 6 = □
	Understand, for example, that: • 5 + 2 equals 2 + 5, but that 5 - 2 is not the same as 2 - 5; • 5 + 2 + 6 = (5 + 2) + 6 or 5 + (2 + 6); and use these properties when appropriate.

As outcomes, Year 2 pupils should, for example:

Understand, use and begin to read:
more, add, sum, total, altogether, equals, sign...
and read and write the plus (+) and equals (=) signs.

Continue to develop understanding of addition as:
- combining sets to make a total;
- counting on steps along a number line.

Understand that adding zero leaves a number unchanged.

Begin to understand that addition reverses subtraction (addition is the inverse of subtraction).

See also using the relationship between addition and subtraction (page 35).

Respond rapidly to oral or written questions phrased in a variety of ways, such as:
- 27 add 10.
- Add 60 to 30.
- 4 plus 18.
- What is the sum/total of 18 and 4?
- How many are 5 and 14 altogether?
- Which two/three numbers could have a sum of 15?
- What must I add to 14 to make 15?
- I think of a number. I add 10. The answer is 30. What is my number?

Record mental additions in a number sentence using the + and = signs.

Recognise the use of symbols such as □ or △ to stand for unknown numbers, and complete, for example:
- with rapid recall, based on facts to 10:
  4 + 5 = □   □ + △ = 9
- using 10p and 1p coins, or a number line or square, then mental strategies, explaining method:
  61 + 14 = □   △ + □ = 50
  36 + 50 = □

Understand, for example, that:
- 15 + 26 = 26 + 15, but that
  15 – 6 is not the same as 6 – 15;
- 15 + 2 + 7 = (15 + 2) + 7 or 15 + (2 + 7);

and use these properties when appropriate.

As outcomes, Year 3 pupils should, for example:

Use, read and begin to write:
more, add, sum, total, altogether, equals, sign...
and the plus (+) and equals (=) signs.

Continue to develop understanding of addition as counting on steps along a number line.

Understand that addition reverses subtraction (addition is the inverse of subtraction).

See also using the relationship between addition and subtraction (page 35), and checking results (page 59).

Respond rapidly to oral or written questions phrased in a variety of ways, such as:
- 94 add 10.
- Add 60 to 14.
- 70 plus 50.
- What is the sum/total of 26 and 9?
- How many are 11 and 35 altogether?
- Which two/three numbers could have a total of 23?
- What must I add to 4 to make 23?
- I think of a number. I add 45. The answer is 90. What is my number?

Record mental additions in a number sentence using the + and = signs.

Recognise the use of symbols such as □ or △ to stand for unknown numbers, and complete, for example:
- with rapid recall, based on facts to 20:
  13 + 6 = □   □ + △ = 20
- using 10p and 1p coins, or a number line or square, then mental strategies, explaining method:
  36 + 58 = □   △ + □ = 100
  127 + 40 = □

Understand, for example, that:
- 225 + 136 = 136 + 225, but that
  645 – 236 is not the same as 236 – 645;
- 115 + 432 + 347 = (115 + 432) + 347 or 115 + (432 + 347);

and use these properties when appropriate.

Pupils should be taught to:	As outcomes, Year 1 pupils should, for example:

Understand that more than two numbers can be added together

With the aid of apparatus

Add three numbers.
For example, use rods or a number line to:

- Explore three hops to 10 (or any other suitable number).
  Keep a record by completing, for example:
  6 + 3 + □ = 10
- Choose three of the numbers from this set: 4, 5, 6, 9.
  Add them up.
  What different totals can you make?
- Write 12 as the sum of three numbers.
  Do it in different ways.
- A plum costs 5p. Find the cost of three plums, using coins if necessary.

Mentally

Add mentally three small numbers, within the range of 1 to about 12.

Respond to oral questions, explaining the strategy used.
For example:

- Find the sum or total of:
  3 + 1 + 4 2 + 2 + 2 6 + 3 + 2
- Choose three numbers from the set 1 to 5. Add them up.
  What different totals can you make?
- Tell me three numbers that add up to 11.
  Are there any others?

Record simple mental additions in a number sentence using the + and = signs: for example, 5 + 3 + 1 = 9.

As outcomes, Year 2 pupils should, for example:

With the aid of apparatus

Add three numbers.
For example, use rods, a number line or square to:

- Explore three hops to 100 (or any other suitable number) and keep a record by completing:
  32 + □ + △ = 100
- Find the missing number in:
  1 + □ + 5 = 35
- Choose three of these numbers: 14, 15, 16, 19.
  Add them up.
  What different totals can you make?
- Using coins if necessary, total a shopping bill such as:
  29p
  36p
  18p

Mentally

Add mentally three small numbers, within the range of 1 to about 20.

Respond to oral/written questions, explaining the strategy used. For example:

- Add 5, 2 and 13.
- 2 plus 19 plus 1.
- What is the sum/total of 3, 6 and 7?
- How many altogether are 7, 4 and 2?
- Tell me three numbers that add up to 20.
  Are there any others?

Record mental additions in a number sentence using the + and = signs.

Work mentally to complete written questions like:
2 + 7 + 4 = □   1 + □ + 5 = 17
and explain method.

See also adding three numbers (page 33).

As outcomes, Year 3 pupils should, for example:

With the aid of apparatus

Add three numbers.
For example, use a number line or square to:

- Explore three hops to 500 (or any other suitable number) and keep a record by completing:
  120 + □ + △ = 500
- Find the missing number in:
  21 + □ + 63 = 150
- Find all the different totals you can make by using three of these five numbers:
  19, 63, 54, 106, 97.
- Using coins if necessary, total a shopping bill such as:
  £2.45
  £0.36
  £4.50

Mentally

Add mentally three or more small numbers, within the range of 1 to about 50.

Respond to oral/written questions, explaining the strategy used. For example:

- Add 15, 6, 15 and 1.
- 7 plus 5 plus 9.
- What is the sum/total of 13, 12 and 3?
- How many altogether are 11, 17 and 6?
- Tell me three numbers that add up to 30.
  Are there any others?

Record mental additions in a number sentence using the + and = signs.

Work mentally to complete written questions like:
16 + 5 + 3 + 7 = □   14 + □ + 6 = 37
and explain method.

See also adding several numbers (page 33).

Pupils should be taught to:	As outcomes, Year 1 pupils should, for example:
Understand the operation of subtraction and the related vocabulary	Understand and use in practical contexts: *take away, subtract, how many are left, how much less is … than …, difference between, how much more is … than …, how many more to make …* and read and write the minus (–) sign.

Understand subtraction as:

- taking away;
- finding the difference between;
- 'how many more to make…' (complementary addition).

Begin to understand that subtracting zero leaves a number unchanged.

Respond rapidly to oral questions phrased in a variety of ways, such as:

- 4 take away 2.
- Take 2 from 7.
- 7 subtract 3.
- Subtract 2 from 11.
- 8 less than 9.
- What number must I take from 14 to leave 10?
- What is the difference between 14 and 12?
- How many more than 3 is 9?
- How many less than 6 is 4?
- 6 taken from a number leaves 3. What is the number?
- Find pairs of numbers with a difference of 2.
- I think of a number. I take away 3. My answer is 7. What is my number?

Record simple mental subtractions in a number sentence using the - and = signs.

Recognise the use of symbols such as □ or △ to stand for unknown numbers, and complete, for example:

- with rapid mental recall, based on facts to 5:
  5 - 3 = □ □ - 1 = 2 △ - □ = 3
- using rods, counters or cubes, 10p and 1p coins, or a number line, then mental strategies, explaining method:
  15 - 8 = □ 21 - □ = 10 □ - △ = 9

As outcomes, Year 2 pupils should, for example:

Understand, use and begin to read:
take away, subtract, how many are left, how much less is … than …, difference between, how much more is … than …, how many more to make …
and read and write the minus (-) sign.

Continue to develop understanding of subtraction as:
- taking away;
- finding the difference between;
- complementary addition.

Understand that:
- subtracting zero leaves a number unchanged;
- 4 - 2, for example, is different from 2 - 4.

Begin to understand the principle that subtraction reverses addition (subtraction is the inverse of addition).

See also using the relationship between addition and subtraction (page 35).

Respond rapidly to oral or written questions phrased in a variety of ways, such as:
- 7 take away 3.
- Take 30 from 70.
- 14 subtract 2.
- Subtract 30 from 70.
- 3 less than 7.
- What number must I take from 20 to leave 3?
- What is the difference between 10 and 18?
- How many more is 11 than 3?
- How many less is 7 than 18?
- 5 taken from a number is 11. What is the number?
- 8 added to a number is 18. What is the number?
- Find pairs of numbers: with a difference of 10… with a difference of 9…

Record mental subtractions in a number sentence using the - and = signs.

Recognise the use of symbols such as □ or △ to stand for unknown numbers, and complete, for example:
- with rapid mental recall, based on facts to 10:
  7 - 3 = □   □ - 6 = 2   □ - △ = 8
- using 10p and 1p coins, or a number line or square, then mental strategies, explaining method:
  25 - 8 = □   25 - □ = 16   △ - □ = 16
  86 - 50 = □   □ - 40 = 28   □ - △ = 40

As outcomes, Year 3 pupils should, for example:

Use, read and begin to write:
take away, subtract, how many are left, how much less is … than …, difference between, how much more is … than …, how many more to make …
and the minus (-) sign.

Continue to develop understanding of subtraction as:
- taking away;
- finding the difference between;
- complementary addition.

Understand that:
- 41 - 35, for example, is different from 35 - 41.

Understand the principle that subtraction reverses addition (subtraction is the inverse of addition).

See also using the relationship between addition and subtraction (page 35), and checking results (page 59).

Respond rapidly to oral or written questions phrased in a variety of ways, such as:
- 15 take away 8.
- Take 8 from 15.
- 63 subtract 40.
- Subtract 8 from 15. Subtract 40 from 95.
- 10 less than 43. 100 less than 437.
- What must I take from 14 to leave 6?
- What is the difference between 22 and 5?
- How many more than 4 is 49?
- How many less than 28 is 12?
- 20 taken from a number is 35. What is the number?
- 8 added to a number is 48. What is the number?
- Find pairs of numbers: with a difference of 30… with a difference of 29…

Record mental subtractions in a number sentence using the - and = signs.

Recognise the use of symbols such as □ or △ to stand for unknown numbers, and complete, for example:
- with rapid mental recall, based on facts to 20:
  17 - 9 = □   13 - □ = 4   □ - △ = 11
- using 10p and 1p coins, or a number line or square, then mental strategies, explaining method:
  36 - 15 = □   □ - 15 = 19   △ - □ = 19
  178 - 56 = □   20 - △ - □ = 5

Pupils should be taught to:	As outcomes, Year 1 pupils should, for example:

Know by heart addition and subtraction facts

Know by heart all **addition and subtraction facts for all numbers up to and including 5**. For example, recall rapidly all the pairs for 4:

0 + 4 = 4	4 + 0 = 4
1 + 3 = 4	3 + 1 = 4
2 + 2 = 4	
4 − 0 = 4	4 − 4 = 0
4 − 1 = 3	4 − 3 = 1
4 − 2 = 2	

Begin to know by heart number bonds for numbers up to 10, for both addition and subtraction.

Understand and use in practical contexts:
double, halve, half...

- Know by heart **addition doubles** from 1 + 1 to at least 5 + 5, such as 4 + 4 = 8.
- Begin to know doubles from 6 + 6 to 10 + 10, such as 7 + 7 = 14.

Respond rapidly to oral questions phrased in a variety of ways, such as:
- Double 4.
- Half of 6.
- Two fives.
- I roll double 3. What's my score?
- How many toes are there on two feet?
- How many socks in two pairs?

Know by heart all **pairs of numbers that total 10**.
For example, rapidly:
- find pairs of cards with a total of 10;
- say how many more counters are needed to make 10 altogether;
- say how many steps must be taken to get from 4 to 10 on a number line, or from 10 back to 4;
- put numbers in the boxes to make 10:
  □ + 4 = 10   □ + △ = 10

As outcomes, Year 2 pupils should, for example:

Know by heart all **addition and subtraction facts for all numbers up to and including 10**. For example, recall rapidly all the pairs for 7:

0 + 7 = 7	7 + 0 = 7
1 + 6 = 7	6 + 1 = 7
2 + 5 = 7	5 + 2 = 7
3 + 4 = 7	4 + 3 = 7
7 − 0 = 7	7 − 7 = 0
7 − 1 = 6	7 − 6 = 1
7 − 2 = 5	7 − 5 = 2
7 − 3 = 4	7 − 4 = 3

Derive quickly these **addition doubles**:

- doubles of numbers from 1 + 1 to 15 + 15, such as 13 + 13 = 26;
- doubles of multiples of 5 from 5 + 5 to 50 + 50, such as 45 + 45 = 90.

For more on doubles, see page 53.

Know by heart all **pairs of numbers that total 20**. For example, rapidly:

- find pairs of cards with a total of 20;
- say how many more counters or cubes are needed to make 20 altogether;
- say how many steps must be taken to get from 13 to 20 on a number line, or from 20 back to 13;
- put numbers in the boxes to make 20:
  □ + 4 = 20 □ + △ = 20

Know by heart all **pairs of multiples of 10 that total 100**. For example, rapidly:

- say how many steps must be taken to get from 40 to 100 on a number line, or from 100 back to 70;
- put numbers in the boxes to make 100:
  □ + 20 = 100 △ + □ = 100

As outcomes, Year 3 pupils should, for example:

Know by heart all **addition and subtraction facts for all numbers up to and including 20**. For example, recall rapidly all the pairs for 15:

… 11 + 4 = 15	4 + 11 = 15
10 + 5 = 15	5 + 10 = 15
9 + 6 = 15	6 + 9 = 15 …
… 15 − 4 = 11	15 − 11 = 4
15 − 5 = 10	15 − 10 = 5
15 − 6 = 9	15 − 9 = 6 …

Derive quickly these **addition doubles**:

- doubles of numbers from 1 + 1 to 20 + 20, such as 19 + 19 = 38;
- doubles of multiples of 5 from 5 + 5 to 100 + 100, such as 95 + 95 = 190.

For more on doubles, see page 53.

Derive quickly all **pairs of multiples of 5 that total 100**. For example, rapidly:

- find pairs of cards such as 65 and 35;
- say how many steps must be taken to get from 65 to 100 on a number line, or from 100 back to 45;
- put numbers in the boxes to make 100:
  □ + 15 = 100 □ + △ = 100

Know by heart all **pairs of multiples of 100 that total 1000**. For example, rapidly:

- say how many steps must be taken to get from 400 to 1000 on a number line, or from 1000 back to 700;
- put numbers in the boxes to make 1000:
  □ + 200 = 1000 △ + □ = 1000

Pupils should be taught to:	As outcomes, Year 1 pupils should, for example:
Use knowledge that addition can be done in any order	For example, **put the larger number first** in order to count on: • arrange 4 + 7 as 7 + 4, and count on 4 from 7.
	Begin to **partition and recombine** by breaking units of 6, 7, 8 or 9 into '5 and a bit'. • For example, work out mentally that: 5 + 8 = 5 plus (5 and 3) = 5 + 5 + 3 = 10 + 3 = 13
Find a small difference by counting up	
Identify near doubles	For example, work out mentally that: • 5 + 6 = 11 and explain that it is double 5 plus 1, or double 6 minus 1.

As outcomes, Year 2 pupils should, for example:

For example, **put the larger number first** in order to count on:

- arrange 5 + 36 as 36 + 5, and count on in ones from 36;
- arrange 30 + 60 as 60 + 30, and count on in tens from 60.

Add three numbers by using strategies such as:

- look for pairs that make 10 and do these first;
- start with the largest number.

Work out mentally questions like:

2 + 7 + 4 = □   1 + □ + 5 = 17

Partition and recombine. For example:

- Break units of 6, 7, 8 or 9 into '5 and a bit'.
  For example, work out mentally and explain that:
  9 + 8 = (5 + 4) plus (5 + 3)
  = 5 + 5 + 4 + 3
  = 10 + 7
  = 17
- Partition into tens and units.
  For example, work out mentally and explain that:
  12 + 23 = (10 + 2) plus (20 + 3)
  = (10 + 20) + (2 + 3)
  = 30 + 5
  = 35
  or
  12 + 23 = 12 + 20 + 3
  = 32 + 3
  = 35

Recognise that when two numbers are close together, it is easier to find a difference by counting up, not counting back.
For example, work out mentally that:

- 82 – 79 = 3 and explain that counting up from 79 to 82 gives 3.

For example, work out mentally that:

- 6 + 7 = 13 and explain that it is double 6 plus 1, or double 7 minus 1;
- 40 + 39 = 79 explaining that it is double 40 take away 1.

As outcomes, Year 3 pupils should, for example:

For example, **put the larger number first** in order to count on:

- calculate 8 + 127 by counting on in ones from 127;
- calculate 40 + 53 by counting on in tens from 53.

Add several numbers by using strategies such as:

- look for pairs that make 10 and do these first;
- start with the largest number;
- look for pairs that make 9 or 11, and add these to the total by adding 10 and then adjusting by 1

Work out mentally questions like:

16 + 5 + 3 + 7 = □   14 + □ + 6 = 37

Partition and recombine. For example:

- Continue to break 6, 7, 8 or 9 into '5 and a bit'.
  For example, work out mentally and explain that:
  55 +16 = 55 plus (15 + 1)
  = 55 + 15 + 1
  = 70 + 1
  = 71
- Partition into tens and units.
  For example, work out mentally and explain that:
  36 + 53 = (30 + 6) plus (50 + 3)
  = (30 + 50) + (6 + 3)
  = 80 + 9
  = 89
  or
  36 + 53 = 36 + 50 + 3
  = 86 + 3
  = 89

See also using jottings (pages 43 and 45).

Recognise that when two numbers are close together, it is easier to find a difference by counting up, not counting back.
For example, work out mentally that:

- 504 – 498 = 6 and explain that counting up from 498 to 504 gives 6.

For example, work out mentally that:

- 36 + 35 = 71 explaining that it is double 35 plus 1;
- 60 + 70 = 130 explaining that it is two 60s plus 10, or two 70s minus 10;
- 18 + 16 = 34 explaining that it is double 20, minus 2, minus 4.

Pupils should be taught to:	As outcomes, Year 1 pupils should, for example:
Add or subtract 9, 19, 29... or 11, 21, 31... by adding or subtracting 10, 20, 30... and adjusting by 1	Add 9 to single-digit numbers by adding 10 then subtracting 1. For example: $6 + 9 = 6 + 10 - 1$.
Use patterns of similar calculations	Develop and recognise a pattern such as: $7 + 0 = 7$ $10 - 0 = 10$ $6 + 1 = 7$ $10 - 1 = 9$ $5 + 2 = 7$ $10 - 2 = 8$ ... ... and so deduce that: $3 + 4 = 7$ $10 - 6 = 4$
Use the relationship between addition and subtraction	

As outcomes, Year 2 pupils should, for example:

Mentally add or subtract 11 or 21, or 9 or 19, to/from any two-digit number. For example:
- 58 + 21 = 79 because it is the same as 58 + 20 + 1;
- 70 - 11 = 59 because it is the same as 70 - 10 - 1;
- 24 - 9 = 15 because it is the same as 24 - 10 + 1;
- 35 + 19 = 54 because it is the same as 35 + 20 - 1.

Develop and recognise a pattern such as:

3 + 5 = 8   4 - 3 = 1
13 + 5 = 18   14 - 3 = 11
23 + 5 = 28   24 - 3 = 21
...   ...

and so deduce that:

63 + 5 = 68   54 - 3 = 51

Recognise and use the pattern in, for example:

4 + 3 = 7
40 + 30 = 70
400 + 300 = 700

Say or write the subtraction fact corresponding to a given addition fact, and vice versa. For example:

15 + 4 = 19 implies that 19 - 4 = 15
4 + 15 = 19 implies that 19 - 15 = 4
and vice versa.

Without apparatus, answer oral questions like:
- You know that 12 + 4 = 16.
  What is 4 + 12, or 16 - 12, or 16 - 4?
- You know that 17 - 3 = 14.
  What is 17 - 14, or 3 + 14, or 14 + 3?

Given three numbers, say or write four different sentences relating these numbers. For example:
- Given 2, 7 and 9, say or write:

  7 plus 2 equals 9   7 + 2 = 9
  2 plus 7 equals 9   2 + 7 = 9
  9 minus 2 equals 7   9 - 2 = 7
  9 minus 7 equals 2   9 - 7 = 2

As outcomes, Year 3 pupils should, for example:

Mentally add or subtract 9 or 11 to/from any three-digit number. For example:
- 284 - 9 = 275 because it is the same as 284 - 10 + 1;
- 543 + 11 = 554 because it is the same as 543 + 10 + 1.

Mentally add or subtract 9, 19, 29... or 11, 21, 31... to/from any two-digit number without crossing 100. For example:
- 63 + 29 = 92 because it is the same as 63 + 30 - 1;
- 78 - 49 = 29 because it is the same as 78 - 50 + 1.

Develop and recognise a pattern such as:

14 + 3 = 17   68 - 5 = 63
14 + 13 = 27   68 - 15 = 53
14 + 23 = 37   68 - 25 = 43
...   ...

and so deduce that:

14 + 83 = 97   68 - 45 = 23

Recognise and use the pattern in, for example:

4 + 8 = 12
40 + 80 = 120
400 + 800 = 1200

Recognise and use the pattern in an addition table.

+	1	2	3	4
1	2	3	4	5
2	3	4	5	6
3	4	5	6	7
4	5	6	7	8

Say or write the subtraction fact corresponding to a given addition fact, and vice versa. For example:

56 + 27 = 83 implies that 83 - 27 = 56
27 + 56 = 83 implies that 83 - 56 = 27
and vice versa.

Without apparatus, answer oral questions like:
- You know that 32 + 14 = 46.
  What is 14 + 32, or 46 - 32, or 46 - 14?
- You know that 87 - 42 = 45.
  What is 87 - 45, or 42 + 45, or 45 + 42?

Given three or more numbers, say or write different sentences relating these numbers. For example:
- Given 5, 8 and 13, say or write:

  8 plus 5 equals 13   8 + 5 = 13
  5 plus 8 equals 13   5 + 8 = 13
  13 minus 8 equals 5   13 - 8 = 5
  13 minus 5 equals 8   13 - 5 = 8
- Using only the numbers 15, 17, 32, 34, 49, write as many different number sentences as you can.

See also checking results (page 59).

Pupils should be taught to:	As outcomes, Year 1 pupils should, for example:
Use known number facts and place value to add or subtract a pair of numbers mentally	*Add or subtract a single digit to or from a single digit, without crossing 10*

Add or subtract a single digit to or from a single digit, without crossing 10

- Respond to oral questions like:
  2 + 4   6 + 4   8 − 5
- Work mentally to complete written questions like:
  2 + 3 = □   2 + □ = 5   □ + 3 = 5
  7 − 3 = □   7 − □ = 4   □ − 3 = 4

Add or subtract a single digit to or from a 'teens' number, without crossing 20 or 10

- Respond to oral questions like:
  15 + 3   18 − 6
  and explain method.
- Work mentally to complete written questions like:
  15 + 4 = □   15 + □ = 19   □ + 4 = 19
  17 − 5 = □   17 − □ = 12   □ − 5 = 12

Add or subtract a single digit to or from 10, then 20

- Respond to oral questions like:
  10 + 3   10 − 4   20 + 6   20 − 4
- Work mentally to complete written questions like:
  10 + 4 = □   10 + □ = 14   □ + 4 = 14
  10 − 4 = □   6 + □ = 10   □ + 4 = 10
  20 + 4 = □   20 + □ = 24   □ + 4 = 24
  20 − 4 = □   16 + □ = 20   □ + 4 = 20

Begin to add a 'teens' number to a 'teens' number, without crossing the tens boundary

- Respond to oral questions like:
  14 + 11   12 + 13
  and explain method.
- Work mentally to complete written questions like:
  15 + 12 = □

Use and apply these skills in a variety of contexts, in mathematics and other subjects.

As outcomes, Year 2 pupils should, for example:

Add or subtract a single digit to or from any two-digit number, without crossing the tens boundary

- Respond to oral questions like:
  36 + 3   98 − 6
  and explain method.
- Work mentally to complete written questions like:
  32 + 5 = □   32 + □ = 37   □ + 5 = 37
  86 − 4 = □   86 − □ = 82   □ − 4 = 82

Add a single digit to a multiple of 10 or 100

- Respond to oral questions like:
  30 + 6   200 + 4
  and explain method.
- Work mentally to complete written questions like:
  30 + 4 = □   30 + □ = 34   □ + 4 = 34
  600 + 7 = □   600 + □ = 607   □ + 7 = 607

Subtract a single digit from a multiple of 10

- Respond to oral questions like:
  30 − 3   100 − 5
  and explain method.
- Work mentally to complete written questions like:
  80 − 4 = □   80 − □ = 76   □ − 4 = 76
  60 − 7 = □   60 − □ = 53   □ − 7 = 53

Begin to add a two-digit number to a multiple of 10, without crossing 100

- Respond to oral questions like:
  30 + 28   50 + 16
  and explain method.
- Work mentally to complete written questions like:
  40 + 24 = □   40 + □ = 64   □ + 24 = 64

Add/subtract a 'teens' number to/from a two-digit number, without crossing the tens boundary or 100

- Respond to oral questions like:
  45 + 13   68 − 17
  and explain method.
- Work mentally to complete written questions like:
  45 + 11 = □   58 + □ = 70   □ + 13 = 43
  37 − 12 = □   29 − □ = 18

Use and apply these skills in a variety of contexts, in mathematics and other subjects.

As outcomes, Year 3 pupils should, for example:

Add or subtract a single digit to or from any three-digit number, without crossing the tens boundary

- Respond to oral questions like:
  365 + 4   629 + 1   499 + 1
  675 − 3   768 − 5   919 − 8
  and explain method.
- Work mentally to complete written questions like:
  493 + 6 = □   435 + □ = 439   □ + 4 = 567
  287 − 3 = □   456 − □ = 450   □ − 7 = 391

Add a two-digit number to a multiple of 100

- Respond to oral questions like:
  200 + 64   400 + 18
  and explain method.
- Work mentally to complete written questions like:
  600 + 27 = □   600 + □ = 627   □ + 27 = 627

Subtract a single digit from a multiple of 100

- Respond to oral questions like:
  800 − 6   400 − 4
  and explain method.
- Work mentally to complete written questions like:
  600 − 7 = □   600 − □ = 593   □ + 7 = 600

Add a two-digit number to a multiple of 10, crossing 100

- Respond to oral questions like:
  80 + 24   60 + 66
  and explain method.
- Work mentally to complete written questions like:
  80 + 24 = □   80 + □ = 104   □ + 24 = 104

Add or subtract a pair of two-digit numbers, without crossing the tens boundary or 100

- Respond to oral questions like:
  45 + 23   68 − 47
  and explain method.
- Work mentally to complete written questions like:
  45 + 31 = □   45 + □ = 76   □ + 31 = 76
  97 − 25 = □   97 − □ = 72   □ − 25 = 72

Use and apply these skills in a variety of contexts, in mathematics and other subjects.

Pupils should be taught to:	As outcomes, Year 1 pupils should, for example:
Use known number facts and place value to add or subtract a pair of numbers mentally (continued)	*Add 10 to a single-digit number and subtract 10 from a 'teens' number* • Respond to oral questions like: 5 + 10 14 − 10 • Work mentally to complete written questions like: 6 + 10 = □ 6 + □ = 16 □ + 10 = 16 19 − 10 = □ 19 − □ = 9 □ − 10 = 9
	Use and apply these skills in a variety of contexts, in mathematics and other subjects.

As outcomes, Year 2 pupils should, for example:

Add or subtract 10 to or from any two-digit number, without crossing 100

- Respond to oral questions like:
  26 + 10 48 − 10
  and explain method.
- Work mentally to complete written questions like:
  25 + 10 = □ 25 + □ = 35 □ + 10 = 35
  49 − 10 = □ 49 − □ = 39 □ − 10 = 39

Add or subtract a pair of multiples of 10, without crossing 100

- Respond to oral questions like:
  40 + 50 80 − 30
  and explain method.
- Work mentally to complete written questions like:
  20 + 40 = □ 20 + □ = 60 □ + 40 = 60
  70 − 30 = □ 70 − □ = 40 □ − 30 = 40

Find what must be added to a two-digit multiple of 10 to make 100

- Respond to oral questions like:
  What must be added to 30 to make 100?
  and explain method.
- Work mentally to complete written questions like:
  40 + □ = 100 70 + □ = 100

Add or subtract a multiple of 10 to or from a two-digit number, without crossing 100

- Respond to oral questions like:
  52 + 30 82 − 30
  and explain method.
- Work mentally to complete written questions like:
  52 + 30 = □ 52 + □ = 82 □ + 30 = 82
  76 − 40 = □ 76 − □ = 36 □ − 40 = 36

Add or subtract a pair of multiples of 100, without crossing 1000

- Respond to oral questions like:
  500 + 300 800 − 200
  and explain method.
- Work mentally to complete written questions like:
  200 + 400 = □ 200 + □ = 600
  700 − 300 = □ □ − 300 = 400

Use and apply these skills in a variety of contexts, in mathematics and other subjects.

As outcomes, Year 3 pupils should, for example:

Add or subtract 10 to or from any two- or three-digit number, including crossing the hundreds boundary

- Respond to oral questions like:
  96 + 10 231 + 10 408 − 10 456 − 10
  and explain method.
- Work mentally to complete written questions like:
  256 + 10 = □ 256 + □ = 266 □ + 10 = 266
  405 − 10 = □ 405 − □ = 395 □ − 10 = 395

Begin to add or subtract a pair of multiples of 10, crossing 100

- Respond to oral questions like:
  40 + 70 120 − 30
  and explain method.
- Work mentally to complete written questions like:
  90 + 40 = □ 90 + □ = 130 □ + 40 = 130
  110 − 30 = □ 110 − □ = 80 □ − 30 = 80

Find what must be added to a three-digit multiple of 10 to make the next higher multiple of 100

- Respond to oral questions like:
  What must be added to 730 to make 800?
  and explain method.
- Work mentally to complete written questions like:
  540 + □ = 600 260 + □ = 300

Add or subtract a multiple of 10 to or from a two-digit number, crossing 100

- Respond to oral questions like:
  52 + 60 112 − 30
  and explain method.
- Work mentally to complete written questions like:
  52 + 80 = □ 52 + □ = 132 □ + 80 = 132
  126 − 40 = □ 126 − □ = 86 □ − 40 = 86

Add or subtract a pair of multiples of 100, crossing 1000

- Respond to oral questions like:
  500 + 800 1200 − 300
  and explain method.
- Work mentally to complete written questions like:
  200 + 900 = □ 200 + □ = 1100
  1500 − 800 = □ □ − 800 = 700

Add or subtract 100 to or from any three-digit number, without crossing 1000

- Respond to oral questions like:
  342 + 100 809 − 100
  and explain method.
- Work mentally to complete written questions like:
  347 + 100 = □ 347 + □ = 447
  613 − 100 = □ □ − 100 = 513

Use and apply these skills in a variety of contexts, in mathematics and other subjects.

Pupils should be taught to:

Add or subtract a pair of numbers mentally (continued) by bridging through 10 or 100, or a multiple of 10 or 100, and adjusting

As outcomes, Year 1 pupils should, for example:

Begin to add a pair of single-digit numbers, crossing 10

- Use two steps and cross 10 as a middle stage.
  For example, work out mentally that:
  6 + 7 = 13
  and explain that:
  6 + 7 = 6 + 4 + 3 = 10 + 3 = 13
- Work mentally to complete written questions like:
  9 + 4 = □ 9 + □ = 13 □ + 4 = 13

Begin to add a single digit to a 'teens' number, crossing 20

- Use two steps and cross 20 as a middle stage.
  For example, work out mentally that:
  18 + 5 = 23
  and explain that:
  18 + 5 = 18 + 2 + 3 = 20 + 3 = 23

Use and apply these skills in a variety of contexts, in mathematics and other subjects.

As outcomes, Year 2 pupils should, for example:

Add a pair of single-digit numbers, or subtract a single digit from a 'teens' number, crossing 10

- Use two steps and cross 10 as a middle stage. For example, work out mentally that:
  6 + 7 = 13 or 15 - 8 = 7
  and explain that:
  6 + 7 = 6 + 4 + 3 = 10 + 3 = 13
  15 - 8 = 15 - 5 - 3 = 10 - 3 = 7
- Work mentally to complete written questions like:
  7 + 8 = □ 7 + □ = 15 □ + 8 = 15
  17 - 9 = □ 17 - □ = 8 □ - 9 = 8

Add a single digit to a 'teens' number, or subtract a single digit from a 'twenties' number, crossing 20

- Use two steps and cross 20 as a middle stage. For example, work out mentally that:
  16 + 7 = 23
  and explain that:
  16 + 7 = 16 + 4 + 3 = 20 + 3 = 23
  or work out mentally that:
  22 - 7 = 15
  and explain that:
  22 - 7 = 22 - 2 - 5 = 20 - 5 = 15
- Work mentally to complete written questions like:
  15 + 8 = □ 15 + □ = 23 □ + 8 = 23
  23 - 6 = □ 23 - □ = 17 □ - 6 = 17

Find a small difference between a pair of numbers lying either side of 20, or another multiple of 10

- For example, work out mentally that:
  23 - 18 = 5
  by counting up from 18 to 20, then 20 to 23;
  or work out mentally that:
  102 - 97 = 5
  by counting up from 97 to 100, then 100 to 102.
- Work mentally to complete written questions like:
  22 - 17 = □ 19 + □ = 22
  103 - 96 = □ 95 + □ = 101
  64 - 58 = □ 87 + □ = 94

Use and apply these skills in a variety of contexts, in mathematics and other subjects.

As outcomes, Year 3 pupils should, for example:

Consolidate subtracting a single digit from a 'teens' number, crossing 10

- Use two steps and cross 10 as a middle stage. For example, work out mentally that:
  15 - 8 = 7
  and explain that:
  15 - 8 = 15 - 5 - 3 = 10 - 3 = 7
- Work mentally to complete written questions like:
  13 - 6 = □ 13 - □ = 7 □ - 6 = 7

Add or subtract a single digit to/from a two-digit number, crossing the tens boundary

- Use two steps, crossing a multiple of 10 as a middle stage. For example, work out mentally that:
  68 + 7 = 75
  and explain that:
  68 + 7 = 68 + 2 + 5 = 70 + 5 = 75
  or work out mentally that:
  62 - 7 = 55
  and explain that:
  62 - 7 = 62 - 2 - 5 = 60 - 5 = 55
- Work mentally to complete written questions like:
  45 + 8 = □ 45 + □ = 53 □ + 8 = 53
  93 - 6 = □ 93 - □ = 87 □ - 6 = 87

Find a small difference between a pair of numbers lying either side of a multiple of 100 from 100 to 1000

- For example, work out mentally that:
  605 - 596 = 9
  by counting up from 596 to 600, then 600 to 605;
  or work out mentally that:
  1008 - 995 = 13
  by counting up from 995 to 1000, then 1000 to 1008.
- Work mentally to complete written questions like:
  804 - 798 = □ 396 + □ = 405
  1003 - 992 = □ 988 + □ = 1001

Begin to add or subtract any pair of two-digit numbers

- For example, work out that 28 + 54 = 82
  and explain that 28 + 54 = 28 + 50 + 4 = 78 + 4 = 82;
  or work out that 61 - 23 = 38
  and explain that 61 - 23 = 61 - 20 - 3 = 41 - 3 = 38.
- Work mentally to complete written questions like:
  25 + 38 = □ 25 + □ = 63 □ + 38 = 63
  83 - 47 = □ 83 - □ = 36 □ - 47 = 36

See also using jottings (pages 43 and 45).

Use and apply these skills in a variety of contexts, in mathematics and other subjects.

Pupils should be taught to:

Develop pencil and paper methods for additions that cannot, at this stage, be done mentally

As outcomes, Year 1 pupils should, for example:

As outcomes, Year 2 pupils should, for example:

As outcomes, Year 3 pupils should, for example:

Use informal pencil and paper methods (jottings) to support, record and explain partial mental methods, building on existing mental strategies. Discuss and compare methods and explain orally how they work.

TU + TU, developing to HTU + TU or HTU + HTU

Do this first not crossing the tens or hundreds boundary, then crossing either the tens or the hundreds boundary. For example:

A: counting on in multiples of 100, 10 or 1

86 + 57 = 86 + 50 + 7 = 136 + 7 = 143

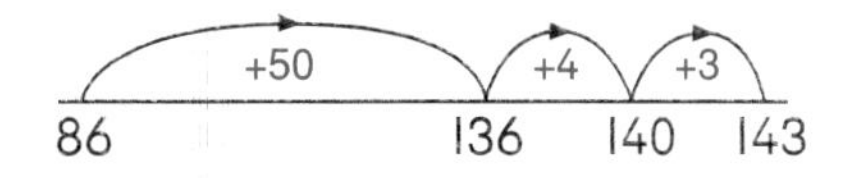

356 + 427 = 356 + (400 + 20 + 7)
= 756 + 20 + 7
= 776 + 7
= 783

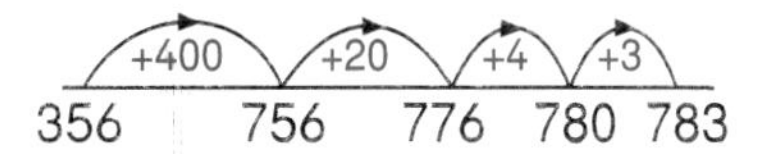

Begin to record calculations in preparation for an efficient standard method. Know that units line up under units, tens under tens, and so on.

B: adding the most (or least) significant digits first

67 + 24 = (60 + 20) + (7 + 4) = 80 + 11 = 91
or:
67 + 24 = (7 + 4) + (60 + 20) = 11 + 80 = 91

```
   67         83
+  24      +  42
   80        120    ] add mentally from top
   11          5    ] or bottom
   91        125

   75        267
+  48      +  85
   13         12    ] add mentally from top
  110        140    ] or bottom
  123        200    ]
             352
```

Pupils should be taught to:	As outcomes, Year 1 pupils should, for example:
Develop pencil and paper methods for subtractions that cannot, at this stage, be done mentally	

As outcomes, Year 2 pupils should, for example:

As outcomes, Year 3 pupils should, for example:

Use informal pencil and paper methods (jottings) to support, record and explain partial mental methods, building on existing mental strategies. Discuss and compare methods and explain orally how they work.

TU – TU, developing to HTU – TU or HTU – HTU

Do this first not crossing the tens or hundreds boundary, then crossing either the tens or the hundreds boundary. For example:

A: counting up from the smaller to the larger number (complementary addition)

84 – 56   56 + 4 + 20 + 4 = 84

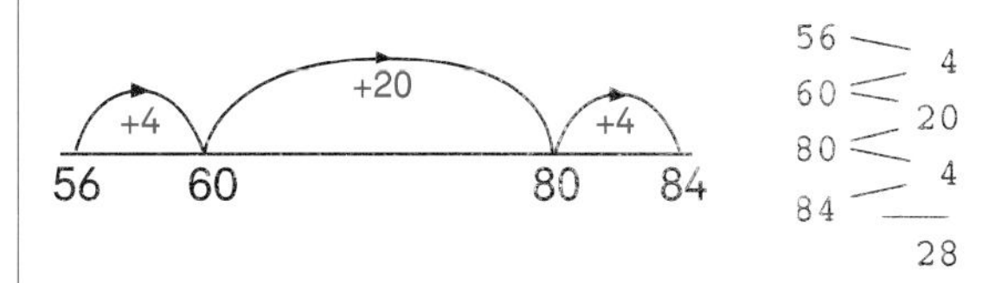

783 – 356

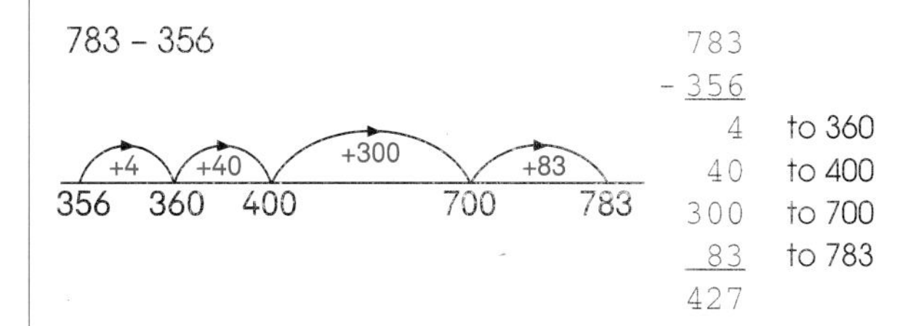

B: compensation (take too much, add back)

84 – 56 = 84 – 60 + 4 = 24 + 4 = 28

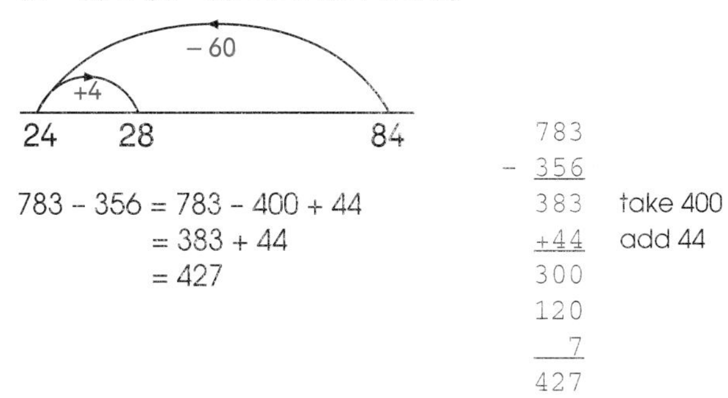

783 – 356 = 783 – 400 + 44
= 383 + 44
= 427

For column recording, know that units line up under units, tens under tens, and so on.

C: decomposition
Begin to record calculations in preparation for an efficient standard method.

```
  81  =  80 + 1  =  70 + 11
- 57     50 + 7     50 +  7
                    20 +  4 = 24
```

Pupils should be taught to:	As outcomes, Year 1 pupils should, for example:
Understand the operation of multiplication and the associated vocabulary, and that multiplication can be carried out in any order	

As outcomes, Year 2 pupils should, for example:

Understand, use and begin to read:
double, times, multiply, multiplied by, multiple of... lots of, groups of... times as (big, long, wide...)
and read and write the × sign.

Understand multiplication as:

- **repeated addition**: for example, 5 added together 3 times is 5 + 5 + 5, or 3 lots of 5, or 3 times 5, or 5 × 3 (or 3 × 5).
- **describing an array**: for example,

■■■■ 4 × 2 = 8
■■■■
2 × 4 = 8

Begin to recognise from arranging arrays that multiplication can be done in any order: for example, 4 lots of 2 and 2 lots of 4 are the same.

Understand and use the principle that doubling reverses halving (doubling is the inverse of halving). For example, knowing a double such as 11 × 2 = 22 implies that half of 22 is 11, or 22 ÷ 2 = 11.

Respond rapidly to oral or written questions such as:
- Two fives... Double 5...
- 6 times 2
- 5 multiplied by 2... Multiply 4 by 2

Record simple mental multiplications in a number sentence using the × and = signs.

Recognise the use of symbols such as □ or △ to stand for unknown numbers, and complete, for example:
- with rapid mental recall:
  6 × 2 = □ 9 × □ = 18 □ × 2 = 14
  6 × 10 = □ 2 × □ = 20 □ × 10 = 40
- using rods or diagrams (e.g. arrays or a number line), then mental strategies, explaining method:
  5 × 4 = □ 5 × □ = 15 □ × 4 = 8
  6 × 10 = □ □ × △ = 12

Begin to interpret situations as multiplication calculations, and explain reasoning. For example:
- How many wheels are there on 3 cars?
- Jo's box is 5 cm wide. Mary's box is twice as wide as Jo's box. How wide is Mary's box?

As outcomes, Year 3 pupils should, for example:

Use, read and begin to write:
double, times, multiply, multiplied by, product, multiple of... times as (big, long, wide...)
and read and write the × sign.

Understand multiplication **(see Year 2)** as:

- **repeated addition**;
- **describing an array**;
- **scaling** (a number of times as wide, tall...): e.g. Take the blue ribbon. Find the ribbon that is 4 times as long.
  Make a red tower 5 cubes high. Make a blue tower 3 times as high.

Understand that multiplication can be done in any order, for example, 5 × 8 = 8 × 5, but that 16 ÷ 2 is not the same as 2 ÷ 16, and use this property appropriately.

Understand the principle that multiplication reverses division (multiplication is the inverse of division).

See also using the relationship between multiplication and division (page 55), and checking results (page 59).

Respond rapidly to oral or written questions such as:
- Two tens... Double 2... 3 times 4...
- 9 multiplied by 2... Multiply 5 by 8...
- Is 20 a multiple of 5?

Record mental multiplications in a number sentence using the × and = signs.

Recognise the use of symbols such as □ or △ to stand for unknown numbers, and complete, for example:
- with rapid mental recall:
  5 × 2 = □ 10 × □ = 80 □ × 5 = 30
  4 × 4 = □ 3 × □ = 15 □ × 4 = 20
- using rods or diagrams (e.g. arrays or a number line), then mental strategies, explaining method:
  5 × 3 = □ 8 × □ = 40 □ × 9 = 45
  6 × 20 = □ □ × △ = 60

Interpret situations as multiplication calculations, and explain reasoning. For example:
- A baker puts 6 buns in each of 4 rows. How many buns does she bake?
- Sue has 10 stamps. Tim has 3 stamps for every one of Sue's. How many stamps has Tim?
- Alex has 4 stickers. Jo has 3 times as many stickers as Alex. How many stickers does Jo have?

Pupils should be taught to:	As outcomes, Year 1 pupils should, for example:
Understand the operation of division and the associated vocabulary	

As outcomes, Year 2 pupils should, for example:

Understand, use and begin to read:
one each, two each... share, halve, divide, left over, divided by... equal groups of ...
and read and write the division sign ÷.

Understand the operation of division as:

- **sharing equally**: for example,
  6 sweets are shared equally between 2 people. How many sweets does each one get?

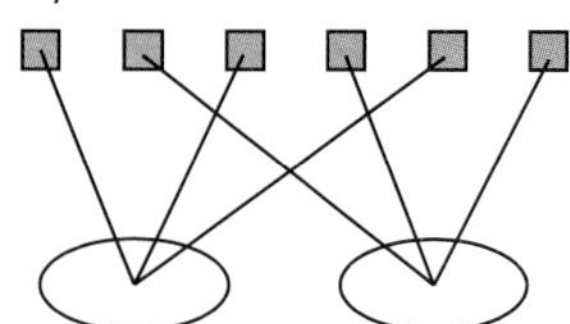

- **grouping**, or repeated subtraction: for example, There are 18 apples in a box. How many bags of 3 apples can be filled?
  Count from zero in tens, for example, to 60. How many tens did you count?

  Interpret 8 ÷ 2 as 'how many 2s make 8?'

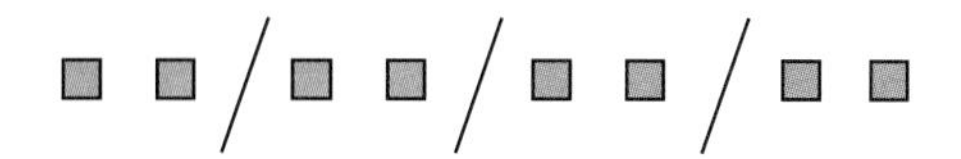

Respond rapidly to oral or written questions phrased in a variety of ways, such as:
- Share 18 between 2.
- Divide 6 by 3.
- How many tens make 80?
- How many sticks of 4 cubes can you make from a stick of 20 cubes?
- How many £2 coins do you get for £20?
- How many 2 cm lengths can you cut from 10 cm of tape?

Record simple simple mental divisions in a number sentence using the ÷ and = signs.

Recognise the use of symbols such as □ or △ to stand for unknown numbers, and complete, for example:
- with rapid mental recall:
  6 ÷ 2 = □ 20 ÷ □ = 2 □ ÷ 10 = 3
- using counters (for sharing) or a number line (for repeated subtraction), then mental strategies, explaining method:
  16 ÷ 4 = □ 24 ÷ □ = 6 □ ÷ 3 = 8
  70 ÷ 10 = □

As outcomes, Year 3 pupils should, for example:

Use, read and begin to write:
share, halve, divide, divided by...
equal groups of... the sign ÷, and understand that ½ means one divided into two equal parts.

Understand division **(see Year 2)** as:
- **grouping**, or repeated subtraction, including interpreting, for example, 35 ÷ 5 as 'how many 5s make 35?'
- **sharing**.

Know that dividing a whole number by 1 leaves the number unchanged: for example, 12 ÷ 1 = 12.

Understand that 16 ÷ 2 does not equal 2 ÷ 16.

Understand that division reverses multiplication (division is the inverse of multiplication).

Solve division calculations by using multiplication strategies. For example:
- Calculate 18 ÷ 3 by counting how many hops of 3 on a number line are needed to reach 18.
- Solve 20 ÷ 4 by interpreting this as 'How many fours make 20?'

Respond rapidly to oral or written questions phrased in a variety of ways, such as:
- Share 18 between 2.
- Divide 25 by 5.
- How many fives make 45?
- How many 5p coins do you get for 35p?
- How many lengths of 10 m can you cut from 80 m of rope?
- Is 35 a multiple of 5?

Record simple mental divisions in a number sentence using the ÷ and = signs.

Recognise the use of symbols such as □ or △ to stand for unknown numbers, and complete, for example:
- with rapid mental recall:
  16 ÷ 2 = □ 30 ÷ □ = 6 □ ÷ 5 = 7
- using counters (for sharing) or a number line (for repeated subtraction), then mental strategies, explaining method:
  16 ÷ 4 = □ 24 ÷ □ = 6 □ ÷ 3 = 8
  26 ÷ 2 = □ 24 ÷ □ = 12 □ ÷ 10 = 8

Interpret 'in every' situations as division calculations. For example:
- A baker bakes 24 buns.
  She puts 6 buns in every box.
  How many boxes of buns can she fill?
- William has made a pattern using 12 tiles.
  One tile in every four is red.
  How many tiles are red?

Pupils should be taught to:	As outcomes, Year 1 pupils should, for example:
Understand the idea of a remainder	
Make sensible decisions about rounding up or down after division in the context of a problem	

As outcomes, Year 2 pupils should, for example:

As outcomes, Year 3 pupils should, for example:

Use, read and begin to write:
left over, remainder...

Give a whole-number remainder when one number is divided by another. For example, work out that:
- $16 \div 3$ is 5 remainder 1;
- $75 \div 10$ is 7 remainder 5.

Respond to oral or written questions, such as finding how many are left or how much is left when you:
- share 18 between 5;
- divide 25 by 10;
- cut as many lengths of 10 cm as you can you from 81 cm of tape.

Work mentally to complete written questions like:

$46 = 10 \times 4 + \square$ $\quad 17 = 5 \times 3 + \square$

Make sensible decisions about rounding down or up after division, depending on the context of the problem.

For example, $46 \div 5$ is 9 remainder 1, but whether the answer should be rounded up to 10 or rounded down to 9 depends on the context.

Examples of rounding down
I have £46. Tickets cost £5 each.
I can only buy 9 tickets.

I have 46 cakes. One box holds 5 cakes.
I could fill only 9 boxes of cakes.

Examples of rounding up
I have 46 cakes. One box holds 5 cakes.
I will need 10 boxes to hold all 46 cakes.

There are 46 children. A table seats 5.
10 tables are needed to seat all the children.

Pupils should be taught to:	As outcomes, Year 1 pupils should, for example:
Know simple multiplication and division facts by heart	
Derive doubles and halves quickly	

As outcomes, Year 2 pupils should, for example:

Know by heart multiplication facts for:

- 2 up to 2×10
- 10 up to 10×10

and derive quickly the corresponding division facts.

Begin to know multiplication facts for:

- 5 up to 5×10

and derive the corresponding division facts.

For example, for multiplication and division by 2, know or derive quickly:

$1 \times 2 = 2$ $\quad 2 \div 2 = 1$
$2 \times 2 = 4$ $\quad 4 \div 2 = 2$
... ...
$9 \times 2 = 18$ $\quad 18 \div 2 = 9$
$10 \times 2 = 20$ $\quad 20 \div 2 = 10$

Respond rapidly to oral or written questions phrased in a variety of ways, such as:

- Six twos.
- 3 times 2.
- 5 multiplied by 2.
- Multiply 4 by 2.
- How many twos in 12?
- Divide 20 by 2.

Understand, use and begin to read:
double, twice, half, halve, whole, divide by 2, divide into 2...

Use known facts to derive quickly:

- doubles of numbers 1 to 15;
- doubles of 5, 10, 15... to 50;
- halves of even numbers to 20;
- halves of multiples of 10 up to 100.

For example, respond quickly to oral or written questions phrased in a variety of ways, such as:

- Double 8... Double 35...
- Half of 18... Half of 70...
- Twice 6... Twice 50...
- ½ of 12.
- Sarah spent half of her 60p pocket money. How much did she spend?
- Two ices cost 80p. What does one ice cost?

Complete written questions, for example:

- with rapid recall:
  $8 + 8 = \square$ $\quad 7 + \square = 14$
  $8 \times 2 = \square$ $\quad 14 \div \square = 7$
- using rods, cubes or a number line, then derive quickly:
  $12 + 12 = \square$ $\quad$ half of 14
  $35 \times 2 = \square$ $\quad 22 \div 2 = \square$
  $\square \times 2 = 26$ $\quad \square \div 2 = 11$

As outcomes, Year 3 pupils should, for example:

Know by heart multiplication facts for:

- 2 up to 2×10
- 5 up to 5×10
- 10 up to 10×10

and derive quickly the corresponding division facts.

Begin to know multiplication facts for:

- 3 up to 3×10
- 4 up to 4×10

and derive the corresponding division facts.

For example, for multiplication and division by 10, know or derive quickly:

$1 \times 10 = 10$ $\quad 10 \div 10 = 1$
$2 \times 10 = 20$ $\quad 20 \div 10 = 2$
... ...
$9 \times 10 = 90$ $\quad 90 \div 10 = 9$
$10 \times 10 = 100$ $\quad 100 \div 10 = 10$

Respond quickly to oral or written questions phrased in a variety of ways, such as:

- Six fives.
- 3 times 5.
- 5 multiplied by 3.
- Multiply 4 by 5.
- How many fives in 35?
- Divide 30 by 5.

Use, read and begin to write:
double, twice, half, halve, whole, divide by 2, divide into 2...
and ½ as one half.

Use known facts to derive quickly:

- doubles of all numbers 1 to 20;
- doubles of 5, 15, 25... up to 100;
- doubles of 50, 100, 150, 200... up to 500;

and the corresponding halves.

For example, respond quickly to oral or written questions phrased in a variety of ways, such as:

- Double 19... Double 75... Double 350...
- Half of 36... Half of 150... Half of 700...
- ½ of 600... ½ of 34...
- Twice 85.
- Anil spent half of his £1.40 savings. How much did he spend?
- How many centimetres is half a metre?

Complete written questions, for example:

- derive quickly:
  $60 + 60 = \square$ $\quad 80 + \square = 160$
  $60 \times 2 = \square$ $\quad 160 \div \square = 80$
- using cubes or a number line, then derive quickly:
  $42 + 42 = \square$ $\quad$ half of 68
  $34 \times 2 = \square$ $\quad 42 \div 2 = \square$
  $\square \times 2 = 86$ $\quad \square \div 2 = 43$

Pupils should be taught to:	As outcomes, Year 1 pupils should, for example:
Shift the digits of a number one place to the left/right to multiply/divide by 10	
Use knowledge of doubles and halves to multiply or divide	
Say or write a division statement corresponding to a given multiplication statement	

As outcomes, Year 2 pupils should, for example:

As outcomes, Year 3 pupils should, for example:

Observe and describe the effect of multiplying and dividing by 10, using an abacus, an OHP calculator or multibase apparatus to develop patterns as on this grid:

1	2	3	4	5...	9
10	20	30	40	50...	90
100	200	300	400	500...	900

Use doubling, working mentally, and explaining reasoning. For example:

- work out the four times-table facts by doubling the two times-table facts;
- work out:

  $1 \times 25 = 25$, and deduce by doubling that:
  $2 \times 25 = 50$
  $4 \times 25 = 100$
  $8 \times 25 = 200$
  $16 \times 25 = 400$ and so on.

Explain how to find quarters by finding half of one half. For example, work out mentally that:

- one quarter of 28 is 7 (because one half of 28 is 14 and half again is 7);
- one quarter of 100 is 25 (because one half of 100 is 50 and half again is 25);
- one quarter of 600 is 150 (because one half of 600 is 300 and half again is 150);
- one quarter of 140 is 35 (because one half of 140 is 70 and half again is 35).

Say or write a division statement corresponding to a given multiplication statement. For example:

$7 \times 5 = 35$ implies that $35 \div 5 = 7$
$5 \times 7 = 35$ implies that $35 \div 7 = 5$

Given three numbers, such as 2, 5 and 10, say or write four different multiplication or division statements relating the numbers.

Without apparatus, answer oral questions like:

- You know that $4 \times 6 = 24$.
  What is 6×4, or $24 \div 6$, or $24 \div 4$?
- You know that $40 \div 5 = 8$.
  What is $40 \div 8$, or 5×8, or 8×5?

See also checking results (page 59).

Pupils should be taught to:	As outcomes, Year 1 pupils should, for example:
Use knowledge of number facts and place value to multiply or divide mentally	

As outcomes, Year 2 pupils should, for example:

Multiply a single digit by 1 or 10
For example:
3×1 7×10
Work mentally to complete written questions like:
$7 \times 1 = \square$ $2 \times \square = 20$ $\square \times 10 = 50$

Divide a two-digit multiple of 10 by 1 or 10
For example:
$20 \div 1$ $80 \div 10$
Respond to oral questions like:
- How many tens in 60?
- Divide 30 by 1.

Work mentally to complete written questions like:
$6 \div 1 = \square$ $40 \div \square = 4$ $\square \div 10 = 6$

Begin to double any multiple of 5 up to 50
For example, double 40, double 15.
Work mentally to complete written questions like:
$20 \times 2 = \square$ $\square \times 2 = 60$
Explain how you did them.

Begin to halve any multiple of 10 to 100
For example, find half of 80, half of 30.
Work mentally to complete written questions like:
$40 \div 2 = \square$ $\square \div 2 = 15$
one half of 20
Explain how you did them.

Multiply a single digit up to 5 by 2, 3, 4, 5
Respond to oral questions like:
2×3 4×5
and explain method.
Work mentally to complete written questions like:
$7 \times 2 = \square$ $2 \times \square = 18$ $15 = 3 \times \square$

Use and apply these skills in a variety of contexts, in mathematics and other subjects.

As outcomes, Year 3 pupils should, for example:

Multiply a single digit by 1, 10 or 100
For example:
7×10 4×100
Work mentally to complete written questions like:
$6 \times 100 = \square$ $8 \times \square = 80$

Divide a three-digit multiple of 100 by 10 or 100
For example:
$800 \div 100$ $300 \div 10$
Respond to oral questions like:
- Find one hundredth of 400…
- Find one tenth of 60… of 500…

Work mentally to complete written questions like:
$\square \div 100 = 6$ $900 \div 10 = \square$ $600 \div \square = 60$

Double any multiple of 5 up to 50
For example, double 30, double 45.
Work mentally to complete written questions like:
$35 \times 2 = \square$ $\square \times 2 = 50$
Explain how you did them.

Halve any multiple of 10 to 100
For example, find half of 70, half of 90.
Work mentally to complete written questions like:
$50 \div 2 = \square$ $\square \div 2 = 35$
one half of 80 one half of 100
Explain how you did them.

Multiply a two-digit multiple of 10 up to 50 by 2, 3, 4, 5 or 10
Respond to oral questions like:
20×3 40×5 60×10
one third of 30 one fifth of 50
and explain method.
Work mentally to complete written questions like:
$70 \times 2 = \square$ $20 \times \square = 100$
$\square \times 10 = 500$ $30 = 3 \times \square$

Multiply a two-digit number by 2, 3, 4 or 5 without crossing the tens boundary
Respond to oral questions like:
23×2 11×5
and explain method.
Work mentally to complete written questions:
$32 \times 3 = \square$ $14 \times \square = 28$
$26 = 13 \times \square$

Use and apply these skills in a variety of contexts, in mathematics and other subjects.

Pupils should be taught to:	As outcomes, Year 1 pupils should, for example:
Check with the inverse operation	
Repeat addition or multiplication in a different order	
Do an equivalent calculation	

As outcomes, Year 2 pupils should, for example:

For example, check:

11 + 19	with 19 + 11;
6 + 13 + 5	with 13 + 6 + 5.

For example, check:

31 − 7	with 30 − 7 + 1 = 23 + 1 = 24, or with 31 − 10 + 3 = 21 + 3 = 24.

As outcomes, Year 3 pupils should, for example:

Check subtraction with addition.

Check halving with doubling.

Check division with multiplication.

For example, check:

12 + 59	with 59 + 12;
12 + 18 + 20	with 20 + 18 + 12;
2 × 5 × 10	with 10 × 5 × 2.

For example, check:

40 + 36	with 40 + 30 + 6, or with double 40 minus 4;
35 × 2	with 30 × 2 plus 5 × 2, or with two 40s minus two 5s.

Pupils should be taught to:

Choose and use appropriate number operations and ways of calculating to solve problems

As outcomes, Year 1 pupils should, for example:

Understand and use in practical contexts:
operation, sign, number sentence…

Choose and use appropriate number operations and mental strategies to solve problems in a wide variety of contexts, in mathematics and other subjects.

Decide whether the calculation can be done mentally or needs the use of apparatus such as counters, cubes or rods, coins, squared paper, a number track…

Explain and record how the problem was solved.

For examples of problems see sections on: reasoning about numbers, 'real life', money, measures and time (pages 62–71).

Make up 'number stories' to reflect statements like:

$3 + 4 = 7 \qquad 11 - 2 = 9$

$\square + 2 = 5 \qquad 6 - \square = 3$

For example:

There were 11 apples in the bag. I ate 2 of them.
There were 9 apples left.

As outcomes, Year 2 pupils should, for example:

Understand, use and begin to read:
operation, sign, symbol, number sentence...

Choose and use appropriate number operations and ways of calculating (e.g. mental, mental with jottings) to solve problems in a wide variety of contexts, in mathematics and other subjects.

Decide whether the calculation can be done mentally or needs the use of apparatus such as counters, cubes or rods, coins, squared paper, a number track or line or 100 square...

Explain and record how the problem was solved.

For examples of problems see sections on: reasoning about numbers, 'real life', money, measures and time (pages 62–71).

Make up 'number stories' to reflect statements like:

$13 + 14 = 27$ $4 \times 3 = 12$

$\square - 2 = 19$ $20 \div \square = 5$

For example:

A tricycle has three wheels.
Four tricycles have 12 wheels.

What sign does each ✱ stand for?

24 ✱ 8 = 32 94 ✱ 5 = 89

As outcomes, Year 3 pupils should, for example:

Use, read and begin to write:
operation, sign, symbol, number sentence, equation...

Choose and use appropriate number operations and ways of calculating (e.g. mental, mental with jottings, pencil and paper) to solve problems in a wide variety of contexts, in mathematics and other subjects.

Decide whether the calculation can be done mentally or needs the use of apparatus such as cubes, rods or blocks, coins, squared paper, a number line or 100 square, pencil and paper...

Explain and record how the problem was solved.

For examples of problems see sections on: reasoning about numbers, 'real life', money, measures and time (pages 62–71).

Make up 'number stories' to reflect statements like:

$135 + 145 = 280$ $14 \times 2 = 28$

$\square - 25 = 45$ $32 \div \square = 16$

For example:

A burger cost £1.35 and a large fries cost £1.45.
They cost £2.80 altogether.

What operation sign does each ✱ represent?

63 ✱ 98 = 161 150 ✱ 21 = 129 18 ✱ 5 = 90

Look at different calculations using, say, subtraction. Say which is hardest to do and justify why.

Pupils should be taught to:

Solve mathematical problems or puzzles, recognise simple patterns or relationships, generalise and predict. Suggest extensions by asking 'What if...?' or 'What could I try next?'

As outcomes, Year 1 pupils should, for example:

Solve puzzles and problems such as:

- Which dominoes have a total of 5 spots? 7 spots? 10 spots?
- How many different ways can you score 4 by rolling two dice? What about 6?

- Investigate different ways of putting 7 buttons in 3 boxes. Now try 10 buttons.

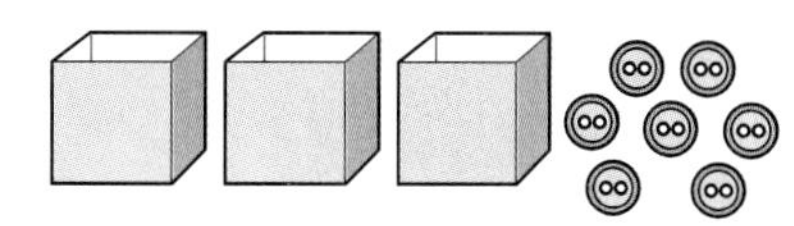

- Ann is 2 years older than Tom. How old could each of them be?
- How many different ways can you colour two squares using a red pen and a blue pen?

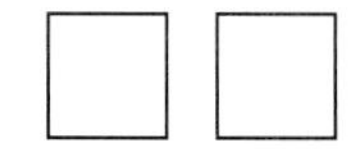

- Put the numbers 1 to 4 in the circles so that the difference between each pair of joined numbers is more than 1.

- Put 1, 2 or 3 in each circle so that each side adds up to 5. You can use each number as often as you like. Find different ways of doing it.

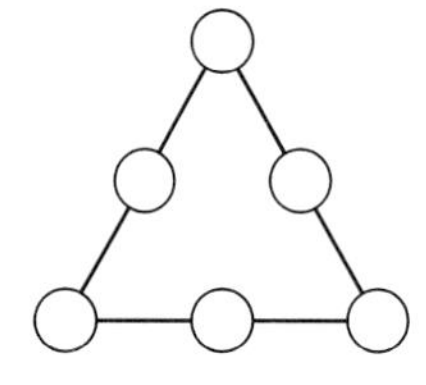

- Write as many different ways as you can of making the number 12.
- Cut up two different birthday cards into five or six pieces. Shuffle the pieces, then reassemble the two pictures.

As outcomes, Year 2 pupils should, for example:

Solve puzzles and problems such as:

- How many dominoes have an odd total of spots?
- Using three dice, find different ways of scoring 12.
- Explore different ways of adding three odd numbers to make 11.
- Put 15 buttons in three boxes so that each box has 3 more buttons than the one before.

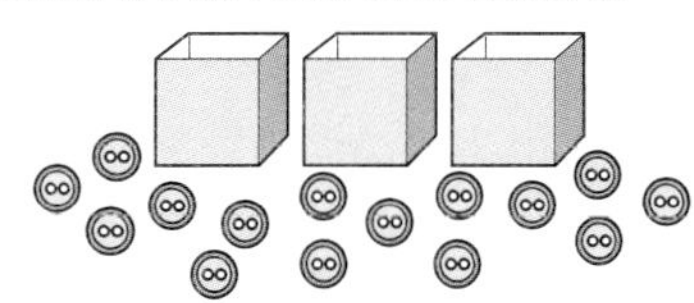

- Write as many different ways as you can of making the number 30.
- Solve a problem presented in a computer program: for example, find a strategy for buying stamps at a post office or using coins in a toy shop.
- Use 1, 4 and 5, and the signs +, – and =. What different answers can you make?
- Put the numbers 1 to 5 in the circles so that the difference between each pair of joined numbers is more than 1.

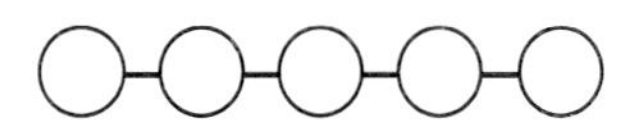

- Find ways of rearranging the digits so that the sum of each row, column and diagonal is the same.

1	1	1
2	2	2
3	3	3

Now try with different digits: for example, 4, 5, 6.

- Complete a pattern to make it symmetrical: for example, using pegboards or pinboards, or gummed shapes on squared paper…

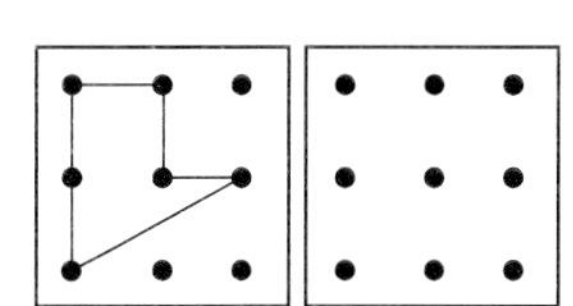

As outcomes, Year 3 pupils should, for example:

Solve puzzles and problems such as:

- How many different ways can you choose two dominoes with a total of 8 spots?
- Using three 1 to 6 dice, what even totals can you get? What if you used other dice?
- Explore different ways of adding four odd numbers to make 20.
- Find a pair of numbers with:
  a sum of 7 and a product of 10;
  a sum of 5 and a product of 6;
  a sum of 19 and a product of 90.
- Each ◆ marks a missing digit.
  Find the digits that are missing.
  a. 1◆ + ◆7 = 32
  b. 3◆ – ◆4 = 4
- Use a computer program to develop a strategy for rearranging the order of objects: for example, to change over two sets of 'frogs' in a line.
- Use 2, 4 and 5, and the signs +, × and =. How many different answers can you make between 40 and 200?
- Put the numbers 1 to 9 in the circles so that the difference between each pair of joined numbers is odd.

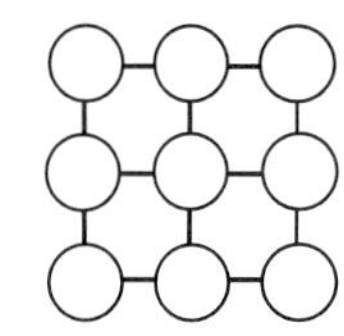

- Put the numbers 1 to 6 in the circles so that each side of the triangle totals 9.
  Now try 10, 11 or 12.

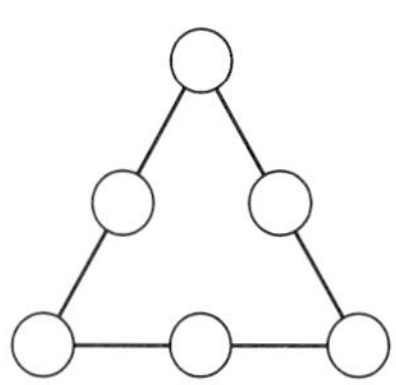

- Fit shapes together to make a symmetrical shape. For example, make symmetrical patterns from a set of three shapes such as:

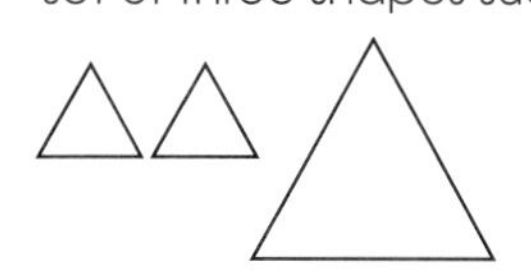

or

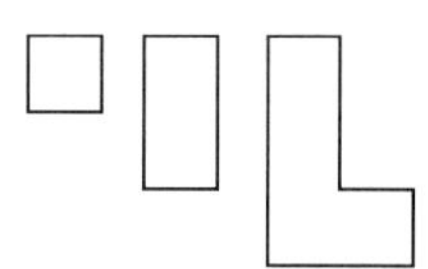

Discuss the lines of symmetry in the patterns.

Pupils should be taught to:

Investigate a general statement about familiar numbers or shapes: for example, by finding examples that satisfy it

As outcomes, Year 1 pupils should, for example:

Give examples to match statements such as:

- *I can make 6 by adding two numbers.*
  For example: 0 + 6 = 6
  1 + 5 = 6
  2 + 4 = 6
  3 + 3 = 6

- *I can pay for anything from 1p to 5p if I have two 2p and one 1p coins.*
  For example: 3p = 2p + 1p   5p = 2p + 2p + 1p

- *When I add 10 to a number the units number stays the same.*
  For example: 3 + 10 = 13   16 + 10 = 26

- *I can add numbers in any order and the answer is the same.*
  For example: 3 + 10 = 10 + 3 = 13

- *I can make four different numbers with two different digits.*
  For example: with 2 and 3, I can make 22, 23, 32, 33

- *All triangles have 3 sides.*
  For example: the white shape is a triangle but the blue shape is not a triangle.

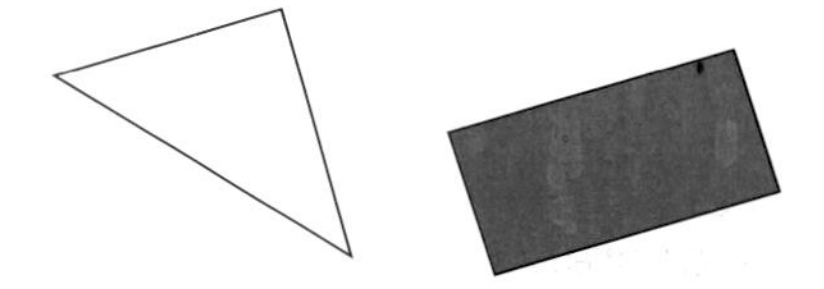

Explain methods of calculation and reasoning about numbers orally and, where appropriate, in writing

For example, explain orally that:

- 5 + 6   5 add 6 is 11 because 5 and 5 is 10 and one more is 11.

- 14 – 5   14 take away 4 is 10. Take away one more is 9.

As outcomes, Year 2 pupils should, for example:

Give examples to match statements such as:

- *When I subtract 10 from a number the units number stays the same.*
  For example: 43 − 10 = 33 86 − 10 = 76
- *I can add 9 by adding 10 and taking away 1.*
  For example: 16 + 9 = 16 + 10 − 1 = 25
- *If a number ends in 2 then it is even.*
  For example: 12, 32, 82
- *If a number ends in 0 then it divides exactly by 10.*
  For example: 10, 40, 90, 100
- *There are three numbers less than 10 that divide exactly by 3.*
  For example: 3, 6, 9
- *Odd numbers have 1 left over when you divide them by 2, but even numbers do not.*
  For example: 9 ÷ 2 is 4 remainder 1
  15 ÷ 2 is 7 remainder 1
- *A cube has six square faces.*

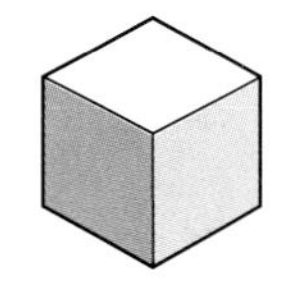
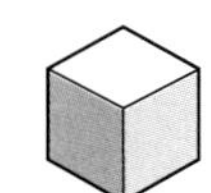

For example, explain orally or record that:

- 8 + 7 I did 7 + 7 + 1, which is double 7 plus 1; or I made the 8 into 10 then I added 5.
- 23 − 7 I did 23 − 3 = 20 then 20 − 4 = 16.
- 21 + 32 I did 20 + 30 = 50 then 1 + 2 = 3, so it's 53.

As outcomes, Year 3 pupils should, for example:

Give examples to match statements such as:

- *There are five odd numbers between 10 and 20.*
  For example: 11, 13, 15, 17, 19
- *If you multiply numbers either way round, the answer is the same.*
  For example: 5 × 6 = 6 × 5 = 30
- *Any odd number is one more than an even number.*
  For example: 23 = 22 + 1 15 = 14 + 1
- *Any even number can be written as the sum of two odd numbers.*
  For example: 6 = 3 + 3 12 = 5 + 7 30 = 13 + 17
- *The multiplication table for 4 is always even.*
  For example: 7 × 4 = 28, which is even.
- *A multiple of 5 is always half a multiple of 10.*
  For example: 15 = 30 ÷ 2 40 = 80 ÷ 2
- *All squares are rectangles.*
- *A square always has four equal sides and four right-angled corners.*

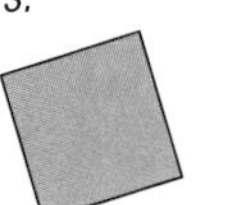

For example, explain orally or write that:

- 23 + 17 I added 17 and 3 to get 20, then 20 more to get 40.
- 50 − 29 I did 50 take away 30, which makes 20, then added 1.
- 25 × 2 25 + 25 = 50, so 25 × 2 = 50.
- 46 ÷ 2 I know double 23 is 46, so half of 46 is 23.

Pupils should be taught to:

Solve simple word problems set in 'real life' contexts and explain how the problem was solved

As outcomes, Year 1 pupils should, for example:

Use own mental strategies to solve 'story' problems about numbers in real life, choosing an appropriate operation (counting, addition, subtraction, halving or doubling).

Explain methods and reasoning orally and record in own way how the problem was solved.

Examples of problems

One-step operations

- I think of a number, then add 2.
  The answer is 7.
  What was my number?

- Lisa has 5 pens and Tim has 2 pens.
  How many pens do they have altogether?
  How many more pens has Lisa than Tim?

- Tina rolled double 6 on her two dice.
  What was her score?

Two-step operations

- Scores in a game are:

Josh	2 + 3
Sam	3 + 5
Ny	4 + 2

  How many did Sam and Ny score altogether?
  How many more did Sam score than Josh?

- Some hens lay 2 eggs, 4 eggs and 3 eggs.
  How many eggs did they lay altogether?

- Half of the cakes in this box of 10 are gone.
  How many are left?

See also problems involving money (page 68), measures and time (page 70).

As outcomes, Year 2 pupils should, for example:

Use mental addition or subtraction, or simple multiplication, and own strategies to solve 'story' problems about numbers in real life, choosing the appropriate operation and way to calculate: mental, mental with jottings...

Explain methods and reasoning orally and, where appropriate, write a number sentence to show how the problem was solved.

Examples of problems

One-step operations

- I think of a number, then halve it.
  The answer is 9.
  What was my number?

- There are 16 plums.
  8 children share them equally.
  How many plums does each child have?

- Two people have 8 cakes each.
  How many cakes have they altogether?
  One person gives 2 cakes to the other.
  How many cakes does each one have now?

Two-step operations

- 7 people are on a bus.
  8 more get on and 3 get off.
  How many people are on the bus now?

- There are 25 bean bags.
  Kim takes 11 and Amit takes 9.
  How many bean bags are left?

- There are 2 red buttons and 4 blue buttons on a card of buttons.
  How many buttons are there on 10 cards?

See also problems involving money (page 69), measures and time (page 71).

As outcomes, Year 3 pupils should, for example:

Use any of the four operations to solve 'story' problems about numbers in real life, choosing the appropriate operation and way to calculate: mental, mental with jottings, pencil and paper...

Explain methods and reasoning orally and, where appropriate, write a number sentence to show how the problem was solved.

Examples of problems

One-step operations

- I think of a number, then subtract 12.
  The answer is 26.
  What was my number?

- A spider has 8 legs.
  How many legs do 5 spiders have?
  Now work out how many legs 6 spiders have.

- A box holds 35 nuts.
  How many nuts are left if you eat 17 nuts?
  How many people can have 5 nuts each?
  How many nuts are there in 3 boxes?
  How many boxes are needed: to hold 70 nuts?
  ...to hold 80 nuts?

Two-step operations

- There are 19 books on the top shelf and 32 books on the bottom shelf.
  24 of the books are removed.
  How many books are left on the shelves?

- There are 18 apples, 21 pears and 19 bananas in some boxes of fruit.
  How many pieces of fruit are there altogether?

- I think of a number, double it and add 5.
  The answer is 35.
  What was my number?

See also problems involving money (page 69), measures and time (page 71).

Pupils should be taught to:	As outcomes, Year 1 pupils should, for example:
Recognise coins and notes of different values	Recognise all coins. Exchange coins up to 10p for an equivalent value in smaller coins. Extend to 20p. Total coins: for example, how much is this? 
Solve simple word problems involving money and explain how the problem was solved	Understand and use in practical contexts: *coin, penny, pence, pound, price, cost, costs more/less, change, total, pay, how much?* Use own mental strategies to solve problems involving money in contexts such as the classroom shop. Explain methods and reasoning orally and record in own way how the problem was solved. For example: *Find totals and give change* • How much altogether is 5p + 2p + 1p? • Tim spent 4p. What was his change from 10p? • Anil spent 6p and 3p on toffees. What change from 10p did he get? • Rosie had 15p. She spent 6p. How much does she have left? • Chews cost 5p each. What do 3 chews cost? *Solve problems: what to buy and how to pay* • Gita paid 6p for chews with no change. What coins could she use? • Apples are 6p each. What do two apples cost? Which two coins would pay for them exactly? • Describe different ways of paying 7p exactly. And 13p? • Which three coins make: 14p, 15p, 16p, 17p? Can you make 18p using three coins? **See also problems involving 'real life' (page 66), measures and time (page 70).**

As outcomes, Year 2 pupils should, for example:

Recognise and appreciate the value of all coins.

Exchange coins for their equivalent value using two or three smaller coins.

Total coins: for example, how much is this?

Understand, use and begin to read: *coin, pound, £, pence, price, cost, pay, costs more/less, change, total, how much?*

Begin to appreciate, for example, that £4.65 means £4 and 65p. Respond to questions such as:

- How many pence is £1.50?
- Write 125p in £ and pence (£1.25).
- Write in £ and pence the total of three £1 coins and six 1p coins (£3.06).

Use mental addition or subtraction, or simple multiplication, and own strategies to solve money problems. Explain methods and reasoning orally and, where appropriate, write a number sentence to show how the problem was solved. For example:

Find totals and give change

- I have £14. I am given another £9. How much do I have now?
- A pear costs 15p more than an apple. An apple costs 12p. What does a pear cost?
- Rhian spent 24p. She spent 8p more than Amy. How much did Amy spend?
- Patrick bought three choc bars at 15p each. How much change from 50p did he get?

Solve problems: what to buy and how to pay

- Investigate ways of using silver coins to pay 50p.
- You have three 10p and three 5p coins in a purse. You use two of the coins to buy a lolly. What might the lolly cost? What if you used three coins?
- Ruth has two coins of the same value. How much might she have altogether?
- Jo has three 20p and two 15p stamps. What values can he make using one or more of the stamps?

See also problems involving 'real life' (page 67), measures and time (page 71).

As outcomes, Year 3 pupils should, for example:

Recognise the value of £5, £10 and £20 notes.

Exchange a note for its equivalent value in smaller notes, or £2 or £1 coins or silver coins.

Use, read and begin to write: *coin, pound, £, pence, note, price, cost, cheaper, more/less expensive, pay, change, total, value, how much?*

Use decimal notation for money. Respond to questions such as:

- How many pence is £9.05?
- Write 465p in £ and pence.
- Write in £ and pence the total of ten £1 coins and five 1p coins (£10.05).

Use any of the four operations and own strategies to solve money problems. Explain methods and reasoning orally and, where appropriate, write a number sentence to show how the problem was solved. For example:

Find totals and give change

- It costs 75p for a child to swim. How much does it cost for two children?
- Anna has a 50p coin and three 20p coins. She pays 90p for a Big Dipper ride. How much does she have left?
- A set of paints costs £3. Parveen saves 20p a week. How many weeks must she save to buy the paints?
- Dad bought three packets of cornflakes at 70p each. What was his change from £3?

Solve problems: what to buy and how to pay

- Which five coins make 74p? What other amounts can you make with five different coins?
- Winston offered two silver coins to pay for a 17p toy. Investigate how much change he got.
- Small pizzas cost: £4.20 £4.40 £4.50 £3.80 £4.25
Big pizzas cost: £5.50 £5.75 £6.00 £4.95 £5.40
Which two pizzas can you buy for exactly £10?
- You have £5. Some toys are priced at: £2.70, £1.80, £1.40, £1.60, £2.20, £1.20. Investigate which three you could buy.

See also problems involving 'real life' (page 67), measures and time (page 71).

Pupils should be taught to:

Solve simple word problems involving measures and explain how the problem was solved

As outcomes, Year 1 pupils should, for example:

Use own mental strategies to solve measurement problems in classroom contexts.

Explain methods and reasoning orally and record in own way how the problem was solved, using a number sentence and signs (+, –, =) where appropriate. For example:

Length, mass, capacity

- The classroom is 15 metres long.
  The library is 12 metres long.
  The classroom is longer than the library.
  How much longer?

- 8 bricks balance an apple.
  10 bricks balance a pear.
  The apple and the pear are together on the scales.
  How many bricks will balance them?

- A full jug hold 6 cups of water.
  How many cups of water do 2 full jugs hold?

Time

- How long is it from 2 o'clock to 6 o'clock?

- It is now half past seven. What time was it 2 hours ago?

- It is 5 o'clock.
  What time will it be 4 hours from now?
  What time was it 3 hours ago?
  If you had tea at 3 o'clock, how long ago was that?
  If you go to bed at 8 o'clock, how many hours until bed time?

See also problems involving 'real life' (page 66) and money (page 68).

As outcomes, Year 2 pupils should, for example:

Use mental calculation strategies to solve measurement problems set in a variety of contexts.

Explain methods and reasoning orally and, where appropriate, write a number sentence using numbers and signs (+, −, ×, ÷, =) to show how the problem was solved. For example:

Length, mass, capacity

- My cat is 30 cm tall.
  My dog is 25 cm taller.
  How tall is my dog?
- There are 5 kg of pears in 1 box.
  How many kilograms of pears are in 3 boxes?
- You have 50 litres of water.
  How many 10 litre buckets can you fill?

Time

- Sue got on the bus at 9 o'clock.
  The journey took half an hour.
  What time did she get off the bus?
- Mary went into a shop at 10:30.
  She came out at 10:45.
  How long was she in the shop?
- James walked from 9:45 until 10:15.
  For how many minutes did he walk?

See also problems involving 'real life' (page 67) and money (page 69).

As outcomes, Year 3 pupils should, for example:

Use mental calculation strategies to solve measurement problems set in a variety of contexts.

Explain methods and reasoning orally and, where appropriate, write a number sentence using numbers and signs (+, −, ×, ÷, =) to show how the problem was solved. For example:

Length, mass, capacity

- Two rolls of tape are 35 cm and 41 cm long.
  What is their total length?
  What is the difference in their lengths?
- An egg weighs about 50 grams.
  Roughly how much do 6 eggs weigh?
- A big potato weighs about ¼ kg on the scales.
  Roughly, what would be the weight on the scales of 10 big potatoes?
- A bottle of medicine holds 35 millilitres.
  A teaspoon holds 5 millilitres.
  How many teaspoons of medicine in the bottle?

Time

- Mark got into the pool at 3:30 pm.
  He swam for 40 minutes.
  What time did he get out?
- The cake went in the oven at 10:20.
  It came out at 10:45.
  How long was it in the oven?
- Lunch takes 50 minutes. It ends at 1:00 pm.
  What time does it start?

See also problems involving 'real life' (page 67) and money (page 69).

Pupils should be taught to:

Understand and use the vocabulary related to length, mass and capacity; begin to know relationships between standard metric units

As outcomes, Year 1 pupils should, for example:

Understand and use in practical contexts:
- length and distance: *long, short, tall, high, low, wide, narrow, deep, shallow, thick, thin, far, near, close...*
- mass: *weight, weighs, heavy, light, balances...*
- capacity: *full, empty, holds...*

and comparative words such as: *longer, longest...*

Measure and compare:
- **by direct (side by side) comparison;**
- **using uniform non-standard units;**
- **using standard units**

Length, mass, capacity: direct comparison

Make direct comparisons (side by side, no counting) in a variety of contexts: for example, compare the lengths of two different ribbons, the weights of two different objects, the capacities of two different cups... For example:

- Compare the heights of two children standing back to back.
- Use a balance to find out which of four parcels is the heaviest.
- Find out which of three or more things holds most by filling with rice, water, sand... and pouring from one to the other.

Length, mass, capacity: non-standard and standard units

Use uniform non-standard and standard units to measure, count and solve problems in a variety of contexts.

For example:

- How many:
  cubes balance this shoe;
  rulers fit along this line;
  cups fill this jug?

- 7 rulers fit across the table. 10 rulers fit across the door. Which is wider, the table or the door? How much wider is it?

- Estimate the distance (number of steps forward) that a floor robot should move from a marked spot to different objects. Check estimates, and respond to questions such as:
  Is that far enough? Too far?
  How many more steps forward are needed?

As outcomes, Year 2 pupils should, for example:

Understand, use and begin to read:
- length and distance: *long, short, tall, high, low, wide, narrow, deep, shallow, thick, thin, far, near, close...*
- mass: *weight, weighs, heavy, light, balances...*
- capacity: *full, empty, holds...*

and comparative words such as: *longer, longest...*

Know that:

1 metre	= 100 centimetres
1 kilogram	= 1000 grams
1 litre	= 1000 millilitres

Length, mass, capacity: non-standard/standard units

Make direct comparisons by finding or suggesting things, for example:
- longer or shorter than 1 metre, or 1 centimetre, or 10 centimetres;
- heavier or lighter than 1 kilogram;
- holding more or less than 1 litre.

Use uniform non-standard and standard units to measure and solve problems in a variety of contexts.

For example:

- Find out which of two or more things is longest/ shortest by measuring in metres or centimetres...
  For example, use a metre stick marked in centimetres to measure the reach and the stride of a partner, measuring to the nearest centimetre, and compare with own measurements.
- Find out which of two or more things is heaviest/ lightest by balancing with and counting: cubes, plastic weights, kilograms...
- Find out which of two or more things holds most/ least by filling with and counting: cups of water, litres...

As outcomes, Year 3 pupils should, for example:

Use, read and begin to write:
- length and distance: *long, short, tall, high, low, wide, narrow, deep, shallow, thick, thin, far, near, close, distance...*
- mass: *weight, weighs, heavy, light, balances...*
- capacity: *full, empty, holds...*

and comparative words such as: *longer, longest...*

Know that:

1 kilometre	= 1000 metres
1 metre	= 100 centimetres
1 kilogram	= 1000 grams
1 litre	= 1000 millilitres

Begin to recognise that 3.5 m represents three and a half metres, and that 3.05 m is 3 metres and 5 centimetres.

Length, mass, capacity: standard units

Solve problems involving length, mass and capacity in a variety of contexts, using standard units such as:
- miles, kilometres, metres, centimetres...
- kilograms, half kilograms, units of 100 g...
- litres, half litres, units of 100 ml...

Use standard units to measure and solve problems in a variety of contexts.

For example:

- Use a ruler or tape measure to measure the hand span and round the wrist of a partner, measuring to the nearest half centimetre.
  Compare with own measurements.
- Work out a recipe for 8 people or 2 people by doubling or halving quantities in a simple recipe for 4 people.

Pupils should be taught to:

Suggest suitable units to estimate or measure length, mass or capacity

As outcomes, Year 1 pupils should, for example:

Understand and use in practical contexts:
guess, roughly, nearly, close to, about the same as...
too many, too few, enough, not enough...

Suggest uniform units to measure or estimate. For example:

- Guess roughly, then check:
  how far up the wall you can reach;
  how far you can jump from this line;
  how many cubes would fit across your book;
  if the red parcel is heavier than the blue one;
  how many cubes would balance the parcel;
  if the tall thin container holds more or less than the short fat one;
  how many bottles full of water would fill the bucket.

- Suggest things that could be measured using:
  rulers, garden canes, matchsticks... metre sticks...
  cubes, matchboxes filled with sand (taped up)...
  egg cups, cups... litre jugs...

- Suggest a unit you could use to measure:
  the height of a table;
  the width of a book;
  across the classroom;
  the weight of a parcel;
  how much a big saucepan holds.

See also problems involving measures (page 70).

As outcomes, Year 2 pupils should, for example:

Understand, use and begin to read:
guess, estimate...
roughly, nearly, about, close to...

Suggest suitable units to measure or estimate. For example:

- Estimate, then check:
  how many matches fit round a book;
  how many bean sticks/metres fit across the hall;
  how many cubes/centimetres fit across the table;
  how many plastic weights/kilograms balance the potatoes...

- Identify in a collection of different bottles or containers those which hold 1 litre or 2 litres.

- Suggest things that could be measured using:
  metres, centimetres...
  kilograms, grams...
  litres...

- Suggest a unit to measure:
  the width of the classroom;
  the height of a flower;
  how much water will fill a bowl.

Respond to oral or written questions like:

- What is about 1 cm, 10 cm, 100 cm long/tall/wide/deep?
- What will balance about 1 kg, 5 kg?
- What holds about 1 litre, 5 litres?

See also problems involving measures (page 71).

As outcomes, Year 3 pupils should, for example:

Use, read and begin to write:
guess, estimate...
roughly, nearly, about, approximately...

Suggest suitable standard units to measure or estimate. For example:

- Estimate, then check, using standard units:
  how wide/tall the classroom is;
  how long/thick a pencil is;
  how many kilograms balance a house brick;
  how much a big saucepan holds;
  how far it is round a bottle, or a tree trunk...

- Collect and display labels from:
  tins holding between 100 grams and 500 grams...
  bottles holding from 50 millilitres to 250 millilitres...

- Suggest things that could be measured using:
  miles or kilometres, metres, centimetres...
  kilograms, grams...
  litres, millilitres...

- Suggest a standard unit to measure:
  how far it is to London;
  the height of a door;
  the length and width of a greetings card;
  the capacity of a kitchen bucket.

Respond to oral or written questions like:

- Would you expect:
  a front door to be 1, 2 or 5 metres tall;
  a hand span to be 5, 15 or 50 centimetres wide;
  a new born baby to be 3 kg or 30 kg;
  a teapot to hold 1 litre, 10 litres or 100 litres?

See also problems involving measures (page 71).

Pupils should be taught to:

Suggest and use simple measuring equipment, reading and interpreting number scales with some accuracy

As outcomes, Year 1 pupils should, for example:

Choose and use, for example, sticks, cubes, cups...
to measure with.

Make simple measuring devices. For example:

- Mark a long stick (such as a garden cane) to find out which of two or more lengths is greatest.
- Use string to find out which of two or more non-straight lines is longest.

Use a balance with two pans, or two identical containers, to compare two objects, or capacities, directly.

Record estimates or measurements as 'about 3 beakers full' or 'about as heavy as 20 cubes'.

As outcomes, Year 2 pupils should, for example:

Choose and use measuring equipment such as rulers, tape measures, metre sticks, balances, jugs, beakers…

Make simple measuring devices. For example:

- Make a paper tape measure to measure with.
- Put a vertical strip on a large jar to measure cups full. Use the jar to measure the capacity of some smaller containers.

Use a ruler to measure and draw lines that are a multiple of 1 cm, or to join two points and measure the distance between them.

Use a metre stick to measure lines that are a multiple of 10 cm.

Read a simple scale to the nearest labelled division. For example:

- What is the height of the table?

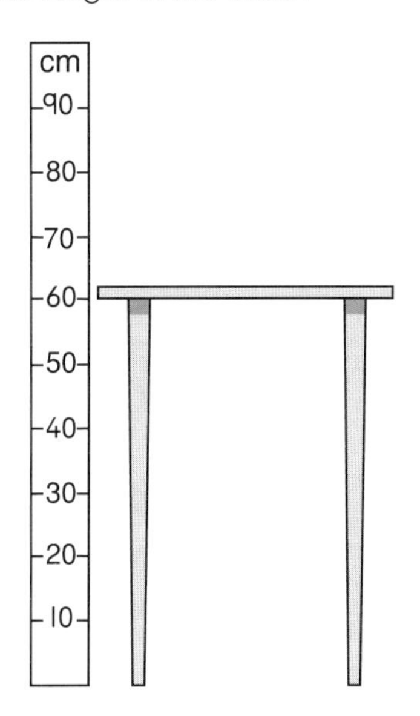

Record estimates and measurements to the nearest metre or centimetre, kilogram, or litre, using own notation: for example, 'three and a bit metres long', 'nearly three kilograms heavy', 'just less than a litre full'.

As outcomes, Year 3 pupils should, for example:

Choose and use a range of measuring equipment such as rulers, tapes, scales, jugs, beakers…

Use a ruler to measure and draw lines to the nearest half centimetre (for example, 8.5 cm, 13.5 cm).

Read a scale to the nearest marked division. For example:

- What length is shown?

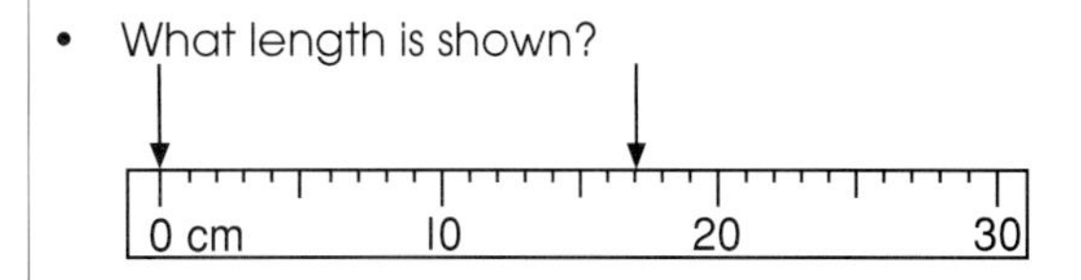

- What measurement is shown on the scales?
- How much is in the jug?

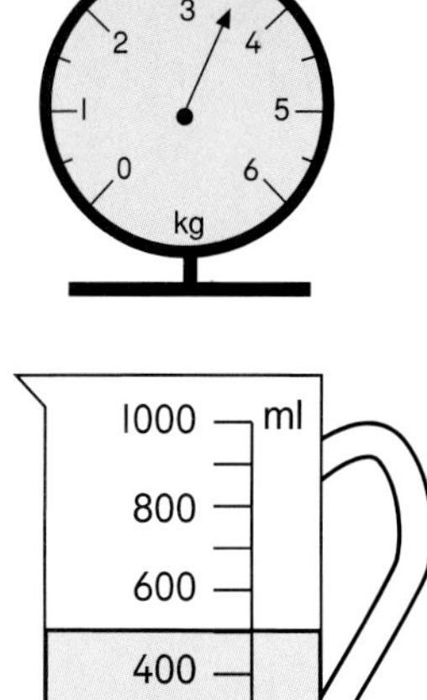

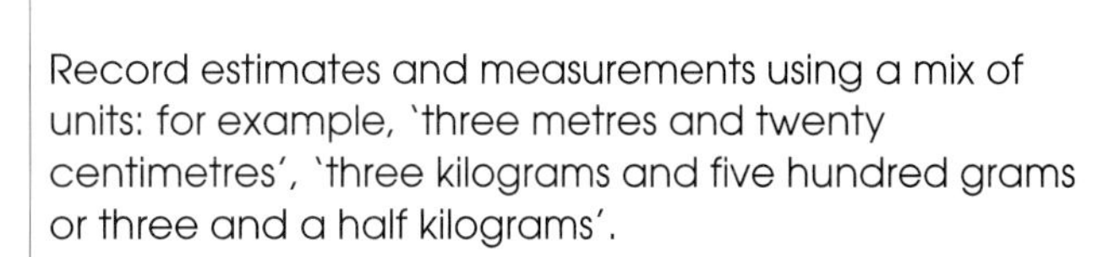

Record estimates and measurements using a mix of units: for example, 'three metres and twenty centimetres', 'three kilograms and five hundred grams or three and a half kilograms'.

Record to the nearest half metre, half kilogram or half litre using whole and half units: for example, 'about 3.5 kg' or 'about 2.5 m'.

Pupils should be taught to:

Understand and use the vocabulary related to time; know and use units of time and the relationships between them; read the time from clocks; solve problems involving time, and explain how the problem was solved

As outcomes, Year 1 pupils should, for example:

Understand and use in context:
names of days of the week, seasons of the year...
hour, day, week, month, year, season, morning, afternoon, evening, night, midnight, weekend, today, yesterday, tomorrow, now, soon, early, late, before, after, first, second, next...
quick, fast, slow...
how long ago, how long will it be to, how long will it take to...
how often... always, never, often, sometimes, usually...
once, twice...
and comparatives such as: *faster, slower, takes longer...*

Know that:
1 week = 7 days
1 day = 24 hours

Know in order the days of the week.
Order familiar events in a day or week, or in a story.
Talk about how often events occur, using vocabulary such as: *often, sometimes, always, usually, never...*

Read the time to the hour or half hour on an analogue clock.

Make estimates and check using a simple timer in PE, science... or at home. For example:

- What can you do while the sand runs through the timer?
- What time will this clock show in one hour's time?

See also problems involving time (page 70).

As outcomes, Year 2 pupils should, for example:

Understand, use and begin to read the vocabulary from the previous year, and extend to:
names of months... and
fortnight, minute, second...

Know that:

1 week	= 7 days
1 day	= 24 hours
1 hour	= 60 minutes
1 minute	= 60 seconds

Know in order the months and seasons of the year.
Know significant times in the day or year: for example, own bedtime, own birthday (day and month).

Read the time to the half or quarter hour on a digital clock or an analogue clock, knowing, for example, that the time is quarter to 5 or 15 minutes to 5.

Make estimates and check using a simple timer in PE, science... or at home. For example:

- Estimate, then check:
  who takes least/most time to hop across the hall;
  how long it takes to change for PE...
- Suggest a suitable unit of time to measure the time needed to walk home, sleep each night...
- What takes about 10 seconds, 1 minute, 1 hour?

See also problems involving time (page 71).

As outcomes, Year 3 pupils should, for example:

Use, read and begin to write the vocabulary from the previous year, and extend to:
century... calendar... date...
am and pm...

Know that:

1 year	= 365 days or 52 weeks or 12 months
1 week	= 7 days
1 day	= 24 hours
1 hour	= 60 minutes
1 minute	= 60 seconds

Use a calendar and write the date correctly.
Know own date of birth (day, month, year).

Read the time to five minutes on a digital clock and an analogue clock, knowing, for example, that the time is 8:35 or 35 minutes past 8 or 25 minutes to 9.
Use am and pm.

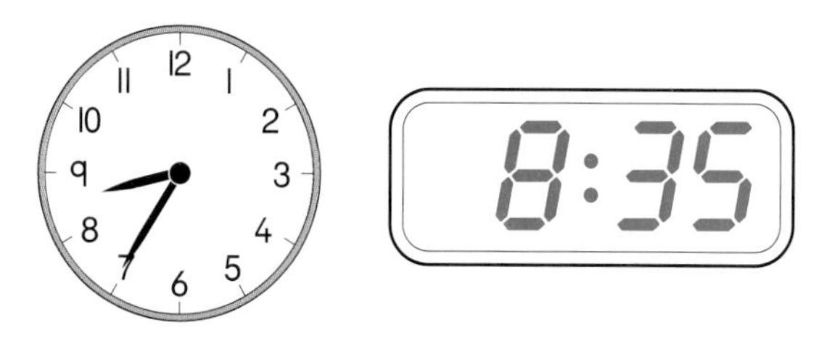

Make estimates and check using a simple timer in PE, science... or at home. For example:

- Estimate, then check:
  the greatest and least time taken to run 200 m;
  how long you will be in school today...
- Suggest a suitable unit of time to measure the time: to the end of the month, to boil an egg...
- What takes about 30 minutes, 5 hours, 4 weeks...?

See also problems involving time (page 71).

Pupils should be taught to:

Describe and classify common 3-D and 2-D shapes according to their properties

As outcomes, Year 1 pupils should, for example:

Understand and use in practical contexts:
shape, pattern… flat, solid, hollow, side, edge, face, straight, curved, round, point, pointed, corner…
sort… make, build, draw…

Use everyday language to name, sort and describe some features of familiar 3-D and 2-D shapes such as:
cube, cuboid, sphere, cone, cylinder…
circle, triangle, rectangle, square…

For example:

3-D shapes

- Identify solid shapes in the classroom: for example, find a cuboid (a box) or a cylinder (baked bean tin)…
- Sort 3-D shapes in different ways according to properties like:
  whether they have any corners;
  whether all their edges are straight;
  whether they are solid or hollow.
- Using a collection of solid shapes, choose an example, and describe it. For example:
  This shape has six faces, and each face is a rectangle.
  This shape has five faces – four are triangles and one is square.
  This cube has 12 edges…
- Recognise a solid shape placed in hands behind back and be able to name it by feeling.

2-D shapes

- Using a collection of flat shapes (thin plastic shapes, or shapes drawn or stuck on card):

  Choose own example, and describe it in everyday language.

  Choose an example to match properties described by the teacher or other children, and name it.
  For example, find and name a shape which:
  has four sides of the same length;
  is round;
  has three corners and three sides which can be different;
  has six points…
  has four corners and two short and two long sides…
  is not square…

- Talk about the shapes and patterns in curtains, clothes, ornaments…

As outcomes, Year 2 pupils should, for example:

Understand, use and begin to read the vocabulary from the previous year, and extend to:
circular, triangular, rectangular...
surface...

Use mathematical vocabulary to name, classify and describe some features of 3-D and 2-D shapes, extending the shapes used to:
pyramid...
pentagon, hexagon, octagon...

For example:

3-D shapes

- Collect examples of cubes, cuboids, cylinders and spheres and match them to name labels.
- Sort 3-D shapes in different ways according to properties of their faces such as whether they:
  have six faces;
  have a triangular face, a rectangular face...
- Using a set of solid shapes, choose an example to match properties described by others.
  For example, find and name a shape with:
  one curved face, and two flat circular faces;
  eight corners and six square faces;
  one square face and four triangular faces...
- Ask 'yes' or 'no' questions about a hidden shape in order to identify it. For example:
  'Does it have a curved face?'

2-D shapes

- Using a collection of flat shapes (thin plastic shapes, paper shapes, shapes drawn on paper):

  Choose own example, name and describe it.

  Choose an example to match properties described by the teacher or other children.
  For example, find and name a shape which:
  has one curved edge;
  has five corners and five sides;
  has four straight equal sides;
  has four square corners but sides that are not all equal...
  is not rectangular...
- Sort a set of flat shapes according to properties such as:
  the numbers of corners;
  the number of sides;
  whether the sides are straight or curved.

As outcomes, Year 3 pupils should, for example:

Use, read and begin to write the vocabulary from the previous year, and extend to:
pentagonal, hexagonal, octagonal...
right-angled... vertex, vertices... layer...
diagram...

Name, classify and describe some properties of 3-D and 2-D shapes, extending the shapes used to:
prism, hemi-sphere...
quadrilateral, semi-circle...

For example:

3-D shapes

- Know that a prism has the same cross-section along its length, and that its two end faces are identical.
- Collect examples of prisms and cylinders and match them to name labels.
- Sort 3-D shapes in different ways according to properties such as:
  whether or not they are prisms;
  the numbers of faces, edges or vertices...
- Name and describe solids. For example:
  A triangular prism has two identical triangular faces at opposite ends, and all the other faces are rectangles.
  A hemi-sphere is a sphere cut in half, and its flat face is circular...

2-D shapes

- Know that a quadrilateral is any flat shape with four straight sides.
- Using a collection of flat shapes, choose an example to match properties described by others.

  For example, find and name a shape which:
  is half of a circle;
  is not a right-angled triangle;
  has eight sides and eight vertices;
  has four right angles and opposite sides equal;
  has five equal sides and two right angles...

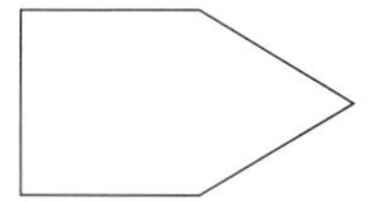

- Sort a set of flat shapes. Display them on a Venn or Carroll diagram according to properties such as:
  the numbers of vertices or sides;
  whether the sides are the same length;
  whether or not at least one angle is a right angle;
  whether or not a shape has a line of symmetry.

Pupils should be taught to:

Make models, shapes and patterns with increasing accuracy, and describe their features

As outcomes, Year 1 pupils should, for example:

Make models, shapes and patterns with increasing accuracy, and describe their features. For example:

3-D shapes

- Make models or patterns using 3-D shapes such as:
  construction kits such as Lego or Duplo;
  everyday materials (packets, rolls, containers…);
  malleable material such as cold clay or Plasticine…

  Describe the model or pattern and say which shapes have been used to make it. For example:
  The top of this tree is a sphere and its trunk is a cylinder.
  This house is made from a cube and its roof is a pyramid…

- Begin to relate 3-D shapes to pictures of them. For example:
  match familiar solids to their pictures;
  use bricks to build models from pictures.

2-D shapes

- Make pictures and patterns using 2-D shapes such as:
  straws and pipe cleaners;
  thin plastic shapes;
  pre-cut sticky shapes;
  stamping or printing shapes…

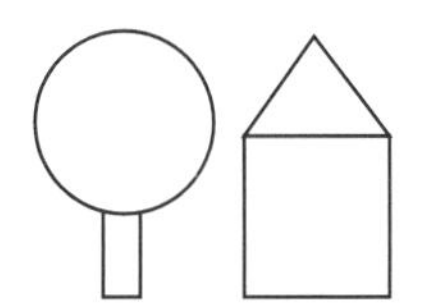
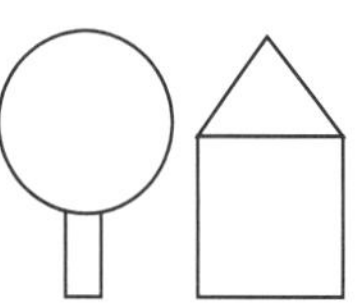

  Describe the picture or pattern and say which shapes have been used to make it. For example:
  This tree is made from a rectangle and a circle.
  This house is made from a square and a triangle.
  This pattern is made from a tree and a house repeating.

- Make halves of paper shapes by folding them.
  Make them into symmetrical patterns: for example, by cutting out small pieces or by ink blot painting…

As outcomes, Year 2 pupils should, for example:

Make models, shapes and patterns with increasing accuracy, and describe their features. For example:

3-D shapes

- Build models out of 3-D shapes and record the shapes used. For example:
  My model was made with 7 cuboids, 10 cubes, 6 cylinders and 1 cone.

- Make a skeleton shape from a construction kit or straws, and count the number of edges or corners.

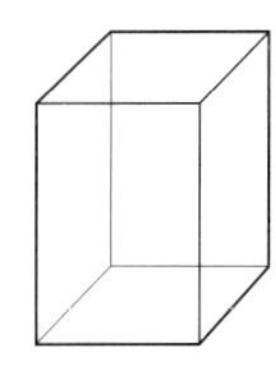
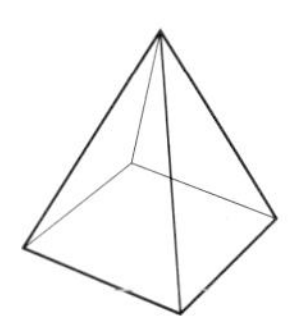

- Relate 3-D shapes to pictures of them.
  For example:
  match familiar solids to their pictures;
  use cubes to make 'single-layered' solids from pictures.

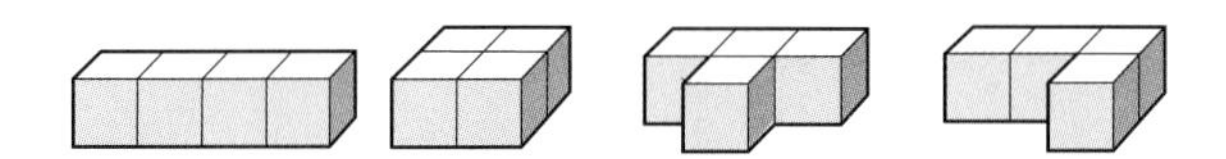

2-D shapes

- Use 2-D shapes to make and describe pictures and patterns:
  by drawing round them;
  using squared paper;
  using pinboard and elastic bands;

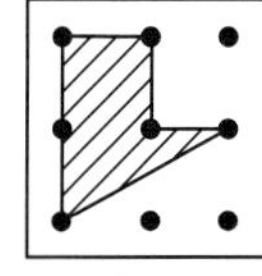
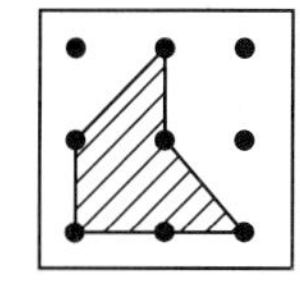

pentagons

  by combining four squares to make new shapes, then counting the number of edges...

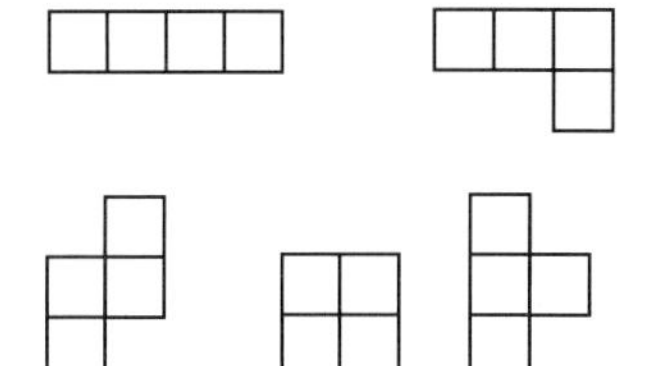

- Use a programmable robot to draw lines, squares and rectangles.

As outcomes, Year 3 pupils should, for example:

Make models, shapes and patterns with increasing accuracy, and describe their features. For example:

3-D shapes

- Recognise that two or more shapes can be put together in different ways to make new shapes. For example, find all the different shapes that can be made by fitting four cubes together face to face.

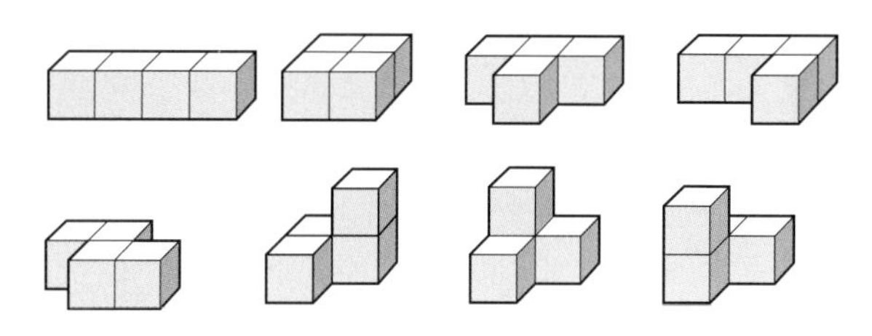

- Relate 3-D shapes to pictures of them.
  For example:
  match familiar solids to their pictures;
  use cubes to build 'double-layered' solids from pictures.

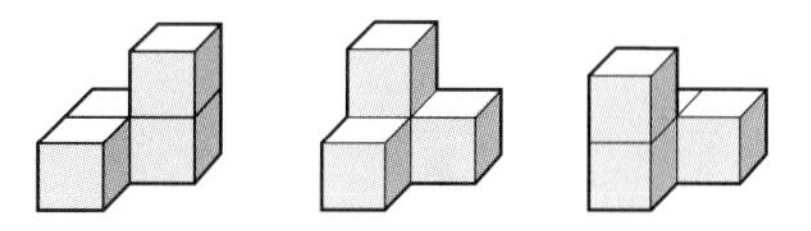

2-D shapes

- Use 2-D shapes to make and describe pictures and patterns:
  by drawing round and cutting out a shape on thin card and using it as a template to make a pattern;
  by folding and cutting paper to make squares, octagons and stars;
  using geo-strips;
  by putting two identical shapes together, then naming the new shapes...

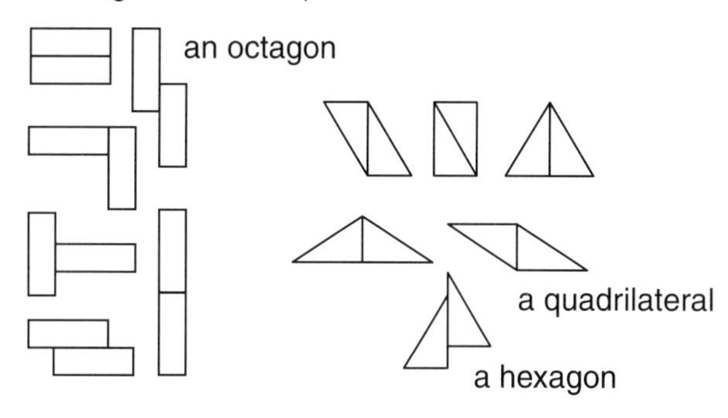

- Use a programmable robot to draw rectilinear shapes such as:

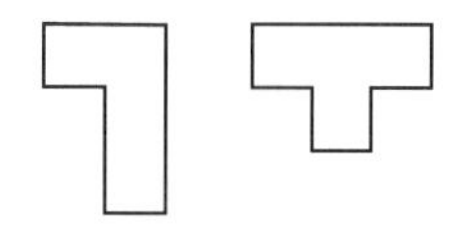

Pupils should be taught to:	As outcomes, Year 1 pupils should, for example:
Recognise line symmetry in simple cases	

As outcomes, Year 2 pupils should, for example:

Understand, use and begin to read:
line of symmetry…
fold, match, mirror line, reflection, symmetrical…

Begin to recognise and sketch a line of symmetry. For example:

- Use toy kaleidoscopes, mirrors, shiny surfaces… to make and describe reflections.
- Make, talk about and describe symmetrical patterns using paint, ink blots, pegboard, gummed shapes on squared paper, interlocking cubes, laying out thin plastic shapes or coloured blocks…

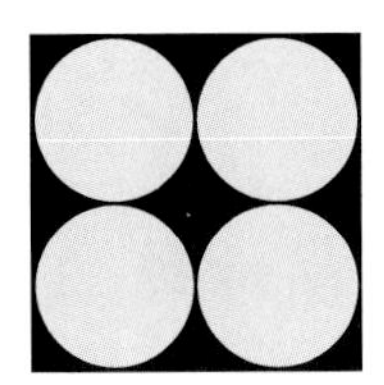

- Recognise and sketch a line of symmetry: for example, in pictures of insects, road signs, flags… testing where appropriate with a mirror.

  For example, draw a line of symmetry:

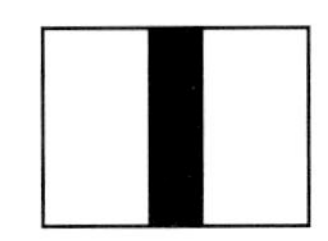

- Complete a symmetrical pattern by drawing or making the other 'half': for example, using a pegboard.

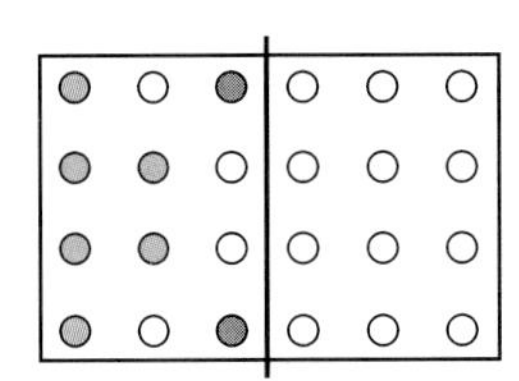

As outcomes, Year 3 pupils should, for example:

Use, read and begin to write the vocabulary from the previous year.

Recognise and sketch more than one line of symmetry. For example:

- Find examples of patterns, capital letters, logos, road signs… with more than one line of symmetry.
- Make patterns with two lines of symmetry at right angles by folding and cutting paper.
- Recognise shapes with no lines of symmetry.

- Recognise and sketch two lines of symmetry: for example, in diagrams of flags or shapes… testing where appropriate with a mirror.

  Draw two lines of symmetry:

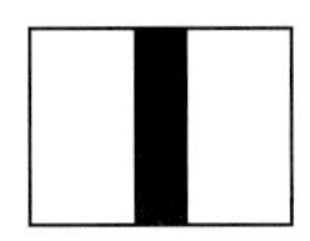

- Sketch the reflection of a simple 2-D shape in a mirror line along one edge, using a mirror to help complete it.

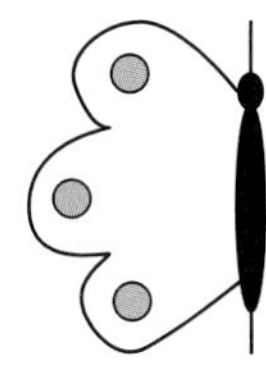

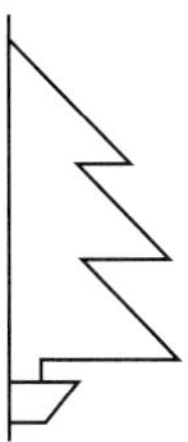

Pupils should be taught to:	As outcomes, Year 1 pupils should, for example:
Describe positions and directions	Understand and use in practical contexts: *position, over, under, underneath, above, below, on, in, outside, inside, in front, behind, beside, before, after, next to, opposite, between... close, far, apart... middle, centre, edge, corner, top, bottom, side... direction, left, right, up, down, forwards, backwards, sideways, across, along, around, through, to, from, towards, away from... journey...*

Use everyday language to **describe positions**. For example:

- In PE, stand in front of, behind, beside, opposite a partner... or between two others...
- Describe how the furniture is arranged in the doll's house; put a chair in front of the TV, a stool under the table, the cooker beside the fridge...
- In the classroom, name an object which is above the door, behind the desk, between the window and the sink...
- Describe where an object is on a large sheet of paper: for example, near the middle, at the edge, at the top...
- Describe the position of an object in a picture or on a magnetic board relative to another object: for example, the house is below the aeroplane, the window is above the door...

Use everyday language to **describe directions**. For example:

- In PE, follow and give instructions to move in particular directions:
  climb upwards, downwards, towards, away from, across, along, through...
  turn to the left or right...
  move forwards, backwards or sideways...
  face towards the door, away from the window...
- Talk about a journey: for example, how to go home from school, how to follow a track painted on the playground...
- Devise instructions to make a floor robot reach a particular place.

As outcomes, Year 2 pupils should, for example:

Understand, use and begin to read the vocabulary from the previous year, and extend to:
higher, lower...
clockwise, anti-clockwise...
route...

Describe positions. For example:

- Respond to oral or written questions or instructions by describing, placing, ticking or drawing objects which are in a position:
  higher than, lower than, next to, below, further away from, on the edge of, at the corner of...
  a given object.

  For instance, describe the position of a feature on a simple map in different ways.

- Use squared paper and a counter to move from a square near the centre of the paper to a square near the edge, describing the route as three squares along and two squares down, or three squares to the left and two squares up...

Describe directions. For example:

- In PE, move clockwise, anti-clockwise, face inwards, face outwards...
- Give instructions for someone else to follow to find a route through a simple maze drawn on squared paper.
- Devise instructions to make a floor robot navigate a floor plan or maze in which all the paths are at right angles to each other and some are dead ends.

As outcomes, Year 3 pupils should, for example:

Use, read and begin to write the vocabulary from the previous year, and extend to:
grid, row, column... map, plan...
compass point, north, south, east, west...
horizontal, vertical, diagonal...
descend, ascend...

Describe and find the position of a square on a grid of squares with the rows and columns labelled.
For example:

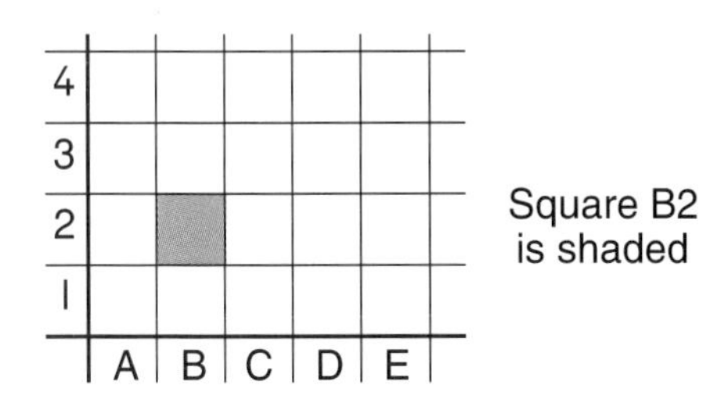

- Play Noughts and Crosses, telling the other player where to put a mark, or games like Battleships or Treasure Hunt.
- In geography, make and use simple maps or plans on squared paper and describe the position of a feature.

Describe directions. For example:

- In geography, recognise the four compass directions N, S, E, W.
- Use squared paper and a counter to move, for example, from A3 to C1, describing the route as two squares east and two squares south...
- Give instructions for a floor robot to navigate a route, based on instructions such as 'Go north 12, west 7...' or 'Go forward 6, turn a right angle anti-clockwise, backward 8...'
- Tell a story which must include key words such as *north, ascend, clockwise, left, horizontal...*

Pupils should be taught to:

Describe movements (in a straight line and turning), and understand angle as a measure of turn

As outcomes, Year 1 pupils should, for example:

Understand and use in practical contexts:
slide, roll, turn...
whole, half...

Recognise and talk about movements.

For example:

- In PE, slide down the bench, roll over on the mat, turn towards the windows, move in a straight line, move in a circle, turn on the spot...
- Talk about things that turn about a point, such as a spinning top, taps, windmill arms, wheels, the hands of a clock, turnstiles, the blades of scissors...
- Talk about things that turn about a line, such as a door, the pages of a book, a hinged lid...
- Find and sort objects that will:
  roll (a ball, an orange, a wooden egg, a sphere);
  slide (a book, a cuboid box, a cube, a pyramid);
  both roll and slide (a cotton reel, a coin, a tin of soup, a cone, a cylinder)...
- In technology, make things that turn, such as a simple clock with hands, a simple windmill...
- Recognise whole turns and half turns. For example:

  In PE, make 2 whole turns to your left, make a half turn to your right...
  Move the windmill sails through 2 whole turns;
  Move the minute hand of the clock through one whole turn, through half a turn, and talk about times like 'half past three'...

- Talk about and make repeating patterns using a variety of media, describing what is happening. For example:

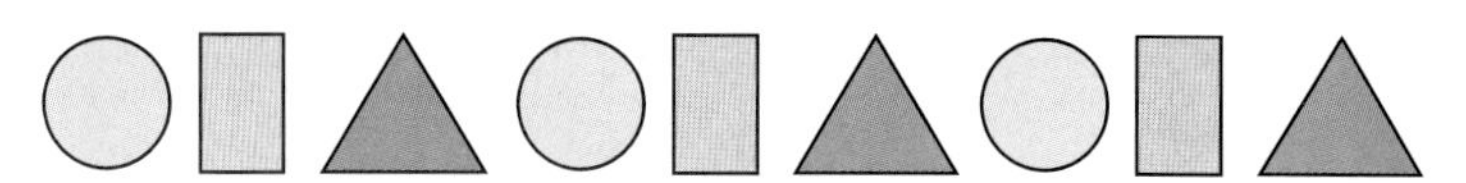

There are 3 shapes in this pattern... a circle, rectangle and triangle, then another circle, rectangle and triangle...

As outcomes, Year 2 pupils should, for example:

Understand, use and begin to read the vocabulary from the previous year, and extend to:
quarter turn...
right angle, straight line...

Recognise whole, half and quarter turns.
Know that a quarter turn is called a right angle.

For example:

- In PE, turn on the spot, turn through whole, half or quarter turns, either clockwise or anti-clockwise...
- In the classroom, recognise that the corners of doors, windows, books, tables... are right angles.
- Recognise that a square and a rectangle have right angles at each corner/vertex.
- Use two geo-strips to make and draw half and quarter turns from the same starting position.

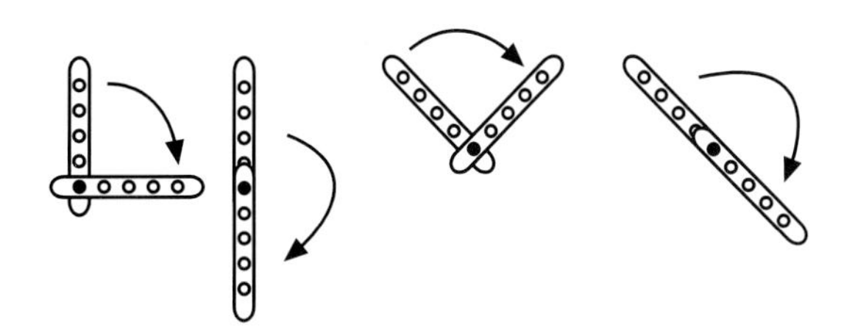

- Talk about and make repeating patterns, describing what is happening. For example:

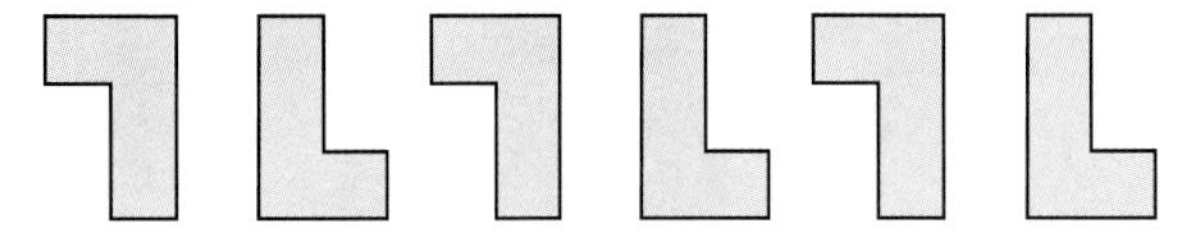

In this pattern the L-shape slides along and turns through half a turn...

As outcomes, Year 3 pupils should, for example:

Use, read and begin to write the vocabulary from the previous year, and extend to:
angle ... is a greater/smaller angle than ...

Recognise whole, half and quarter turns.
Know that a quarter turn is called a right angle and that a straight line is two right angles.

For example:

- In PE, follow instructions such as face west, turn clockwise through one right angle...

  Know that after turning through half a turn, or two quarter turns in the same direction, you are facing the opposite direction.

- Sort 2-D shapes according to whether they have all, some or no right angles...

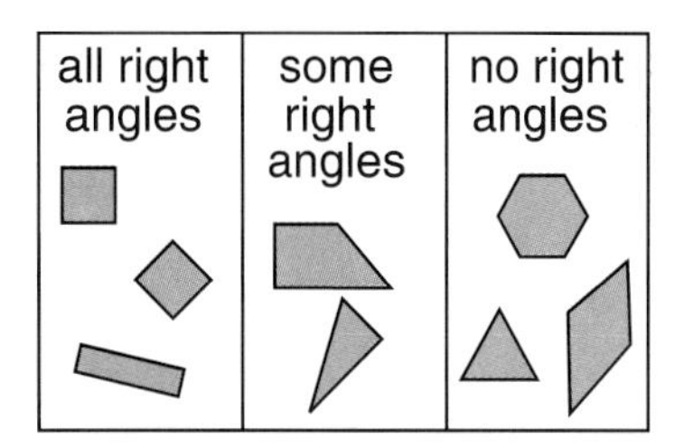

- Fold paper to make a right angle. Use it to find right angles in the classroom.
- Use a template to draw and measure right angles. For example, decide which of these angles are greater than a right angle and which are less than a right angle.

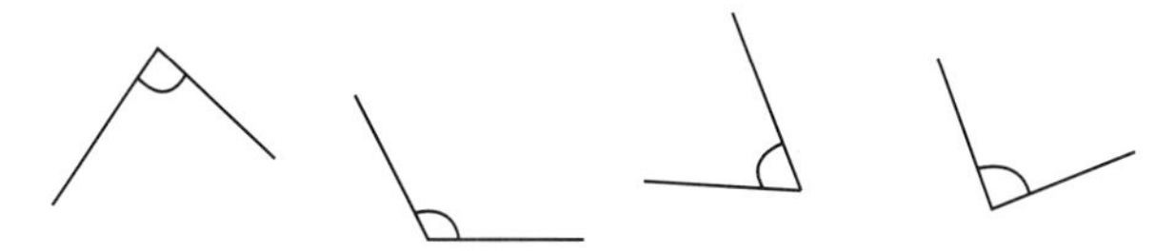

- In this shape, mark:
  the smallest angle with the letter S;
  the largest angle with the letter L.

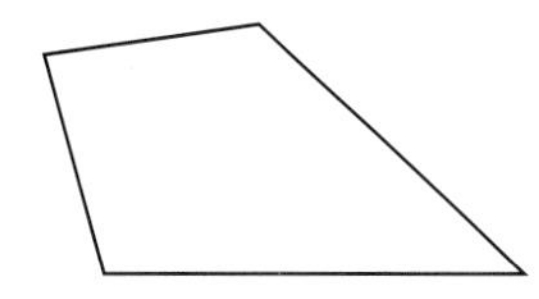

- Use a tiling computer program to create a pattern which is repeated along a line. Reflect the tile in one axis, and describe how the pattern changes.

Pupils should be taught to:

Solve a given problem by collecting, sorting and organising information in simple ways

As outcomes, Year 1 pupils should, for example:

Understand and use in practical contexts:
sort, set, list, count...

Make and organise a **list**, such as:

- all the counting numbers between 14 and 23;
- all the days of the week;
- first names with six letters.

Solve problems such as:
How many cubes can you hold in your hand?

Discuss questions such as:
- How can we find out?
- How shall we organise the information?

Collect data quickly and make and organise a **table**.

Name	Cubes
Mary	8
James	7
Lisa	5
Mark	6

Respond to oral questions such as:
- Who can hold the most cubes?
- Who can hold one more cube than Mark?
- How many more cubes can Mary hold than Lisa?

As outcomes, Year 2 pupils should, for example:

Understand, use and begin to read:
sort, set, represent, graph, table, list, count, label...
most/least common or popular...

Classify numbers and organise them in lists and simple tables. For example, make a list of:

- all the multiples of 10 between 0 and 100;
- five different numbers that are more than 70;
- all the odd numbers from 15 to 35.

Solve a problem such as:
Are names with five letters the most popular?

Respond to questions such as:
- How can we find out?
- What information should we collect?
- How shall we organise it?

Collect data quickly (for example, by holding up a digit card corresponding to the number of letters in your name) and make a simple **table.**

Our names

3 letters	4 letters	5 letters	6 letters
Ann Sam Ali	Kate Ajit Tara Mark	Halim David Jyoti	Pritam Sophie

Discuss the outcomes. Respond orally to questions like:
- What is the most common number of letters in a name?
- How many names have more than 5 letters?
- How many names have fewer than 5 letters?

As outcomes, Year 3 pupils should, for example:

Use, read and begin to write:
sort, set, represent, graph, chart, pictogram, diagram, table, list, count, tally, axis, label, title...
most/least common or popular...

Classify objects, numbers or shapes according to one criterion, progressing to two criteria, and display on a **Carroll or Venn diagram**. Examples might include:

- children who are 8 years old or not 8 years old...
- shapes that are squares or not squares...

Multiples of 5 up to 50	
even	not even

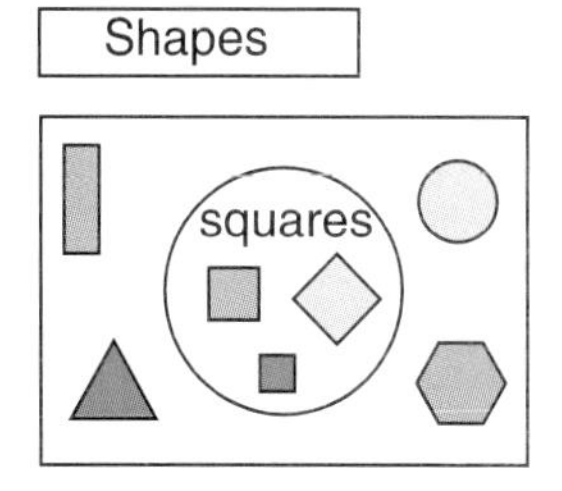

Discuss questions about the properties of the sorted items such as:
- Why is this shape a square?
- Why is this rectangle not a square?

Solve a problem such as:
What is our favourite... sport, comic, TV show, colour...?

Respond to questions such as:
- How can we find out?
- What information should we collect, and how?
- How shall we organise it?

Collect data quickly (for example, by voting in a show of hands) and make a simple **frequency table.**

Favourite colours	Votes
blue	6
green	4
pink	8
red	7

Discuss the outcomes. Respond to questions like:
- Which is the most/least popular?
- Who voted **either** for this **or** for this?
- Which colour had fewer than 5 votes?
- Would the table be the same if we asked Year 6?
- How might the table change if everyone had 2 votes?
- Who might find it useful to know what colours children like?

Pupils should be taught to:

Solve a given problem by collecting, sorting and organising information in simple ways (continued)

As outcomes, Year 1 pupils should, for example:

Solve a simple problem such as finding out children's likes or dislikes. Collect information quickly by voting or sorting, then represent it by drawing or placing objects or pictures. For example, use towers of bricks or linking cubes, placing a brick or cube on the correct tower:

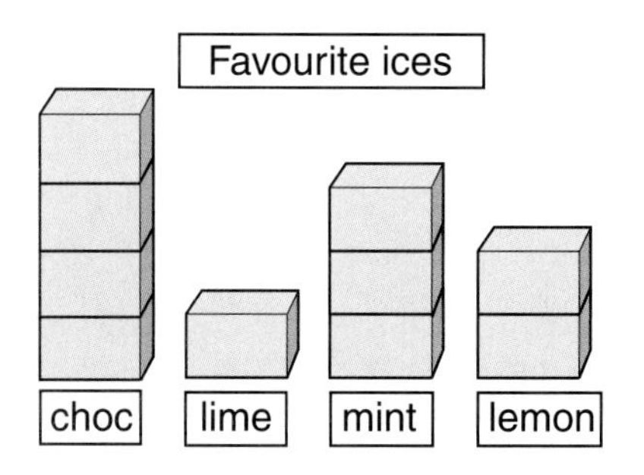

Respond to questions such as:

- How many children did we ask?
- Which ice cream did children like best? How do you know?

As outcomes, Year 2 pupils should, for example:

Solve a problem such as:
What do 6- and 7-year-olds like to drink?
Discuss:

- How can we find out?
- How shall we organise the information?

Make a simple **block graph**.

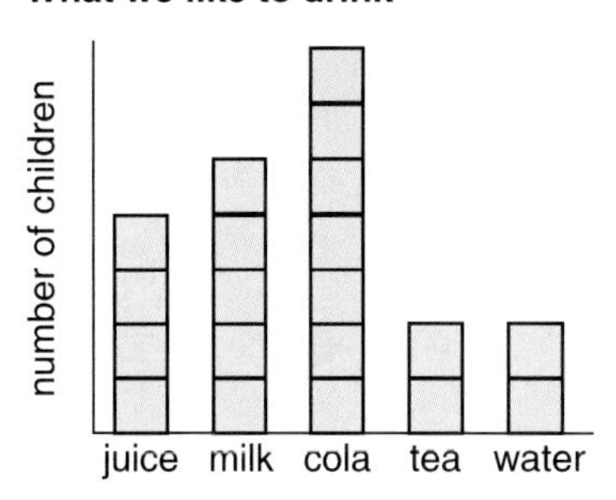

Discuss questions such as:

- What do most children like to drink?
  Why do you think this is?
  Who would find it useful to know?
- How many children did we ask?
- Would the information be different if we asked in the winter?

Test a hypothesis such as:
Children in our class are in bed by half past seven.

Collect data quickly (for example, by a show of hands) then make a simple **pictogram, where the symbol represents one unit**. For example:

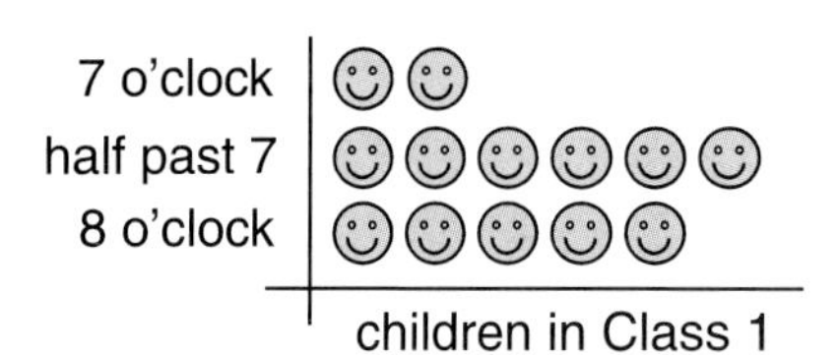

Discuss questions such as:

- How many children are in bed by half past seven?
- How many children go to bed at 8 o'clock?
- Are more children in bed by half past seven than after half past seven?
- How many children altogether in the class?

As outcomes, Year 3 pupils should, for example:

Use the data in a frequency table linked to a problem the class is trying to solve. Make – or use a computer to make – a simple **bar chart**, with the vertical axis labelled in ones, then twos. For example:

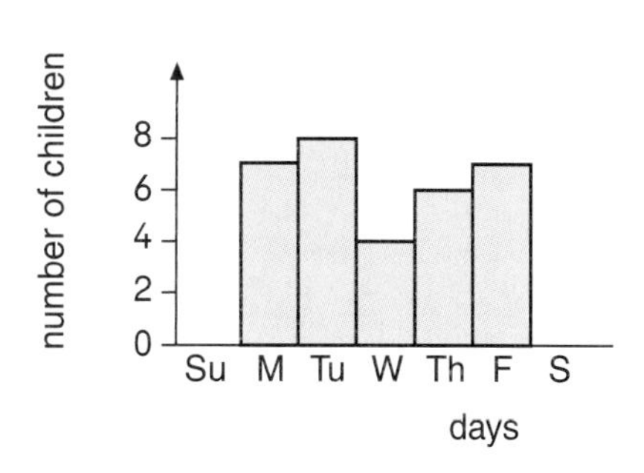

Discuss questions such as:

- Which day had most/least packed lunches?
- How many packed lunches in the whole week?
- Why do you think there are different numbers of packed lunches brought on different days?
- Would next week's graph of packed lunches be the same or different? Why?

Test a hypothesis such as:
We think that most children in our class walk to school.

Decide what data is needed, collect it quickly then make – or use a computer to make – a simple **pictogram, where the symbol represents 2 units**.

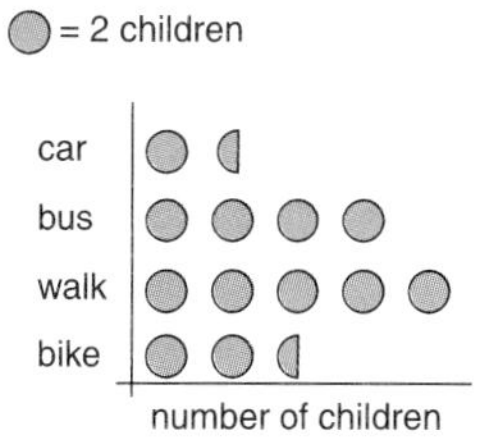

Discuss questions such as:

- Do most children walk to school?
- More children walk than come by bike.
  How many more?
- How many children altogether in the class?
- How would the graph be different:
  if it were a wet day...? or December...?
  if there were no buses...?
  if we asked Year 6...?

Use a computer with a simple graphing program to enter and display data. Discuss how quickly the computer can do it and which chart, graph or table shows the information best.

6

6

Supplement of examples: **Years 4, 5 & 6**

Pupils should be taught to:

Read and write whole numbers, know what each digit in a number represents, and partition numbers into thousands, hundreds, tens and ones

As outcomes, Year 4 pupils should, for example:

Use, read and write:
units or ones, tens, hundreds, thousands...
ten thousand, hundred thousand, million...
digit, one-digit number, two-digit number, three-digit number, four-digit number... numeral... place value...

Respond to oral or written questions such as:

- Read these: 785, 1179, 4601, 3002, 8075...
- Find the card with:
  'two thousand, three hundred and sixty' on it;
  'five thousand and seven' on it;
  'six thousand and seventy-six' on it.
- What number needs to go in each box? Explain why.

3642	=	□	+	600	+	40	+	2
5967	=	5000	+	□	+	60	+	7
4529	=	4000	+	500	+	□	+	9
1398	=	1000	+	300	+	90	+	□

- What does the digit 3 in 3642 represent? The 6? The 4? The 2?
  (They represent 3000 and 600 and 40 and 2.)
- What is the figure 4 worth in the number 7451?
  And the 5?
- Write the number that is equivalent to:
  seven thousands, four hundreds, five tens and six ones (units);
  two thousands, nine hundreds and two ones (units);
  five thousands, four hundreds.
- Write in figures:
  four thousand, one hundred and sixty-seven...
  six thousand, four hundred and nine...
  ten thousand, three hundred and fifty...
- Write in words:
  7001, 5090, 8300...
- Which is less: 4 hundreds or 41 tens?
- What needs to be added/subtracted to change:
  4782 to 9782; 3261 to 3961;
  7070 to 5070; 2634 to 2034?
- Make the biggest/smallest number you can with these digits:
  3, 2, 5, 4, 0.
  Write your number in words.

As outcomes, Year 5 pupils should, for example:

Use, read and write, spelling correctly:
units or ones, tens, hundreds, thousands...
ten thousand, hundred thousand, million...
digit, one-digit number, two-digit number, three-digit number, four-digit number... numeral... place value...

Respond to oral or written questions such as:

- Read these: 3 010 800, 342 601, 630 002, 2 489 075...
- Find the card with:
  'sixty-two thousand, six hundred and twenty' on it;
  'six hundred and forty-five thousand and nine' on it;
  'fifty-six thousand and seventy-six' on it.
- What does the digit 3 in 305 642 represent? And the 5? And the 6? And the 4? And the 2?
- What is the value of the digit 7 in the number 79 451? And the 9?
- Write the number that is equivalent to:
  five hundred and forty-seven thousands, four hundreds, nine tens and two ones (units);
  ninety-two thousands, four hundreds and six units;
  six million, sixty-five thousands, four hundreds.
- Write in figures:
  two hundred and ninety-four thousand, one hundred and sixty-one...
  one hundred and sixty-seven thousand, four hundred and nine...
  twenty million, ninety thousand and fifty...
  six million and seven...
  one million, twenty thousand and seventeen...
- Put in your calculator display:
  ninety-nine thousand, five hundred and two;
  two hundred and fifty-two thousand and forty.
- Write in words:
  207 001, 594 090, 5 870 300, 10 345 602...
- Which is less: 4 thousands or 41 hundreds?
- What needs to be added/subtracted to change:
  47 823 to 97 823; 207 070 to 205 070?
  Use your calculator. Make the change in one step.
- Make the biggest/smallest integer you can with these digits: 8, 3, 0, 7, 6, 0, 2.
  Write your number in words.

As outcomes, Year 6 pupils should, for example:

Pupils should be taught to:

Add or subtract 1, 10, 100 or 1000 to/from whole numbers, and count on or back in tens, hundreds or thousands from any whole number up to 10 000

As outcomes, Year 4 pupils should, for example:

From any three- or four-digit number, count on or back in ones, tens, hundreds or thousands, including crossing boundaries.

Respond to oral questions such as:

- Count on, for example:
  6 in ones from 569…
  60 in tens from 569…
  600 in hundreds from 569…
  6000 in thousands from 2300… from 7300…

- Count back, for example:
  6 in ones from 732…
  60 in tens from 732…
  600 in hundreds from 732…
  6000 in thousands from 8700…

- Starting with 23, how many tens do you need to add to get more than 100?

- Starting with 374, how many hundreds do you need to add to get more than 1000?

Answer oral or written questions such as:

- What is 1 more than: 3485… 4569… 4599… 4999…?
- What is 1 less than: 2756… 6540… 6500… 6000…?
- What is 10, 100 or 1000 more/less than the numbers above?

- What is 1p, 10p, 100p, 1000p… more/less than 1005p?
- What is 1 ml, 10 ml, 100 ml, 1000 ml… more/less than 3250 ml?
- What is 1 g, 10 g, 100 g, 1000 g… more/less than 1200 g?
- What is 1 m, 10 m, 100 m, 1000 m… more/less than 5000 m?

- Write the correct numbers in the boxes.

6500 —1000 more is→ ☐ ☐ —1000 less is→ 2350

As outcomes, Year 5 pupils should, for example:

As outcomes, Year 6 pupils should, for example:

Pupils should be taught to:

Multiply and divide whole numbers, then decimals, by 10, 100 or 1000

As outcomes, Year 4 pupils should, for example:

Demonstrate understanding of multiplying or dividing a whole number by 10.

Understand that:
- when you multiply a number by 10, the digits move one place to the left;
- when you divide a number by 10, the digits move one place to the right.

For example:

- Multiply by 10 using base-10 apparatus on a ThHTU board. For example, put 26 on the board (2 tens, 6 ones) and label with digit cards. Multiply each piece by 10, make the exchanges to become 2 hundreds, 6 tens, 0 ones, and label again with digit cards. Repeat twice. Describe the pattern.

$$26 \times 10 = 260$$
$$260 \times 10 = 2\,600$$
$$2600 \times 10 = 26\,000$$

- Explain this grid (which shows multiplication by 10). Describe what happens when you divide by 10.

1	2	3	4	5	...	9
10	20	30	40	50	...	90
100	200	300	400	500	...	900
1000	2000	3000	4000	5000	...	9000

Extend to multiplying integers less than 1000 by 100.

Respond to oral or written questions such as:
- How many times larger is 260 than 26?
- How many £1 coins are in £15, £150, £1500? How many 10p coins?
- Tins of dog food are put in packs of 10. One tin costs 42p. How much does one pack cost? 10 packs?

Work out mentally the answers to written questions such as:

$6 \times 10 = \square$	$900 \div 10 = \square$
$28 \times 100 = \square$	$50 \div 10 = \square$
$329 \times 10 = \square$	$8000 \div 10 = \square$
$73 \times \square = 730$	$4000 \div \square = 400$

See also decimal place value (page 28).

As outcomes, Year 5 pupils should, for example:

Demonstrate understanding of multiplying or dividing a whole number by 10 or 100.

Understand that:
- when you multiply a number by 10/100, the digits move one/two places to the left;
- when you divide a number by 10/100, the digits move one/two places to the right.

Understand that multiplying by 100 is equivalent to multiplying by 10, and again by 10.

For example:

- Write a single-digit number in the centre of a large sheet of paper. Keep multiplying by 10 and record the result in words and figures, then divide by 10 and by 10 again. Describe the pattern.

six hundred thousand	600 000
sixty thousand	60 000
six thousand	6 000
six hundred	600
sixty	60
six	6
nought point six	0.6
nought point nought six	0.06

Discuss questions like:
- What is 600 times 10? 600 divided by 10?
- What is 600 times 100? 600 divided by 100?
- What is one tenth of 600? Of 60? Of 6?
- What is one hundredth of 6000? Of 600? Of 60?

Observe and comment on the effect of multiplying or dividing by 10 or 100 using a calculator.

Respond to oral or written questions such as:
- How many times larger is 2600 than 26?
- How many £10 notes are in £120, £1200?
  How many £1 coins, 10p coins, 1p coins?
- Tins of dog food at 42p each are put in packs of 10.
  Ten packs are put in a box.
  How much does one box of dog food cost?
  10 boxes? 100 boxes?

Work out mentally the answers to questions such as:

329 × 100 = □	8000 ÷ 100 = □
56 × □ = 5600	7200 ÷ □ = 72
420 × □ = 4200	3900 ÷ □ = 390

See also decimal place value (page 29).

As outcomes, Year 6 pupils should, for example:

Demonstrate understanding of multiplying or dividing a whole number by 10, 100 or 1000.

Understand that:
- when you multiply a number by 10/100/1000, the digits move one/two/three places to the left;
- when you divide a number by 10/100/1000, the digits move one/two/three places to the right.

Understand that multiplying by 1000 is equivalent to multiplying by 10, then by 10, then by 10, or is equivalent to multiplying by 10 and then by 100.

For example:

- Look at a metre stick. Name something about 1 metre in length.
  Now name something about 10 m in length.
  Build up a table, recognising that the table involves multiplying or dividing by 10.

distance to town centre	10 000 m
from the school to the park	1 000 m
length of playground fence	100 m
length of swimming pool	10 m
height of shelves	1 m
length of a pencil	0.1 m
width of a thumb nail	0.01 m
thickness of a 5p coin	0.001 m

Discuss questions like:
- What is about 100 times the width of a thumb nail?
- What is one hundredth of a pencil length?
- What is one thousandth of the length of the fence?
- How many pencils would fit along the pool?
- How many 5p coins would stack under the shelves?

Observe and comment on the effect of multiplying or dividing by 10, 100 or 1000 using a calculator.

Respond quickly to oral questions such as:
- How many times larger is 26 000 than 26?
- How many £100 notes are in £1300, £13 000, £130 000…?
  How many £10 notes, £1 coins, 10p coins, 1p coins?
- Tins of dog food at 42p each are put in packs of 10.
  Ten packs are put in a box.
  Ten boxes are put in a crate.
  How much does 1 crate cost?
  10 crates? 100 crates?

Work out mentally the answers to questions such as:

0.8 × 10 = □	8 ÷ 10 = □
56 × □ = 56 000	72 000 ÷ □ = 72
7.3 × □ = 73	4 ÷ □ = 0.4

See also decimal place value (page 29).

Pupils should be taught to:

Use the vocabulary of comparing and ordering numbers, and the symbols >, <, =; give a number lying between two given numbers and order a set of numbers

As outcomes, Year 4 pupils should, for example:

Use, read and write:
how many, as many as, the same number as, equal to...
more than, fewer than, greater than, less than, smaller than, larger than... most, least, smallest, largest...
order, first, last, before, after, next, between, half way between...
ordinal numbers: *first, second, third, fourth... 1st, 2nd, 3rd, 4th...*
and the < and > signs.

Respond to oral or written questions such as:

- Which is greater: 7216 or 7261?
  Which is longer: 3157 m or 3517 m?
- Jo has walked 4356 metres.
  Ny has walked 4365 metres.
  Who has walked further? How many metres further?
- Indicate on a number line what number is half way between:
  740 and 750 4000 and 4100 2350 and 2380

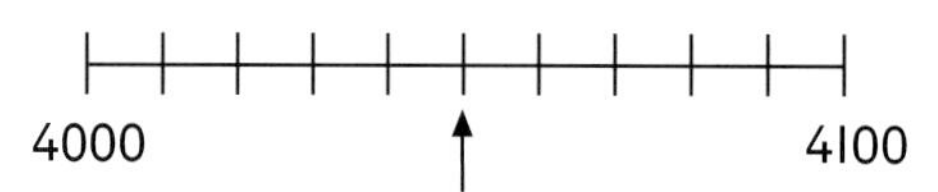

  Now try without a number line.
- A melon weighs between 1090 grams and 1110 grams.
  How heavy could it be?
- An oil tank holds between 5900 litres and 6100 litres of oil.
  What could its capacity be?
- My car cost between £6950 and £7050.
  Suggest what it cost.
- This is part of the number line.
  Fill in the missing numbers.

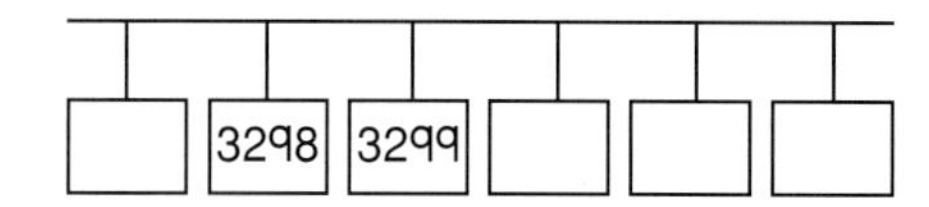

- Here is a row of five cards. Two cards are blank.
  Write a number on each blank card.
  The five numbers must be in order.

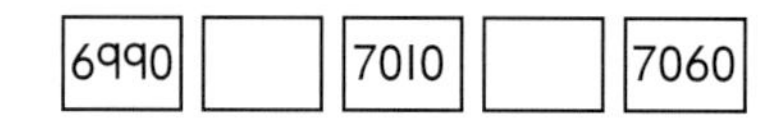

- Put these numbers in order, largest/smallest first:
  4521, 2451, 5124, 2154, 5214.
- If 3160 < □ < 3190, what numbers could □ be?

See also the examples on ordering in:
negative numbers (page 14), fractions (page 22) and decimals (page 28).

As outcomes, Year 5 pupils should, for example:

Use, read and write, spelling correctly, the vocabulary from the previous year, and extend to:
ascending/descending order...
and the ≤ and ≥ signs.

Respond to oral or written questions such as:

- Which is greater: 17 216 or 17 261?
  Which is longer: 43 157 m or 43 517 m?
- Jo has cycled 14 356 metres.
  Ny has cycled 15 365 metres.
  Who has cycled further?
  How many metres further?
- What number is half way between:
  27 400 and 28 000... 45 670 and 45 680...?
- A journey takes about 2 hours, give or take 10 minutes. How long could the journey be?
- The distance to the crossroads is about 1 km, give or take 100 metres.
  How far away could the crossroads be?
- Use knowledge of place value and number operations to place digits in the best position to make the largest/smallest sum, difference, product or quotient, using either a calculator or a computer program.
- Put these numbers in ascending/descending order: 14 521, 126 451, 25 124, 2154, 15 214.
- If 16 240 ≤ □ ≤ 16 320, what numbers could □ be?

See also the examples on ordering in:
negative numbers (page 15), fractions (page 23) and decimals (page 29).

As outcomes, Year 6 pupils should, for example:

Pupils should be taught to:

Use the vocabulary of estimation and approximation; make and justify estimates and approximations of numbers

As outcomes, Year 4 pupils should, for example:

Use, read and write:
guess, estimate, approximate...
round, nearest...
roughly, nearly, approximately...
too many, too few, enough, not enough...

Estimate a number up to about 250, explaining how the estimate was made. For example, estimate how many:

- counters in a big box of them;
- words on one or more pages of a book;
- dots on a piece of dotty paper...

Explain how you worked out each estimate.

Estimate the position of a point on an undivided line: for example, the whole number marked by the arrow. Explain how you made your decision.

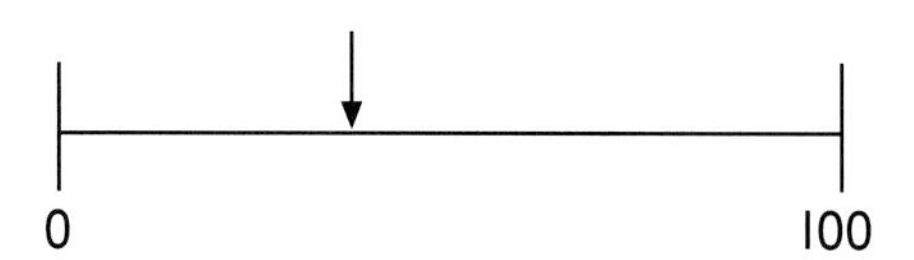

Estimate a simple proportion.
For example:

- This jar holds 100 sweets when it is full.
  Some have been eaten.
  About how many are left?

  What if the jar held 50 sweets?

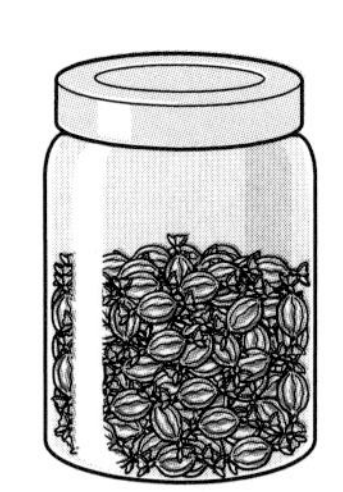

- Compare contents of containers and make statements like 'there is about half as much in this one' or 'there is about one and a half times as much in this one'.

See also estimating measures (page 92).

As outcomes, Year 5 pupils should, for example:

Use, read and write, spelling correctly:
guess, estimate, approximate...
round, nearest...
roughly, nearly, approximately...
too many, too few, enough, not enough...
and the symbol for 'is approximately equal to' (≈).

Estimate, for example, how many:
- penny coins will make a straight line 1 metre long;
- slices there are in a loaf of thick-sliced bread;
- how many slices you eat in a day, a week, a year...
- petals there are in a bunch of daisies;
- bricks there are in a wall.

Explain how you worked out each estimate.

Estimate the position of a point on an undivided line: for example, the whole number or decimal marked by each arrow. Explain how you made your decision.

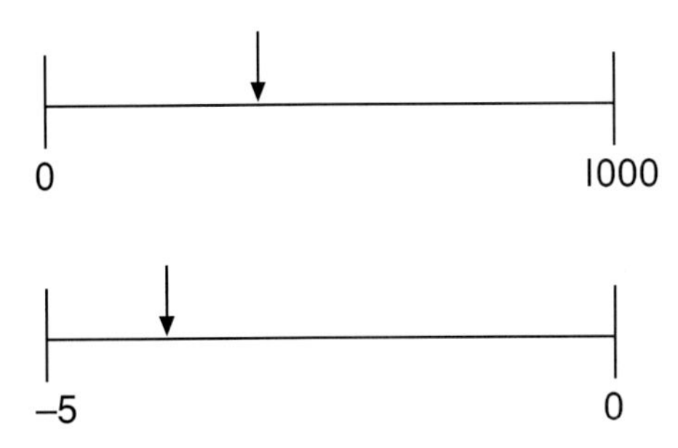

Estimate a proportion: for example, where to cut off one fifth of a piece of rope, or the proportion of dried beans left in a jar.

See also estimating measures (page 93).

As outcomes, Year 6 pupils should, for example:

Use, read and write, spelling correctly:
guess, estimate, approximate...
round, nearest...
roughly, nearly, approximately...
too many, too few, enough, not enough...
and the symbol for 'is approximately equal to' (≈).

Estimate, for example, how many:
- penny coins will make a straight line 1 kilometre long;
- loaves of sliced bread your class will eat in a lifetime;
- leaves of clover there are in a patch of grass;
- leaves there are on a tree;
- bricks there are in the school building;
- words there are in a book;
- entries there are in a telephone directory.

Explain how you worked out each estimate.

Estimate the position of a point on an undivided line: for example, the whole number or decimal marked by each arrow. Explain how you made your decision.

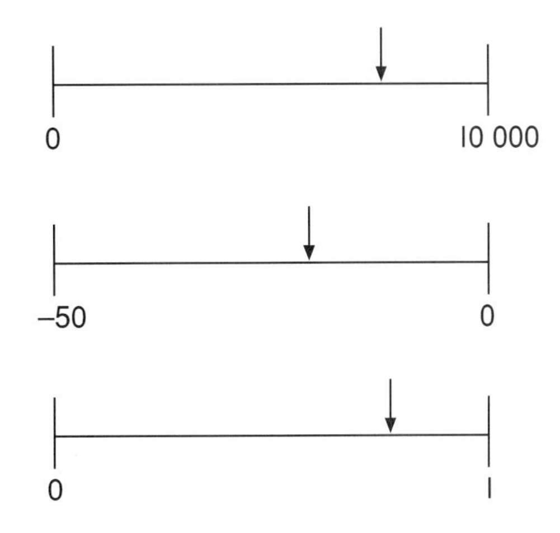

Estimate a proportion: for example, the fraction of a cake that has been eaten, or the proportion of grains of rice left in a jar.

See also estimating measures (page 93).

Pupils should be taught to:

Round whole numbers to the nearest 10, 100 or 1000

As outcomes, Year 4 pupils should, for example:

Round any two- or three-digit number to the nearest 10 or 100. For example:

- 633 is 630 rounded to the nearest ten.
  837 is 840 rounded to the nearest ten.
  935 is 940 rounded to the nearest ten.
- 433 is 400 rounded to the nearest hundred.
  856 is 900 rounded to the nearest hundred.
- 650 is half way between 600 and 700.
  The nearest hundred to 650 is 700, because we round up when the number is half way between two hundreds.

Write a number between 600 and 700 which is nearer to 700 than to 600.

Round measurements in seconds, minutes, hours, metres, kilometres, miles, kilograms, litres to the nearest 10 or 100 units. For example:

- Round these distances from Penzance to the nearest 100 miles, then to the nearest 10 miles.

Aberdeen	660 miles
Edinburgh	542 miles
Fort William	650 miles
Kendal	703 miles
Leeds	375 miles

Estimate calculations by approximating. For example:

- Which of these is the best approximation for 608 + 297?
  600 + 200 700 + 300 600 + 300
  600 + 97 610 + 300
- Which of these is the best approximation for 19×6?
  99×6 20×6 9×60 20×5
- Approximate: 19×16

See also examples on rounding in:
rounding up or down after division (page 56),
rounding measures (page 94) and
estimating calculations (pages 66 and 68).

As outcomes, Year 5 pupils should, for example:

Round any two-, three- or four-digit number to the nearest 10, 100 or 1000. For example:

- 5633 is 5630 rounded to the nearest ten.
  9837 is 9840 rounded to the nearest ten.
- 6433 is 6400 rounded to the nearest hundred.
  2856 is 2900 rounded to the nearest hundred.
- 8215 is 8000 rounded to the nearest thousand.
  8760 is 9000 rounded to the nearest thousand.
- 7500 is half way between 7000 and 8000.
  The nearest thousand to 7500 is 8000, because we round up when the number is half way between two thousands.

Write a number between 6000 and 7000 which is nearer to 7000 than to 6000.

Round measurements in days, metres, kilometres, miles, kilograms, litres to the nearest 10, 100 or 1000 units. For example:

- Round these distances from London to the nearest 1000 miles, 100 miles and 10 miles.

Paris	451 miles
Jeddah	5904 miles
New York	6799 miles
Sydney	19 675 miles
Madras	9981 miles

- A cricket team scored 247 runs in the first innings and 196 runs in the second innings. Approximately how many runs did the team score?
- It is 656 kilometres to Glasgow.
  I have driven 448 kilometres.
  About how much further is it?

Estimate calculations. For example:

- Which is the best approximation for 608 + 96?
  600 + 100   700 + 100   610 + 100   600 + 90
- Which is the best approximation for 19×26?
  99×26 20×26 19×20 20×25
- Approximate: $(37 + 54) \div 28$

**See also examples on rounding in:
rounding up or down after division (page 57),
rounding decimal fractions (page 31),
rounding measures (page 95) and
estimating calculations (pages 67 and 69).**

As outcomes, Year 6 pupils should, for example:

Round any whole number to the nearest multiple of 10, 100 or 1000. For example:

Would you estimate these numbers to the nearest 10, 100, 1000, 10 000, 100 000 or 1 000 000?

- the size of a Premier League football crowd;
- the number of people on a full jumbo jet;
- the number of people on a full bus;
- the number of fish in the sea;
- the number of children in a school;
- the number of children in a class;
- the number of people in the world.

Give an example of a number you would estimate to:
the nearest 10 000… the nearest 1000…
the nearest 100… the nearest 10… the nearest million.

Round to the nearest 10, 100 or 1000 units measurements such as:

- your height in millimetres;
- the capacity of a large saucepan in millilitres;
- the perimeter of the playground in metres.

Estimate calculations. For example:

- Which is the best approximation for 40.8 – 29.7?
  408 – 297   40 – 29   41 – 30   4.0 – 2.9
- Which is the best approximation for 9.18×3.81?
  10×3 10×4 9×3 9×4
- Approximate: $(409 - 155) \div 73$

**See also examples on rounding in:
rounding up or down after division (page 57),
rounding decimal fractions (page 31),
rounding measures (page 95) and
estimating calculations (page 67 and 69).**

Pupils should be taught to:

Recognise and order negative numbers

As outcomes, Year 4 pupils should, for example:

Use, read and write in context:
integer, positive, negative, minus, above/below zero...

Recognise positive and negative whole numbers (integers) in contexts such as rungs on a ladder, above ground and below ground, on a temperature scale, on a weather chart...

Count back through zero:
three, two, one, zero, negative one, negative two...

Respond to questions such as:

- What integers lie between –5 and 3?
- Put these shuffled cards from –15 to 5 in order.
- Fill in the missing numbers on this part of the number line.

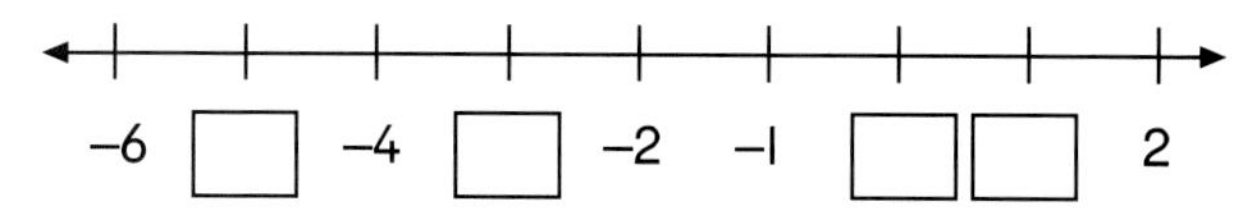

- Draw an arrow to point to –2.

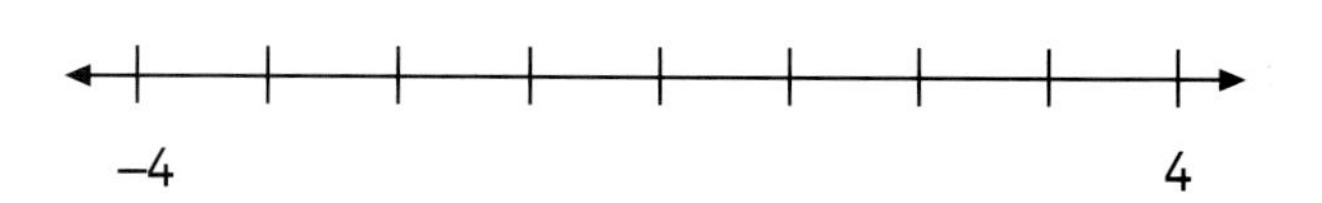

Use negative numbers in the context of temperature.
For example:
- What temperature does this thermometer show? *(minus 2 °C)*

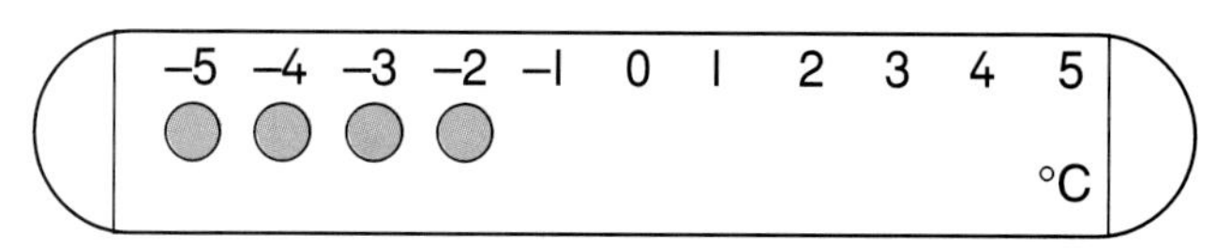

- Use a strip thermometer to take readings of:
  your body temperature;
  the temperature of the classroom window on a cold day;
  the temperature of different objects on a freezing day, such as a wall, car body, your hands...
- Which temperature is lower: –4 °C or –2 °C?
- Put these temperatures in order, lowest first:
  2 °C, –8 °C, –1 °C, –6 °C, –4 °C.

As outcomes, Year 5 pupils should, for example:

Use, read and write, spelling correctly:
integer, positive, negative, minus, above/below zero…

Recognise negative numbers on a calculator.
Use the constant function to generate sequences of negative numbers.

Count back through zero, for example:
seven, three, negative one, negative five…

Respond to questions such as:

- Put these numbers in order, least first:
  -2, -8, -1, -6, -4.
- What number is the arrow pointing to?

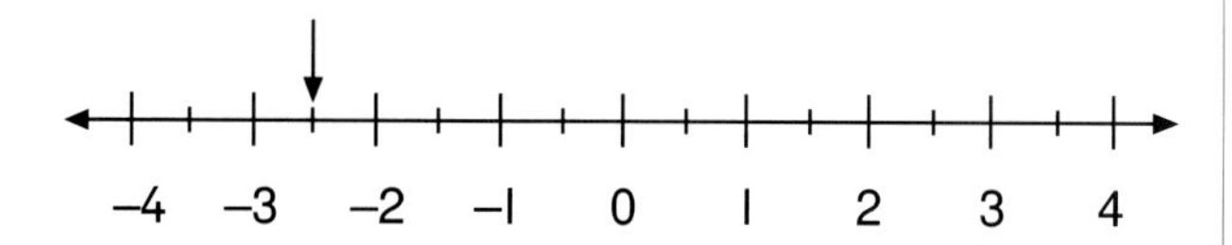

- Here is a row of six cards. Three cards are blank. Write a whole number on each blank card so that the six numbers are in order.

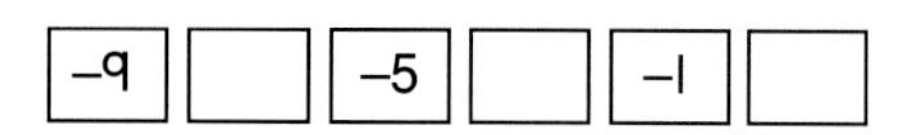

- If $-7 < \square < -4$, what integer could □ be?

Use negative numbers in the context of temperature. For example:

- What temperature does this thermometer show?

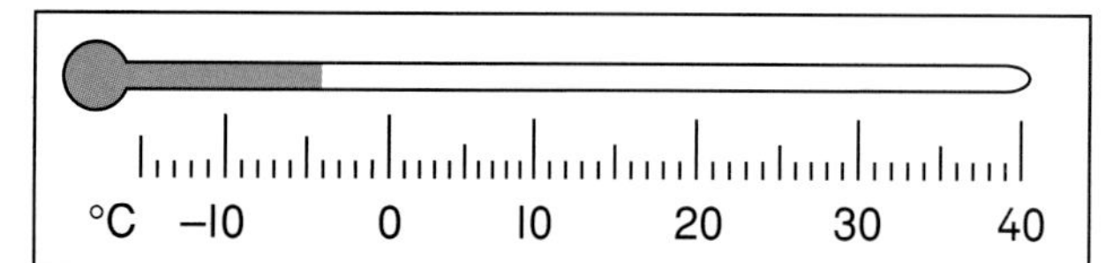

- The temperature rises by 15 degrees. Mark the new temperature reading on the thermometer.
- The temperature falls from 11 °C to -2 °C. How many degrees does the temperature fall?
- The temperature is 6 °C. It falls by 8 degrees. What is the temperature now?
- The temperature is -3 °C. How much must it rise to reach 5 °C?
- What is the difference in temperature between -4 °C and 14 °C?

Use negative numbers in other contexts such as:

- A diver is below the surface of the water at -30 m. He goes up 12 metres, then down 4 metres. Where is he now?

As outcomes, Year 6 pupils should, for example:

Use, read and write, spelling correctly:
integer, positive, negative, minus, above/below zero…

Respond to questions such as:

- Put these integers in order, least first:
  -37, 4, 29, -4, -28.
- In this equation, □ and △ represent whole numbers.

  □ + △ = 17

  Make a table of their possible values.
  Is there a pattern?
- Plot these points on a co-ordinate grid:
  (5, 4) (5, 8) (-3, 4) (-3, 8)
  What shape do they make?
  What is the length of its perimeter?

See also plotting co-ordinates (page 109).

Use negative numbers in the context of temperature. For example:

- The temperature is -5 °C. It falls by 6 degrees. What is the temperature now?
- The temperature is -11 °C. It rises by 2 degrees. What is the temperature now?
- The temperature at the North Pole is -20 °C. How much must it rise to reach -5 °C?
- Draw a line graph to show these temperatures at 9:00 am each day for a week:
  -2 °C, +3 °C, -1 °C…

Use negative numbers in other contexts such as:

- Lena set herself a target of 1 metre for her high jump. She recorded each attempt in centimetres above and below her target.

+2	-3	+2	-2	0	-1

What was her highest (best) jump?
What was her lowest jump?
What was her average jump?

Pupils should be taught to:

Recognise and extend number sequences formed by counting on and back in steps of any size, extending beyond zero when counting back

As outcomes, Year 4 pupils should, for example:

Use, read and write:
next, consecutive, sequence, predict, continue, rule, relationship… sort, classify, property…

Count on and back. For example:

- From any number, count on in 2s, 3s, 4s, 5s to about 100, and then back.
- Count back in 4s from 40.
  What happens when you get to zero? Can you go on?
  What happens if you start at 39?
- Count in 25s to 500, then back.

Describe, extend and explain number sequences and patterns. For example, respond to questions like:

- What are the next three numbers in each sequence?
  38, 47, 56, 65…   135, 137, 139, 141…
  48, 41, 34, 27…   268, 266, 264…
  Explain the rule.

- Fill in the missing numbers in this sequence.
  Explain the rule.
  □, □, 45, 49, □, 57, 61, □

- Take a 6 × 6 number grid.
  Count on in 4s from 0.
  Shade the numbers you land on.
  What do you notice?

  If you went on, would 44 be in your sequence? Or 52?
  How do you know?

  What happens if you start at 2?
  Is the pattern the same?

1	2	3	4	5	6
7	8	9	10	11	12
13	14	15	16	17	18
19	20	21	22	23	24
25	26	27	28	29	30
31	32	33	34	35	36

  Now try a 5 × 5 or a 10 × 10 number grid.

- What do you notice when you count from zero in:

twos	fours	eights
2	4	8
4	8	16
6	12	24
8	16	32

  (4s are double 2s; 8s are double 4s.)

- Count on or back from any number in steps of any single-digit number. Predict what will come next each time.
  What do you notice?

  Now try steps of 11.

See also negative numbers (page 14) and adding or subtracting 10, 100 or 1000 (page 4).

As outcomes, Year 5 pupils should, for example:

Use, read and write, spelling correctly:
next, consecutive, sequence, predict, continue, rule, relationship, formula... classify, property...

Count on and back. For example:

- From zero, count on in 6s, 7s, 8s, 9s to about 100, and then back.
- Count in 11s to 132, then count back.
  Can you go on past zero?
  What happens if you start at 133?
- Count in 25s to 1000, then back.
- Count in steps of 0.1 to 5.0, then back.

Describe, extend and explain number sequences and patterns. For example, respond to questions like:

- Describe and extend this sequence:
  -40, -37, -34...
  Explain the rule orally and in writing.

- Fill in the missing numbers in these sequences.
  Explain the rule orally and in writing.
  38, 49, □, □, 82
  □, □, 71, 62, □, 44

- Take a 9 × 9 number grid.
  Count on in 7s from 0.
  Circle the numbers you land on.
  What do you notice?

  If you went on, would 100 be in your sequence? Or 105? How do you know?

  What happens if you start at a number other than zero? Is the pattern the same?

  Now try a 10 × 10 or an 11 × 11 number grid.

- What do you notice when you count from zero in:

threes	sixes	nines
3	6	9
6	12	18
9	18	27
12	24	36

(6s are double 3s; 9s are 3s plus 6s.)

- Count on or back from any number in steps of 19, 21 or 25. Predict what will come next each time.
  What do you notice?

  Do the same using the constant function on a calculator to generate multiples of, say, 55 or 70.

See also negative numbers (page 15).

As outcomes, Year 6 pupils should, for example:

Use, read and write, spelling correctly:
next, consecutive, sequence, predict, continue, rule, relationship, formula... classify, property...

Count on and back. For example:

- From any number, count on in 6s, 7s, 8s, 9s to about 100, and then back.
- Count in 11s, 15s, 19s, 21s, 25s, then back.
  Can you go on past zero?
- Count in steps of 0.1, 0.5, 0.25 to 10, then back.

Describe, extend and explain number sequences and patterns. For example, respond to questions like:

- Describe and extend this sequence:
  1, 3, 6, 10, 15, 21... (triangular numbers)
  Explain the rule orally and in writing.

- Fill in the missing numbers in these sequences.
  Explain each rule orally and in writing.
  10, 25, □, □, 70...
  1, 4, □, □, 25, 36, □...
  □, □, -61, -42, -23...

- Examine the patterns formed by last digits: for example, when repeatedly adding 4.

  How does the pattern change if you start at 1?

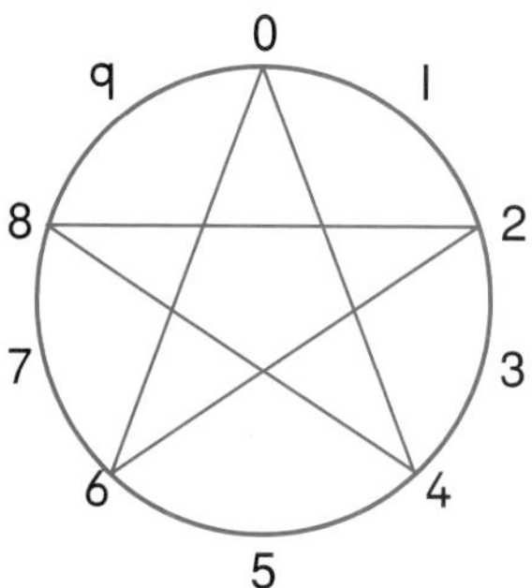

- Take a multiplication square. Find and explain as many patterns as possible: for example, the symmetry in the square, the pattern of square numbers, multiples of 3, multiples of 4...

1	2	3	4	5	6	7	8	9	10
2	4	6	8	10	12	14	16	18	20
3	6	9	12	15	18	21	24	27	30
4	8	12	16	20	24	28	32	36	40
5	10	15	20	25	30	35	40	45	50
6	12	18	24	30	36	42	48	54	60
7	14	21	28	35	42	49	56	63	70
8	16	24	32	40	48	56	64	72	80
9	18	27	36	45	54	63	72	81	90
10	20	30	40	50	60	70	80	90	100

Multiples of 4

See also negative numbers (page 15).

Pupils should be taught to:

As outcomes, Year 4 pupils should, for example:

Recognise odd and even numbers and make general statements about them

Make general statements about odd or even numbers and/or give examples that match them.

For example, explore and give some examples to satisfy these general statements:

- the last digit of an even number is 0, 2, 4, 6 or 8;
- the last digit of an odd number is 1, 3, 5, 7 or 9;
- after 1, every second number is odd;
- the numbers on both sides of an odd number are even;
- if you add two odd numbers, the answer is even.

Recognise multiples and know some tests of divisibility

Use, read and write:
multiple, digit...

Recognise multiples in the 2, 3, 4, 5 and 10 times-tables.

Respond to questions such as:

- Ring the numbers in the box that divide exactly by 4.

3	8	20	27	34	36	48	50

  Which numbers in the box are divisible by both 5 and 2?

- Sean counts his books in fours.
  He has 1 left over.
  He counts his books in fives.
  He has 3 left over.
  How many books has Sean?

- Use a number grid computer program to highlight multiples.
  Use different sizes of grid to explore multiples of 2.
  Describe and explain which grids produce 'diagonal' patterns, and which produce 'vertical' patterns.
  Try multiples of 3.

As outcomes, Year 5 pupils should, for example:

Make general statements about odd or even numbers and/or give examples that match them.

For example, explore and give some examples to satisfy these general statements:

- the sum of three even numbers is even;
- the sum of three odd numbers is odd;
- the difference between one odd and one even number is odd;
- the difference between two odd or two even numbers is even.

Use, read and write, spelling correctly:
multiple, digit, divisible, divisibility, factor...

Recognise multiples in the 6, 7, 8, 9 times-tables, and in the 11 times-table to 99.
Respond to questions such as:

- Ring the numbers in the box that are divisible by 7 (or have a factor of 7).

3	18	21	27	36	42	56

- A line of counters is set out in a pattern:
  two white, four blue, two white, four blue...
  What colour is the 49th counter?
  What position in the line is the 11th blue counter?

- Use a number grid computer program to highlight and explore multiples on different sizes of grid. Describe and explain the patterns produced.

Recognise multiples of more than one number: for example, multiples of both 2 and 3.

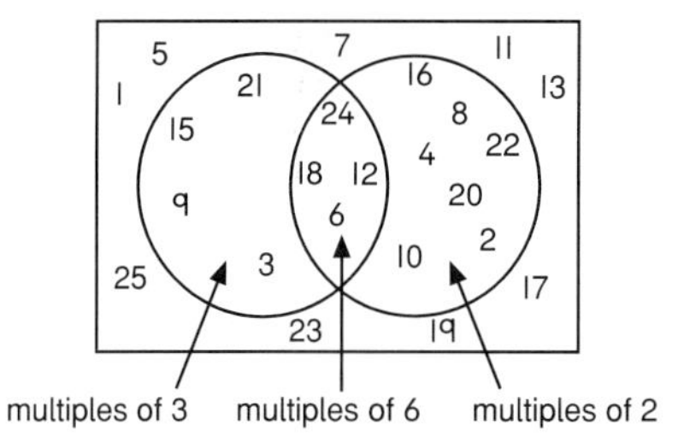

Recognise that a whole number is divisible by:

100	if the last two digits are 00;
10	if the last digit is 0;
2	if its last digit is 0, 2, 4, 6 or 8;
4	if the last two digits are divisible by 4;
5	if the last digit is 0 or 5.

Use this knowledge to work out, for example, that the year 2004 is a leap year because 2004 is divisible by 4.

As outcomes, Year 6 pupils should, for example:

Make general statements about odd or even numbers and/or give examples that match them.

For example, explore and give some examples to satisfy these general statements:

- the product of two even numbers is even;
- the product of two odd numbers is odd;
- the product of one odd and one even number is even;
- an odd number can be written as twice a number plus one (an example is 21, which is $2 \times 10 + 1$).

Use, read and write, spelling correctly:
multiple, digit, divisible, divisibility, factor...

Recognise multiples to at least 10×10.

Respond to questions such as:

- Ring the numbers in the box that are divisible by 12 (or have a factor of 12).

24	38	42	60	70	84	96

- A line of counters is set out in a pattern:
  five white, four blue, five white, four blue...
  What colour is the 65th counter?
  What position in the line is the 17th blue counter?

- Ring the numbers that are divisible by 7.

210	180	497

Find the smallest number that is a common multiple of two numbers such as:

8 and 12
12 and 16
6 and 15

Recognise that a whole number is divisible by:

3	if the sum of its digits is divisible by 3;
6	if it is even and is also divisible by 3;
8	if half of it is divisible by 4, or
	if the last three digits are divisible by 8;
9	if the sum of its digits is divisible by 9;
25	if the last two digits are 00, 25, 50 or 75.

See also tests of divisibility (page 73).

Pupils should be taught to:	As outcomes, Year 4 pupils should, for example:
Recognise square numbers	
Recognise prime numbers and identify factors	

As outcomes, Year 5 pupils should, for example:

Use, read and write, spelling correctly:
square number...
Begin to recognise: 6^2 as *six squared.*

Recognise 1, 4, 9, 16, 25, 36, 49, 64, 81, 100 as square numbers. Relate to drawings of squares.

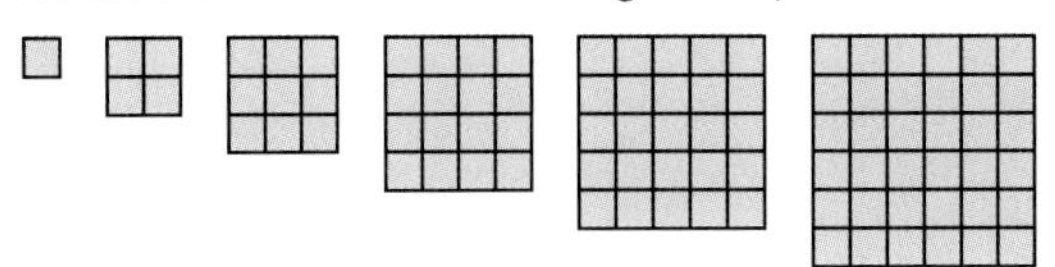

Respond to questions such as:

- What is 4 squared?
- What is the square of 6?
- What is 8^2?
- Which number multiplied by itself gives 36?
- What is the area of a square whose side is 6 cm in length?

Use, read and write, spelling correctly:
factor, divisible by...

Find all the pairs of factors of any number to 100. For example, the pairs of factors of 36 are:
1 and 36, 2 and 18, 3 and 12, 4 and 9, 6 and 6.

Use factors, when appropriate, for finding products mentally: for example,

$16 \times 12 = 16 \times 3 \times 2 \times 2 = 48 \times 2 \times 2 = 96 \times 2 = 192$

As outcomes, Year 6 pupils should, for example:

Use, read and write, spelling correctly:
square number...
Recognise: 6^2 as *six squared.*

Recognise squares up to 12×12, and calculate the values of larger squares: for example, 15^2, 21^2.

Identify two-digit numbers which are the sum of two squares: for example, $34 = 3^2 + 5^2$.

Use a calculator to respond to questions such as:

- Find which number, when multiplied by itself, gives 2809.
- Find two consecutive numbers with a product of 9506.
- The area of a square is 256 cm^2.
  What is the length of its side?

Use, read and write, spelling correctly:
factor, divisible by, prime, prime factor... factorise...

Find all the prime factors of any number to 100. For example, the prime factors of 60 are 2, 2, 3 and 5, since $60 = 2 \times 30 = 2 \times 2 \times 15 = 2 \times 2 \times 3 \times 5$.

Recognise, for example, that since 60 is a multiple of 12, it is also a multiple of all the factors of 12.

Use factors, when appropriate, for finding products mentally: for example,

$32 \times 24 = 32 \times 3 \times 8 = 96 \times 8 = 800 - (4 \times 8) = 768$

Identify numbers with an odd number of factors (squares).

Identify two-digit numbers with only two factors (primes). For example:

- Which of these are prime numbers?
  11 21 31 41 51 61

Recognise prime numbers to at least 20.

Use a computer program to identify or define a number chosen by the computer, using knowledge of number properties such as being greater or less than a given number, being odd, even, prime, square, a multiple of..., a factor of...

Pupils should be taught to:

As outcomes, Year 4 pupils should, for example:

Use fraction notation and recognise the equivalence between fractions

Use, read and write:
fraction...
half, quarter, eighth... third, sixth...
fifth, tenth, twentieth...

Use fraction notation: for example, read and write $^1/_{10}$ as one tenth, $^3/_{10}$ as three tenths.

Recognise that five tenths ($^5/_{10}$) or one half ($^1/_2$) is shaded.

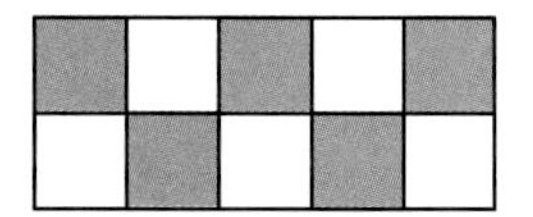

Recognise that two eighths ($^2/_8$) or one quarter ($^1/_4$) of the set of buttons is ringed.

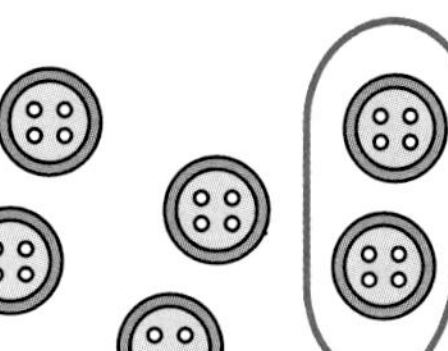
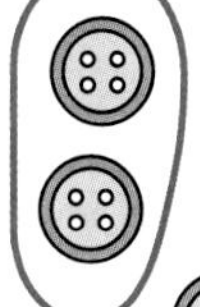
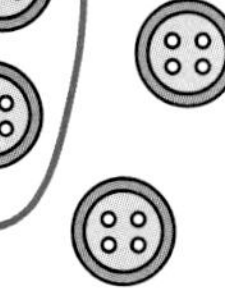

Recognise that one whole is equivalent to two halves, three thirds, four quarters... For example, build a fraction 'wall' using a computer program and then estimate parts.

Begin to know the equivalence between:

- halves, quarters and eighths: for example,
  - $^2/_8$ equals $^1/_4$,
  - $^4/_8$ equals $^2/_4$ or $^1/_2$,
  - $^6/_8$ equals $^3/_4$;
- tenths and fifths: for example,
  - $^2/_{10}$ equals $^1/_5$;
- thirds and sixths: for example,
  - $^2/_6$ equals $^1/_3$,
  - $^4/_6$ equals $^2/_3$.

Order familiar fractions

Recognise from practical work, for example:

- that one half is more than one quarter and less than three quarters;
- which of these fractions are greater than one half:

  $^3/_4$, $^1/_3$, $^5/_8$, $^1/_8$, $^2/_3$, $^3/_{10}$...

As outcomes, Year 5 pupils should, for example:

Use, read and write, spelling correctly:
fraction, proper/improper fraction, mixed number...
numerator, denominator...
half, quarter, eighth; third, sixth, ninth, twelfth;
fifth, tenth, twentieth, hundredth...
equivalent, reduced to, cancel...

Convert improper fractions to mixed numbers, and vice versa: for example, change $\frac{37}{10}$ to $3\frac{7}{10}$.

Recognise from practical work simple relationships between fractions. For example:
- one quarter is half of one half;
- one eighth is half of one quarter;
- one sixth is half of one third;
- one tenth is half of one fifth;
- one twentieth is half of one tenth.

Recognise patterns in equivalent fractions, such as:

$\frac{1}{2} = \frac{2}{4} = \frac{3}{6} = \frac{4}{8} = \frac{5}{10} = \frac{6}{12} = \frac{7}{14} \ldots$

$\frac{1}{3} = \frac{2}{6} = \frac{3}{9} = \frac{4}{12} = \frac{5}{15} = \frac{6}{18} = \frac{7}{21} \ldots$

and similar patterns for $\frac{1}{4}$, $\frac{1}{5}$ and $\frac{1}{10}$.

Start to recognise that:
- $\frac{10}{100}$ is equivalent to $\frac{1}{10}$;
- $\frac{20}{100}$ is equivalent to $\frac{2}{10}$;
- $\frac{50}{100}$ is equivalent to $\frac{5}{10}$ or $\frac{1}{2}$;
- $\frac{25}{100}$ is equivalent to $\frac{1}{4}$;
- $\frac{75}{100}$ is equivalent to $\frac{3}{4}$.

Recognise from practical work that, for example:
- one quarter is more than one eighth;
- one third is more than one ninth;
- two thirds is less than three quarters.

Make a line to 6 showing wholes, thirds, sixths and twelfths.

Answer questions such as:

- Which of these fractions are less than one half?
  $\frac{1}{10}$, $\frac{1}{20}$, $\frac{2}{5}$, $\frac{7}{10}$, $\frac{11}{20}$, $\frac{60}{100}$...
- Mark each of these fractions on a line from 0 to 1 with 20 marked divisions:
  $\frac{3}{10}$, $\frac{3}{4}$, $\frac{2}{5}$, $\frac{1}{2}$, $\frac{7}{10}$, $\frac{4}{5}$, $\frac{13}{20}$.
  Which is the smallest? Which is the largest?
- Place these in order, smallest first:
  $\frac{1}{2}$, $1\frac{1}{2}$, 2, $\frac{1}{4}$, $1\frac{3}{4}$.

As outcomes, Year 6 pupils should, for example:

Use, read and write, spelling correctly, the vocabulary from the previous year, and extend to:
thousandth...

Continue to convert improper fractions to mixed numbers, and vice versa: for example, $\frac{49}{8}$ to $6\frac{1}{8}$.

Recognise from practical work simple relationships between fractions. For example:
- one half is twice as much as one quarter, and three times as much as one sixth;
- one quarter is twice as much as one eighth;
- one tenth is ten times as much as one hundredth.

Recognise that:
- a fraction such as $\frac{5}{20}$ can be reduced to an equivalent fraction $\frac{1}{4}$ by dividing both numerator and denominator by the same number (cancel);
- a fraction such as $\frac{3}{10}$ can be changed to an equivalent fraction $\frac{30}{100}$ by multiplying both numerator and denominator by the same number.

Recognise equivalent fractions, such as:

$\frac{1}{2} = \frac{2}{4} = \frac{3}{6} = \frac{4}{8} = \frac{5}{10} = \frac{6}{12} = \frac{7}{14} = \frac{8}{16} = \frac{9}{18} = \frac{10}{20} \ldots$

$\frac{1}{3} = \frac{2}{6} = \frac{3}{9} = \frac{4}{12} = \frac{5}{15} = \frac{6}{18} = \frac{7}{21} = \frac{8}{24} = \frac{9}{27} = \frac{10}{30} \ldots$

and similar patterns for other unit fractions, relating them to ratios: 1 in every 7, 2 in every 14, and so on.

Answer questions such as:
- Write four more fractions equivalent to:
  $\frac{4}{5}$... $\frac{11}{10}$...
- Copy and complete:
  $\frac{\square}{10} = \frac{20}{100}$ $\frac{6}{21} = \frac{2}{\square}$

Compare or order simple fractions by converting them to a common denominator. For example:

- Suggest a fraction that is greater than one quarter and less than one third.

Answer questions such as:

- Mark each of these fractions on a line from 0 to 1 with 30 marked divisions:
  $\frac{3}{10}$, $\frac{1}{3}$, $\frac{2}{5}$, $\frac{1}{2}$, $\frac{2}{3}$, $\frac{7}{10}$, $\frac{4}{5}$, $\frac{5}{6}$.
  Which is the smallest? Which is the largest?
- Place these in order, smallest first:
  $2\frac{1}{10}$, $1\frac{3}{10}$, $2\frac{1}{2}$, $1\frac{1}{5}$, $1\frac{3}{4}$.
- What number is half way between:
  $5\frac{1}{4}$ and $5\frac{1}{2}$; $5\frac{1}{3}$ and $5\frac{2}{3}$...?

Pupils should be taught to:	As outcomes, Year 4 pupils should, for example:

Find fractions of numbers or quantities

Begin to relate fractions to division. For example:

- understand that finding one half is equivalent to dividing by 2, so that $\frac{1}{2}$ of 16 is equivalent to 16 ÷ 2;
- recognise that when 1 whole cake is divided equally into 4, each person gets one quarter, or 1 ÷ 4 = $\frac{1}{4}$.

Find fractions of numbers and quantities.
For example, answer questions such as:

- What is one tenth of: 100, 30, 500...?
  What is one fifth of: 15, 10, 35...?
- What is $\frac{1}{4}$ of: 8, 16, 40...?
  What is $\frac{1}{10}$ of: 50, 10, 80...?
- What is one tenth, one quarter, one fifth... of £1? Of 1 metre?
- What fraction of £1 is 10p?
  What fraction of 1 metre is 25 cm?
- What fraction of the larger bag of flour is the smaller bag?

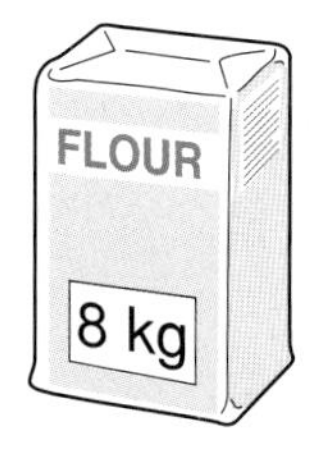

- What fraction of the larger shape is the smaller shape?

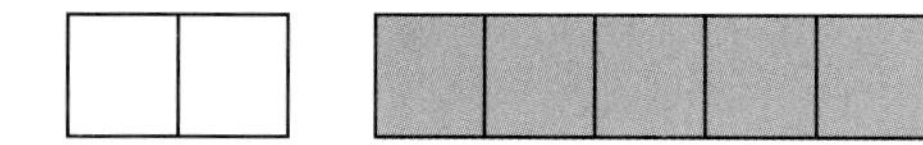

As outcomes, Year 5 pupils should, for example:

Relate fractions to division. For example:
- understand that finding one third is equivalent to dividing by 3, so $\frac{1}{3}$ of 15 is equivalent to 15 ÷ 3;
- when 3 whole cakes are divided equally into 4, each person gets three quarters, or 3 ÷ 4 = $\frac{3}{4}$;
- recognise that $\frac{12}{3}$ is another way of writing 12 ÷ 3.

See also remainders (page 57).

Find fractions of numbers and quantities.
For example, answer questions such as:

- What is one tenth of: 80, 240, 1000…?
  What is one hundredth of: 100, 800, 1000…?
- What is $\frac{3}{10}$ of: 50, 20, 100…?
  What is $\frac{3}{4}$ of: 16, 40, 100…?
- Write $\frac{23}{100}$ of £1 in pence.
  Write $\frac{7}{10}$ of 1 metre in centimetres.
- What fraction of £1 is 33p? 30p?
  What fraction of 1 metre is 27 cm? 20 cm?
- What fraction of 1 km is 250 m? 200 m?
  What fraction of 1 kg is 500 g? 300 g?
  What fraction of 1 litre is 750 ml? 700 ml?
  What fraction of 1 day is 1 hour, 8 hours, 12 hours?
- I work for 8 hours and sleep for 10 hours.
  What fraction of the day do I work?
  What fraction of the day do I sleep?
- What fraction of the smaller shape is the larger?

As outcomes, Year 6 pupils should, for example:

Relate fractions to division. For example:
- understand that finding one tenth is equivalent to dividing by 10, so $\frac{1}{10}$ of 95 is equivalent to 95 ÷ 10;
- when 9 whole cakes are divided equally into 4, each person gets nine quarters, or 9 ÷ 4 = $2\frac{1}{4}$;
- recognise that 60 ÷ 8 is another way of writing $\frac{60}{8}$, which is the same as $7\frac{4}{8}$.

Answer questions such as:
- How many halves in: $1\frac{1}{2}$, $3\frac{1}{2}$, $9\frac{1}{2}$…?
- How many quarters in: $1\frac{1}{4}$, $2\frac{3}{4}$, $5\frac{1}{2}$…?
- How many thirds in: $1\frac{1}{3}$, $3\frac{2}{3}$, $7\frac{1}{3}$…?

See also remainders (page 57).

Find fractions of numbers and quantities.
For example, answer questions such as:

- What is three tenths of: 80, 10, 100…?
  What is seven tenths of: 50, 20, 200…?
  What is nine hundredths of: 100, 400, 1000…?
- What is $\frac{4}{5}$ of: 50, 35, 100…? 2 litres, 5 metres…?
  What is $\frac{5}{6}$ of: 12, 48, 300…? 12 km, 30 kg?
- Write $\frac{3}{10}$ of 2 metres in centimetres.
  Write $\frac{23}{100}$ of 4 kilograms in grams.
  Write $\frac{7}{1000}$ of 1 metre in millimetres.
- What fraction of £1 is 35p? 170p?
  What fraction of 1 metre is 140 cm?
- What fraction of 1 km is 253 m?
  What fraction of 1 kg is 397 g?
  What fraction of 1 litre is 413 ml?
- What fraction of one year is:
  one week; one day; June?

Relate fractions to simple proportions.

See ratio and proportion (page 27).

Pupils should be taught to:

Solve simple problems involving ratio and proportion

As outcomes, Year 4 pupils should, for example:

Use, read and write:
in every, for every…

For example, discuss statements such as:

- In every week I spend 5 days at school.
  So in every 2 weeks I spend 10 days at school,
  and in every 3 weeks I spend 15 days at school.
- For every 2 bags of crisps you buy you get 1 sticker.
  For every 6 bags of crisps you get 3 stickers.
  To get 3 stickers you must buy 6 bags of crisps.
- 1 in every 3 squares is black in this pattern.
  In every 6 squares 2 of them are black.

Make a tile pattern where 1 in every 5 tiles is black.

See also problems involving 'real life' (page 82), money (page 84) and measures (page 86).

As outcomes, Year 5 pupils should, for example:

Use, read and write, spelling correctly, vocabulary to express simple ratios and proportions:
for every... to every... in every... as many as...

Discuss statements such as:

- John has 1 stamp for every 2 that Mark has.

  This means that:
  John has half as many stamps as Mark.
  Mark has twice as many stamps as John.
  John has one third of the total number of stamps and Mark has two thirds.
  If John has 4 stamps, Mark has 8 stamps.
  If Mark has 20 stamps, John has 10 stamps.

Solve simple problems involving 'in every' or 'for every'. For example:

- Chicken must be cooked 50 minutes for every kg. How long does it take to cook a 3 kg chicken?
- At the gym club there are 2 boys for every 3 girls. There are 15 girls at the club. How many boys are there? There are 12 boys at the club. How many girls are there?
- Zara uses 3 tomatoes for every ½ litre of sauce. How much sauce can she make from 15 tomatoes? How many tomatoes does she need for 1 litre of sauce?
- A mother seal is fed 5 fish for every 2 fish for its baby. Alice fed the mother seal 15 fish. How many fish did its baby get? Alice fed the baby seal 8 fish. How many fish did its mother get?
- For every 50p coin Mum gives to Dad, he gives her five 10p coins. Dad gave Mum twenty-five 10p coins. How many 50p coins did Mum give him?

See also problems involving 'real life' (page 83), money (page 85) and measures (page 87).

As outcomes, Year 6 pupils should, for example:

Appreciate that 'two to every three' compares part to part; it is equivalent to 'two in every five', which compares a part to the whole.

For example:

- Here is a tile pattern.

  How many black tiles to white tiles? (1 to every 2)
  What is the proportion of black tiles in the whole line? (⅓)

- Compare shapes using statements such as:

  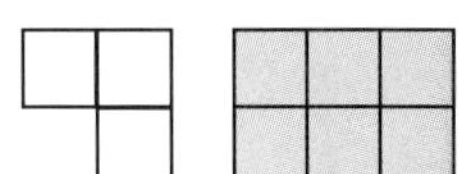

  there is one small square in the small shape for every two small squares in the larger shape;
  the larger shape is twice the size of the smaller shape;
  the smaller shape is half the size of the larger shape.

  Respond to questions such as:

  How many white to shaded squares? (1 to every 2)
  What proportion (fraction) of the total number of squares is shaded? (6/9 or ⅔)
  What fraction of the big shape is the small one? (½)

Solve simple ratio and proportion problems in context. For example:

- Kate shares out 12 sweets. She gives Jim 1 sweet for every 3 sweets she takes. How many sweets does Jim get?
- At the gym club there are 2 boys for every 3 girls. There are 30 children at the club. How many boys are there?
- Dee mixes 1 tin of red paint with 2 tins of white. She needs 9 tins of paint altogether. How many tins of red paint does she need?
- There are 5 toffees to every 2 chocolates in a box of 28 sweets. How many chocolates are there in the box?

See also problems involving 'real life' (page 83), money (page 85) and measures (page 87).

Pupils should be taught to:

Use decimal notation, know what each digit in a decimal fraction represents and order a set of decimal fractions

As outcomes, Year 4 pupils should, for example:

Use, read and write:
decimal fraction, decimal, decimal point, decimal place…

Respond to questions such as:

- What does the digit 6 in 3.6 represent? And the 3?
- What is the figure 4 worth in the number 17.4? And the 7?

- Write the decimal fraction equivalent to:
  four tenths;   fifty-seven and nine tenths.

- Round to the nearest pound:
  £4.58   £19.27

- In one step (operation), change:
  4.7 to 4.9…   6.9 to 6.1…

- Count from zero in steps of one tenth.
- Start at 5.1 and count on or back in steps of 0.1.

- Count along this line and back again.

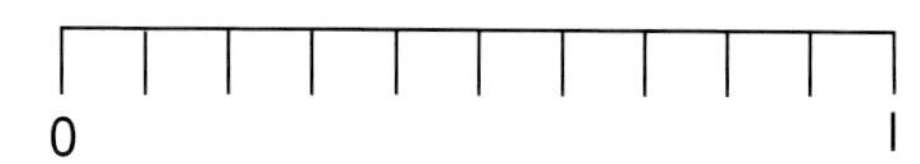

- Place these decimals on a line from 0 to 2:
  0.3, 0.1, 0.9, 0.5, 1.2, 1.9.

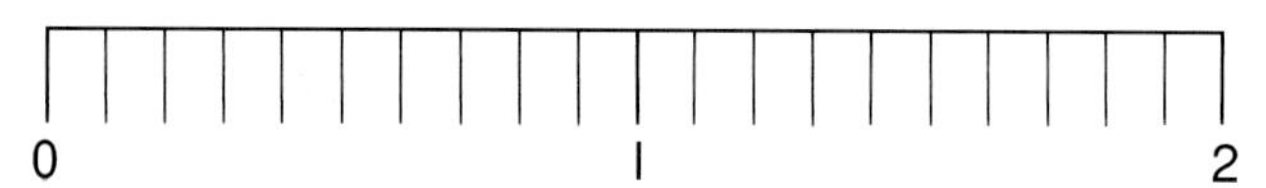

- Which is lighter: 3.5 kg or 5.5 kg?   3.72 kg or 3.27 kg?
  Which is less: £4.50 or £4.05?

- Put in order, largest/smallest first:
  6.2, 5.7, 4.5, 7.6, 5.2;
  99p, £9, 90p, £1.99;
  1.2 m, 2.1 m, 1.5 m, 2.5 m.

Convert pounds to pence, and vice versa. For example:
- Write 578p in £.
- How many pence is £5.98, £5.60, £7.06, £4.00?
- Write in £ the total of ten £1 coins and seven 1p coins. (£10.07)

Write centimetres in metres. For example, write:
125 cm in metres   (1.25 metres).

In the context of word problems, work out calculations involving mixed units of pounds and pence, or metres and centimetres, such as:
£3.86 ± 46p
4 metres ± 65 cm
For example: I cut 65 cm off 4 metres of rope. How much is left?

See also multiplying and dividing by 10 or 100 (page 6).

As outcomes, Year 5 pupils should, for example:

Use, read and write, spelling correctly:
decimal fraction, decimal, decimal point, decimal place...

Respond to questions such as:

- What does the digit 6 in 3.64 represent? The 4?
- What is the 4 worth in the number 7.45? The 5?

- Write the decimal fraction equivalent to:
  two tenths and five hundredths;
  twenty-nine hundredths;
  fifteen and nine hundredths.

- Using a calculator, in one step (operation), change:
  7.82 to 7.86...   15.35 to 15.75...
  5.3 to 53...   89 to 8.9...

- Continue the pattern: 1.2, 1.4, 1.6, 1.8...

- Put these in order, largest/smallest first:
  5.51, 3.75, 7.35, 5.73, 3.77;
  1.21 m, 2.25 m, 1.25 m, 1.52 m.

- Place these decimals on a line from 6.9 to 7.1:
  6.93, 6.91, 6.99, 7.01, 7.06.

- Suggest a decimal fraction between 4.1 and 4.2.

- Use a computer program to zoom in and out of a number line, and position and order decimals.

Begin to convert halves of a metric unit to a smaller unit, and vice versa. For example, write:

7.5 m in centimetres	(750 centimetres);
8.5 cm in millimetres	(85 millimetres);
3.5 kg in grams	(3500 grams).

In the context of word problems, work out calculations involving mixed units such as:
3 kilograms ± 150 grams
6.5 metres ± 40 centimetres

See also multiplying and dividing by 10, 100 or 1000 (page 7).

As outcomes, Year 6 pupils should, for example:

Use, read and write, spelling correctly:
decimal fraction, decimal, decimal point, decimal place...

Respond to questions such as:

- What does the digit 5 in 3.645 represent? And the 4? And the 6?

- Write the decimal fraction equivalent to:
  two tenths, five hundredths and nine thousandths;
  eight and seven thousandths;
  sixteen and twenty-nine thousandths.

- Using a calculator, in one step (operation), change:
  4.7 to 470...   530 to 5.3...
  0.3 to 0.03...   7 to 0.07...   60 to 0.6...

- Continue the pattern: 1.92, 1.94, 1.96, 1.98...

- Put these in order, largest/smallest first:
  5.25, 15.3, 5.78, 5.87, 5.2;
  1.5, 1.375, 1.4, 1.3, 1.35, 1.425;
  7.765, 7.675, 6.765, 7.756, 6.776;
  and other sets involving measures.

- Suggest a decimal fraction between 4.17 and 4.18.

- Use a computer program to zoom in and out of a number line, and position and order decimals.

Convert a larger metric unit to a smaller.
For example, write:

3.125 km in metres	(3125 metres);
1.25 litres in millilitres	(1250 millilitres).

Begin to convert halves, quarters, tenths, hundredths to a larger unit. For example, write:

750 grams in kilograms	(0.75 kilograms);
300 millilitres in litres	(0.3 litres);
3 centimetres in metres	(0.03 metres).

In the context of word problems, work out calculations involving mixed units such as:
1.3 litres ± 300 millilitres
3565 grams ± 2.5 kilograms...

See also multiplying and dividing by 10, 100 or 1000 (page 7).

Pupils should be taught to:	As outcomes, Year 4 pupils should, for example:
Round decimal fractions to the nearest whole number or the nearest tenth	
Recognise the equivalence between decimals and fractions	Know that, for example: 0.5 is equivalent to ½; 0.25 is equivalent to ¼; 0.75 is equivalent to ¾; 0.1 is equivalent to $\frac{1}{10}$; particularly in the context of money and measurement.

As outcomes, Year 5 pupils should, for example:

Round decimals with one decimal place to the nearest whole number. For example:

- Round these to the nearest whole number:
  9.7 25.6 148.3
- Round these lengths to the nearest metre:
  1.5 m 6.7 m 4.1 m 8.9 m
- Round these costs to the nearest £:
  £4.27 £12.60 £14.05 £6.50

See also rounding up or down after division (page 57).

Recognise that, for example:

0.07 is equivalent to $\frac{7}{100}$;
6.35 is equivalent to $6\frac{35}{100}$;

particularly in the context of money and measurement.

Respond to questions such as:

- Which of these decimals is equal to $\frac{19}{100}$?
  1.9 10.19 0.19 19.1
- Write each of these as a decimal fraction:
  $\frac{27}{100}$ $\frac{3}{100}$ $2\frac{33}{100}$

Enter fractions into a calculator and interpret the display to find the equivalent decimal.
Predict the result before confirming.
For example:

$\frac{1}{2}$	one half	0.5
$\frac{1}{4}$	one quarter	0.25
$\frac{3}{4}$	three quarters	0.75
$\frac{1}{10}$	one tenth	0.1
$\frac{1}{5}$	one fifth or two tenths	0.2
$\frac{1}{100}$	one hundredth	0.01
$\frac{75}{100}$	75 hundredths or three quarters	0.75
$\frac{3}{100}$	three hundredths	0.03
$\frac{50}{100}$	fifty hundredths or one half	0.5

Appreciate that a number like 3.6 in a calculator display means £3.60 in the context of money, and that 67p is entered as 0.67 since it is $\frac{67}{100}$ of £1.

As outcomes, Year 6 pupils should, for example:

Round decimals with one or two decimal places to the nearest whole number. For example:

- Round these to the nearest whole number:
  19.7 25.68 148.39

Round decimals with two or more decimal places to the nearest tenth. For example:

- What is 5.28 to the nearest tenth?
- What is 3.82 to one decimal place?

See also rounding up or down after division (page 57).

Recognise that, for example:

0.007 is equivalent to $\frac{7}{1000}$;
6.305 is equivalent to $6\frac{305}{1000}$;

particularly in the context of measurement.

Respond to questions such as:

- Which of these decimals is equal to $\frac{193}{100}$?
  1.93 10.193 0.193 19.13
- Write each of these decimals as a fraction:
  0.27 2.1 7.03 0.08

Continue to enter fractions into a calculator and interpret the display to find the equivalent decimal.
Predict the result before confirming.
For example:

$\frac{1}{1000}$	one thousandth	0.001
$\frac{1}{8}$	one eighth	0.125
$\frac{1}{3}$	one third	0.3333333
$\frac{2}{3}$	two thirds	0.6666666

Use a calculator to compare fractions. For example:

- Which of these two fractions is less?
  $\frac{7}{8}$ or $\frac{4}{5}$ $\frac{3}{4}$ or $\frac{11}{14}$
- Place these fractions in order:
  $\frac{7}{20}$, $\frac{6}{15}$, $\frac{13}{40}$, $\frac{8}{25}$

Pupils should be taught to:

Understand percentage as the number of parts in every 100, recognise the equivalence between percentages and fractions and decimals, and find simple percentages of numbers or quantities

As outcomes, Year 4 pupils should, for example:

As outcomes, Year 5 pupils should, for example:

Respond rapidly to oral or written questions, explaining the strategy used. For example:

- 3754 add 30… Add 700 to 9764…
- 18 add 30 add 29… Add 250, 60, 40, 150 and 3…
- What is the sum/total of 226 and 39? And of 13, 64 and 153?
- How many altogether are 121 and 345? And 61, 237 and 6?
- Increase 190 by 37.
- Which three numbers could have a total of 450? Are there any others?

Complete written questions, for example:

- working rapidly, using known facts:
  □ + 62 = 189 7.6 + 5.8 = □
- using informal pencil and paper jottings:
  □ + 756 = 924 □ + △ = 1
- using a standard written method:
  14 136 + 3258 + 487 = □

Use mental or written methods or a calculator to:

- find the missing number in:
  531 + □ + 160 = 746
- total a shopping bill or set of measurements such as:
  £12.45, £7.36, £24.50
  17.5 km, 55 km, 4.5 km, 28 km
- find all the different totals you can make by using three of these five numbers:
  8, 4008, 562, 3103, 95

See also mental calculation strategies (pages 40–47) and checking results of calculations (page 73).

As outcomes, Year 6 pupils should, for example:

Respond rapidly to oral or written questions, explaining the strategy used. For example:

- Add 4250 to 3536… 66 add 314 add 750…
- Add 1200, 400, 600, 1200 and 15.
- What is the sum/total of 753 and 227? And of 93, 62 and 25?
- How many altogether are 854 and 622? And 91, 88 and 6?
- Increase 250 by 420.
- Which three numbers could have a total of 1? Are there any others?

Complete written questions, for example:

- working rapidly, using known facts:
  □ + 2.56 = 5.38 91 + □ + 48 = 250
- using informal pencil and paper jottings:
  □ + 1475 = 6924 □ + △ = 0.1
- using a standard written method:
  421.36 + 25.7 + 53.25 = □

Use mental or written methods or a calculator to:

- find the missing number in:
  287 + □ + 2485 = 6128
- find all the different totals you can make by using three of these five numbers:
  14 721, 76, 9534, 788, 6
  1.07, 0.3, 37.03, 17.73, 31.7
- find the average (mean): for example, the average price of some goods, the average of a set of measurements or a set of numbers…

See also mental calculation strategies (pages 40–47) and checking results of calculations (page 73).

Pupils should be taught to:	As outcomes, Year 4 pupils should, for example:

Understand the operation of subtraction and the associated vocabulary, and its relationship to addition

Use, read and write:
take away, subtract, how many are left, how much less, difference between, how much more, how many more to make, decrease, inverse... and the minus (–) sign.

Consolidate understanding of subtraction as:
- taking away;
- finding the difference between;
- complementary addition.

Understand that:
- subtraction is non-commutative: that is, 5 – 7 is not the same as 7 – 5;
- when a larger number is subtracted from a smaller number, the answer is negative: for example, 3 – 8 = –5.

Understand that:
- subtracting a (positive) number makes a number less: for example, 260 – 129 is less than 260;
- subtracting zero leaves a number unchanged.

Understand that subtraction is the inverse of addition and use this to check results.

Respond rapidly to oral or written questions, explaining the strategy used. For example:
- 93 take away 8... Take 7 from 62...
- 63 subtract 46... Subtract 120 from 215...
- 170 less than 250... 1000 less than 5437...
- What must I take from 84 to leave 26?
- What is the difference between 28 and 65?
- How many more than 234 is 249?
- How many less than 68 is 42?
- What must I add to 54 to make 93?
- Decrease 72 by 34.
- 28 add a number is 43. What is the number?
- Find pairs of numbers with a difference of 79...

Complete written questions, for example:
- with rapid mental recall:
  27 – 19 = □ 43 – □ = 4 □ – △ = 11
- using a number line or square, then mental strategies:
  136 – 78 = □ □ – 65 = 87 △ – □ = 54
- using jottings or a pencil and paper method:
  1258 – 576 = □ 1258 – □ = 682 □ – △ = 682

Use mental or written methods to:
- find the missing number in:
  91 – □ = 48
- find all the different differences you can make by using two of these five numbers:
  219, 193, 74, 156, 97

See also mental calculation strategies (pages 40–47) and checking results of calculations (page 72).

As outcomes, Year 5 pupils should, for example:

Respond rapidly to oral or written questions, explaining the strategy used. For example:

- 127 take away 35... Take 80 from 373...
- 678 subtract 105... Subtract 50 from 225...
- 500 less than 720.
- What must I take from 220 to leave 55?
- What is the difference between 155 and 390?
- How many more than 952 is 1050?
- How many less than 305 is 94?
- What must I add to 720 to make 908?
- Decrease 92 by 78.
- 570 add a number is 620. What is the number?
- Find pairs of numbers with a difference of 599...

Complete written questions, for example:

- working rapidly, using known facts:
  □ - 62 = 189   7.6 - 5.8 = □
- using informal pencil and paper jottings:
  □ - 256 = 424   □ - △ = 1.2
- using a standard written method:
  141.36 - 32.58 = □

Use mental or written methods or a calculator to:

- find the missing number in:
  931 - □ = 746
- find all the different differences you can make by using two of these five numbers:
  8, 4008, 562, 3103, 95

See also mental calculation strategies (pages 40–47) and checking results of calculations (page 73).

As outcomes, Year 6 pupils should, for example:

Respond rapidly to oral or written questions, explaining the strategy used. For example:

- 750 take away 255... Take 300 from 1240...
- 3500 subtract 2050... Subtract 2250 from 8500...
- 1700 less than 2500... 3000 less than 10 220...
- What must I take from 8.4 to leave 2.6?
- What is the difference between 2.2 and 6.5?
- How much more than 23.4 is 24.9?
- How much less than 6.8 is 4.2?
- What must I add to 5.4 to make 9.3?
- Decrease 5.6 by 1.9.
- 2.8 add a number is 4.3. What is the number?
- Find pairs of numbers with a difference of 13.5...

Complete written questions, for example:

- working rapidly, using known facts:
  □ - 2.56 = 5.38   7.65 - 6.85 = □
- using informal pencil and paper jottings:
  □ - 1475 = 2924   □ - △ = 0.03
- using a standard written method:
  421.3 - 82.57 = □

Use mental or written methods or a calculator to:

- find the missing number in:
  □ - 2485 = 4128
- find all the different differences you can make by using two of these five numbers:
  1.07, 0.3, 37.03, 17.73, 31.7

See also mental calculation strategies (pages 40–47) and checking results of calculations (page 73).

Pupils should be taught to:	As outcomes, Year 4 pupils should, for example:

Know, with rapid recall, addition and subtraction facts

Consolidate knowing by heart all addition and subtraction facts to 20. For example, recall rapidly all the pairs for 15:

$10 + 5 = 15 \quad 5 + 10 = 15$
$9 + 6 = 15 \quad 6 + 9 = 15$
$8 + 7 = 15 \quad 7 + 8 = 15$

$15 - 5 = 10 \quad 15 - 10 = 5$
$15 - 6 = 9 \quad 15 - 9 = 6$
$15 - 7 = 8 \quad 15 - 8 = 7$

For example, with rapid recall:
- say pairs of numbers with a total of 18;
- given a number, say how many more will make 17 altogether;
- say how many steps must be taken to get from 4 to 17 on a number line, or from 17 back to 4.

Derive quickly related facts such as:

$70 + 90 = 160 \quad 160 - 90 = 70$
$700 + 900 = 1600 \quad 1600 - 900 = 700$

Derive quickly:

- number pairs that total 100:
  for example, 36 + 64 or 18 + 82;

- pairs of multiples of 50 that total 1000:
  for example, 250 + 750 or 150 + 850.

Derive quickly addition doubles:

- doubles from 1 + 1 to 50 + 50:
  for example, 38 + 38 = 76;

- multiples of 10 from 10 + 10 to 500 + 500:
  for example, 290 + 290 = 580;

- multiples of 100 from 100 + 100 to 5000 + 5000:
  for example, 1900 + 1900 = 3800.

See also doubling (page 58).

As outcomes, Year 5 pupils should, for example:

Derive quickly related facts such as:

70 + 90 = 160	160 – 90 = 70
700 + 900 = 1600	1600 – 900 = 700
0.7 + 0.9 = 1.6	1.6 – 0.9 = 0.7

Derive quickly, or continue to derive quickly:

- two-digit pairs that total 100:
  for example, 36 + 64 or 18 + 82;
- pairs of multiples of 50 that total 1000:
  for example, 250 + 750 or 150 + 850;
- decimals (tenths) with a total of 1:
  for example, 0.7 + 0.3 or 0.1 + 0.9;
- decimals (ones and tenths) with a total of 10:
  for example, 3.7 + 6.3 or 8.5 + 1.5.

Derive quickly addition doubles:

- doubles from 1 + 1 to 100 + 100:
  for example, 78 + 78 = 156;
- multiples of 10 from 10 + 10 to 1000 + 1000:
  for example, 780 + 780 = 1560;
- multiples of 100 from 100 + 100 to 10 000 + 10 000:
  for example, 6900 + 6900 = 13 800.

See also doubling (page 59).

As outcomes, Year 6 pupils should, for example:

Pupils should be taught to:	As outcomes, Year 4 pupils should, for example:
Find a difference by counting up through the next multiple of 10, 100 or 1000	For example, work out mentally by counting up from the smaller to the larger number: • 92 – 89, 403 – 386, 4000 – 3993
Count on or back in repeated steps of 1, 10, 100, 1000	For example, work out mentally that: • 2003 – 8 = 1995 by counting back in ones from 2003; • 643 + 50 = 693 by counting on in tens from 643; • 387 – 50 = 337 by counting back in tens from 387; • 460 + 500 = 960 by counting on in hundreds from 460.
Partition into hundreds, tens and ones	For example, work out mentally that: • 24 + 58 = 82 because it is 20 + 50 = 70 and 4 + 8 = 12, making 70 + 12 = 82, or it is 24 + 50 + 8 = 74 + 8 = 82; • 98 – 43 = 98 – 40 – 3 = 58 – 3 = 55.
Identify near doubles	For example, work out mentally that: • 38 + 36 = 74 double 40, subtract 2, subtract 4, or double 37; • 160 + 170 = 330 two 160s plus 10, or two 170s minus 10; • 380 + 380 = 760 double 350 plus double 30, or double 400 minus double 20.
Add or subtract the nearest multiple of 10, 100 or 1000 and adjust	Add 9, 19, 29… or 11, 21, 31… to any two-digit number: • 63 + 29 = 92 because it is the same as 63 + 30 – 1; • 58 + 71 = 129 because it is the same as 58 + 70 + 1. Subtract 9, 19, 29… or 11, 21, 31… from any two- or three-digit number: • 84 – 19 = 65 because it is the same as 84 – 20 + 1; • 283 – 71 = 212 because it is the same as 283 – 70 – 1. For example, work out mentally that: • 74 + 58 = 132 because it is 74 + 60 – 2 = 134 – 2 = 132; • 128 – 67 = 61 because it is 128 – 70 + 3 = 58 + 3 = 61.

As outcomes, Year 5 pupils should, for example:

For example, work out mentally by counting up from the smaller to the larger number:

- 705 – 287, 8006 – 2993

For example, work out mentally that:

- 324 + 58 = 382 because it is 320 + 50 = 370 and 4 + 8 = 12, or 370 + 12 = 382, or it is 324 + 50 + 8 = 374 + 8 = 382;
- 428 – 43 = 428 – 40 – 3 = 388 – 3 = 385, or it is 430 – 45 = 430 – 40 – 5 = 390 – 5 = 385.

For example, work out mentally that:

- 1.5 + 1.6 = 3.1 double 1.5 plus 0.1.

Continue to add/subtract 9, 19, 29... or 11, 21, 31... by adding/subtracting 10, 20, 30... then adjusting by 1.

- 458 + 71 = 529 because it is the same as 458 + 70 + 1;
- 583 – 71 = 512 because it is the same as 583 – 70 – 1.

For example, work out mentally that:

- 274 + 96 = 370 because it is 274 + 100 – 4 = 374 – 4 = 370;
- 4005 – 1997 = 2008 because it is 4005 – 2000 + 3 = 2005 + 3 = 2008.

As outcomes, Year 6 pupils should, for example:

For example, work out mentally by counting up from the smaller to the larger number:

- 8000 – 2785 is 5 + 10 + 200 + 5000 = 5215

For example, work out mentally that:

- 421 + 387 = 808 double 400 plus 21 minus 13.

Add/subtract 0.9, 1.9, 2.9... or 1.1, 2.1, 3.1... by adding or subtracting 1, 2, 3... then adjusting by 0.1.

Pupils should be taught to:	As outcomes, Year 4 pupils should, for example:
Use the relationship between addition and subtraction	Continue to recognise that knowing one of: 36 + 19 = 55 19 + 36 = 55 55 − 19 = 36 55 − 36 = 19 means that you also know the other three. Work out mentally one fact such as 58 + 27 or 91 − 25, and then state three other related facts. Working mentally, answer oral questions like: • You know that 56 + 14 = 70. What is: 14 + 56, or 70 − 56, or 70 − 14? • You know that 83 − 25 = 58. What is: 83 − 58, or 25 + 58, or 58 + 25? Use the numbers 25, 37, 52, 77, 87. Write as many different addition or subtraction statements as you can.
Add several numbers	Add mentally several small numbers: for example, 7 + 12 + 9 or 4 + 7 + 9 + 1. Work mentally to complete questions like: 1 + □ + 6 + 9 + 7 = 37 40 + 90 + 60 = □ using strategies such as: • looking for pairs that make 10 or 100 and doing these first; • starting with the largest number; • looking for pairs that make 9 or 11, and adding these to the total by adding 10 and then adjusting by 1. Add a set of numbers such as 6 + 6 + 5 + 7, recognising this as equivalent to 6 × 4. Explain your strategies.

As outcomes, Year 5 pupils should, for example:

Recognise that knowing a fact such as 136 + 319 = 455 makes it possible to find:

455 - 318 or 455 - 137.

Work out mentally one fact such as 15.8 + 9.7 or 101 - 25, and then state three other related facts.

Working mentally, answer oral questions like:

- You know that 560 + 140 = 700. What is: 140 + 560, or 700 - 560, or 700 - 140?
- You know that 835 - 25 = 810. What is: 835 - 810, or 25 + 810, or 810 + 25?

Given the numbers 135, 228 and 363, say or write four different sentences relating these numbers. For example:

228 add 135 equals 363,	228 + 135 = 363;
135 add 228 equals 363,	135 + 228 = 363;
363 subtract 228 equals 135,	363 - 228 = 135;
363 subtract 135 equals 228,	363 - 135 = 228.

Use the numbers 125, 237, 352, 77, 202, 477. Write as many different addition or subtraction statements as you can.

Add mentally:

- several small numbers, such as 3 + 5 + 7 + 2 + 9;
- three multiples of 10, such as 80 + 70 + 40.

Work mentally to complete questions like:

27 + 36 + 13 = □

using strategies such as:

- looking for pairs that make 10 and doing these first;
- starting with the largest number.

Add a set of numbers such as 26 + 28 + 30 + 32 + 34, recognising this as equivalent to 30 × 5.

Explain your strategies.

As outcomes, Year 6 pupils should, for example:

Continue to make use of the relationship between addition and subtraction. For example:

- Work out mentally one fact such as 1.58 + 4.97 or 1001 - 250, and then state three other related facts.
- Use 8036 - 1275 = 6761 to work out:
  8036 - 6760
  6761 + 1270

Add mentally:

- three or more multiples of 10, such as 80 + 70 + 40 + 90.

Work mentally to complete questions like:

31 + □ + 29 = 87   36 + 19 + 24 = □

using strategies such as:

- looking for pairs that make multiples of 10 and doing these first;
- starting with the largest number.

Add sets of numbers such as 70 + 71 + 75 + 77, recognising this as equivalent to (70 × 4) + (1 + 5 + 7).

Explain your strategies.

Pupils should be taught to:

Use known number facts and place value to add or subtract a pair of numbers mentally

As outcomes, Year 4 pupils should, for example:

Continue to add or subtract two-digit multiples of 10

- Respond to oral questions like:
  40 + 70   130 – 50
  and explain method.
- Work mentally to complete written questions like:
  90 + □ = 130   □ – 50 = 80
  then explain method in writing.

Add or subtract a pair of multiples of 100, crossing 1000

- Respond to oral questions like:
  500 + 700   1200 – 500
  and explain method.
- Work mentally to complete written questions like:
  200 + 900 = □   800 + □ = 1300   □ – 600 = 900
  then explain method in writing.

Revise adding/subtracting a multiple of 10 to/from a two- or three-digit number, without crossing the hundreds boundary

- Respond to oral questions like:
  52 + 30   582 – 30
  and explain method.
- Work mentally to complete written questions like:
  52 + 30 = □   52 + □ = 82   □ + 30 = 82
  76 – 40 = □   76 – □ = 36   □ – 40 = 36
  then explain method in writing.

Revise adding a two- or three-digit number to a multiple of 10, 100 or 1000

- Respond to oral questions like:
  90 + 18   350 + 16
  200 + 364   4000 + 518
  and explain method.
- Work mentally to complete written questions like:
  430 + 54 = □   430 + □ = 484   □ + 54 = 484
  610 + 27 = □   610 + □ = 637   □ + 27 = 637
  then explain method in writing.

Find what to add to a two- or three-digit number to make 100 or the next higher multiple of 100

- Respond to oral questions and explain method:
  What must be added to 37 to make 100? 432 to make 500?
- Work mentally to complete written questions like:
  58 + □ = 100   486 + □ = 500   731 + □ = 800
  then explain method in writing.

Find what to add to a four-digit multiple of 100 to make the next higher multiple of 1000

- Respond to oral questions like:
  What must be added to 7300 to make 8000?
  and explain method.
- Work mentally to complete written questions like:
  3200 + □ = 4000   8400 + □ = 9000

Use and apply these skills in a variety of contexts, in mathematics and other subjects.

As outcomes, Year 5 pupils should, for example:

Add or subtract three-digit multiples of 10

- Respond to oral questions like:
  570 + 250   620 - 380
  and explain method.
- Work mentally to complete written questions like:
  240 + 370 = ☐   610 - ☐ = 240   ☐ - 370 = 240
  then explain method in writing.

Add three or more three-digit multiples of 100

- Respond to oral questions like:
  500 + 700 + 400
  and explain method.
- Work mentally to complete written questions like:
  800 + ☐ + 300 = 1500
  then explain method in writing.

Add/subtract a single-digit multiple of 100 to/from a three- or four-digit number, crossing 1000

- Respond to oral questions like:
  638 + 500   1263 - 400
  and explain method.
- Work mentally to complete written questions like:
  300 + 876 = ☐   300 + ☐ = 1176   ☐ + 876 = 1176
  1382 - 400 = ☐   1382 - ☐ = 982   ☐ - 400 = 982
  then explain method in writing.

Add/subtract a three-digit multiple of 10 to/from a three-digit number, without crossing the hundreds boundary

- Respond to oral questions like:
  230 + 364   460 + 518
  and explain method.
- Work mentally to complete written questions like:
  538 + 120 = ☐   538 + ☐ = 658   ☐ + 120 = 658
  742 - 210 = ☐   742 - ☐ = 532   ☐ - 210 = 532
  then explain method in writing.

Continue to find what to add to a three-digit number to make the next higher multiple of 100

- Respond to oral questions and explain method:
  What must be added to 734 to make 800?
- Work mentally to complete written questions like:
  651 + ☐ = 700   247 + ☐ = 300
  then explain method in writing.

Find what to add to a decimal with units and tenths to make the next higher whole number

- Respond to oral questions like:
  What must be added to 3.4 to make 4?
  and explain method.
- Work mentally to complete written questions like:
  4.8 + ☐ = 5   7.3 + ☐ = 8
  then explain method in writing.

Use and apply these skills in a variety of contexts, in mathematics and other subjects.

As outcomes, Year 6 pupils should, for example:

Add or subtract four-digit multiples of 100

- Respond to oral questions like:
  5700 + 2500   6200 - 3800
  and explain method.
- Work mentally to complete written questions like:
  2400 + 8700 = ☐   6100 - ☐ = 3700
  then explain method in writing.

Find what to add to a decimal with units, 10ths and 100ths to make the next higher whole number or 10th

- Respond to oral questions and explain method:
  What must be added to 6.45 to make 7?
  And to 2.78 to make 2.8?
- Work mentally to complete written questions like:
  4.81 + ☐ = 5   7.36 + ☐ = 7.4
  then explain method in writing.

Use and apply these skills in a variety of contexts, in mathematics and other subjects.

Pupils should be taught to:

Use known number facts and place value to add or subtract a pair of numbers mentally (continued)

As outcomes, Year 4 pupils should, for example:

Add a single digit to any three- or four-digit number, crossing the tens boundary

- Respond to oral questions like:
  629 + 3   6745 + 8
  and explain method.
- Work mentally to complete written questions like:
  357 + 7 = □   368 + □ = 372   □ + 5 = 893
  2397 + 9 = □   4128 + □ = 4135   □ + 5 = 1254
  then explain method in writing.

Subtract a single digit from a multiple of 100 or 1000

- Respond to oral questions like:
  900 – 7   4000 – 3
  and explain method.
- Work mentally to complete written questions like:
  600 – 7 = □   600 – □ = 593   □ – 7 = 593
  5000 – 3 = □   5000 – □ = 4997   □ – 3 = 4997
  then explain method in writing.

Subtract a single digit from a three- or four-digit number, crossing the tens boundary

- Respond to oral questions like:
  905 – 7   4641– 3   7003 – 6899
  and explain method.
- Work mentally to complete written questions like:
  626 – 7 = □   626 – □ = 619   □ – 7 = 619
  5952 – 3 = □   5952 – □ = 5949   □ – 3 = 5949
  then explain method in writing.

Find a small difference between a pair of numbers lying either side of a multiple of 1000

- For example, work out mentally that:
  7003 – 6988 = 15
  by counting up 2 from 6988 to 6990, then 10 to 7000, then 3 to 7003.
- Work mentally to complete written questions like:
  6004 – 5985 = □   6004 – □ = 19   □ – 5985 = 19

Add or subtract any pair of two-digit numbers, including crossing the tens boundary

- Respond to oral questions like:
  45 + 27   62 – 27
  and explain method.
- Work mentally to complete written questions like:
  45 + 39 = □   45 + □ = 84   □ + 39 = 84
  92 – 25 = □   92 – □ = 67   □ – 25 = 67
  then explain method in writing.

Use and apply these skills in a variety of contexts, in mathematics and other subjects.

As outcomes, Year 5 pupils should, for example:

Find the difference between a pair of numbers lying either side of a multiple of 1000

- For example, work out mentally that:
  7003 - 6899 = 104
  by counting up 1 from 6899 to 6900, then 100 to 7000, then 3 to 7003.
- Work mentally to complete written questions like:
  8004 - 7985 = □   8004 - □ = 19   □ - 7985 = 19

Add or subtract a pair of decimal fractions each with units and tenths, or with tenths and hundredths, including crossing the units boundary or the tenths boundary

- Respond to oral questions like:
  5.7 + 2.5   6.2 - 3.8   0.56 + 0.72   0.63 - 0.48
  and explain method.
- Work mentally to complete written questions like:
  2.4 + 8.7 = □   0.24 + □ = 0.78
  6.1 - 2.4 = □   0.95 - □ = 0.67
  then explain method in writing.

Use and apply these skills in a variety of contexts, in mathematics and other subjects.

As outcomes, Year 6 pupils should, for example:

Add or subtract a pair of decimal fractions each less than 1 and with up to two decimal places

- Respond to oral questions like:
  0.05 + 0.3   0.7 - 0.26
  and explain method.
- Work mentally to complete written questions like:
  0.67+ 0.2 = □   0.67 + □ = 0.87
  0.5 - 0.31 = □   0.5 - □ = 0.19
  then explain method in writing.

Use and apply these skills in a variety of contexts, in mathematics and other subjects.

Pupils should be taught to:	As outcomes, Year 4 pupils should, for example:

Develop and refine written methods for addition, building on mental methods

Informal written methods
Use pencil and paper methods to support, record or explain calculations, achieving consistent accuracy.
Discuss, explain and compare methods.

Where calculations are set out in columns, know that units should line up under units, tens under tens, and so on...

HTU + TU, then HTU + HTU
Do this crossing the tens boundary, or the hundreds boundary, or both. For example:

A: adding the most significant digits first

```
    625         783         367         205
+  _48_     +  _42_     +  _85_     +  _176_
    600         700         300         300 ]
     60         120         140          70 ]  add mentally
    _13_        __5_        _12_        _11_ ]  from top
    673         825         452         381
```

B: compensation (add too much, take off)

```
    754
+  _86_
    854   (754 + 100)
   _-14_  (86 - 100)
    840
```

Standard written methods
Develop an efficient standard method that can be applied generally. For example:

C: adding the least significant digits, preparing for 'carrying'

```
   358
+  _73_
    11
   120
   _300_
   431
```

leading to 'carrying' below the line

```
    625          783          367
+  _48_      +  _42_      +  _85_
   _673_        _825_        _452_
     1           1           1 1
```

Using similar methods, add several numbers with different numbers of digits. For example, find the total of:

83, 256, 4, 57.

Extend to decimals
Using methods similar to those above, begin to add two or more three-digit sums of money, with or without adjustment from the pence to the pounds. Know that decimal points should line up under each other, particularly when adding or subtracting mixed amounts such as £3.59 ± 78p.
For example:

£4.21 + £3.87
£2.24 + £5.23 + £1.36

As outcomes, Year 5 pupils should, for example:

Informal written methods
Use pencil and paper methods to support, record or explain calculations, achieving consistent accuracy. Discuss, explain and compare methods.

Where calculations are set out in columns, know that units should line up under units, and so on...

HTU + HTU, then ThHTU + ThHTU
For example:

A: adding the most significant digits first

```
    587             7587
+   475        +     675
    900             7000 ]
    150             1100 ] add mentally
     12              150 ] from top
   1062               12 ]
                    8262
```

B: compensation (add too much, take off)

```
    654
+   286
    954  (654 + 300)
    -14  (286 - 300)
    940
```

Standard written methods
Continue to develop an efficient standard method that can be applied generally. For example:

C: using 'carrying'

```
    587             3587
+   475        +     675
   1062             4262
     11              111
```

Extend method to numbers with at least four digits.

Using similar methods, add several numbers with different numbers of digits. For example, find the total of:

58, 671, 9, 468, 2187.

Extend to decimals
Using the chosen method, add two or more decimal fractions with up to three digits and the same number of decimal places. Know that decimal points should line up under each other, particularly when adding or subtracting mixed amounts such as 3.2 m ± 350 cm. For example:

£6.72 + £8.56 + £2.30
72.5 km + 54.6 km

As outcomes, Year 6 pupils should, for example:

Informal written methods
Use pencil and paper methods to support, record or explain calculations, achieving consistent accuracy. Discuss, explain and compare methods.

Where calculations are set out in columns, know that units should line up under units, and so on...

ThHTU + ThHTU, then numbers with any number of digits
For example:

A: adding the most significant digits first

```
    7648            6584
+   1486       +    5848
    8000           11000 ]
    1000            1300 ] add mentally
     120             120 ] from top
      14              12 ]
    9134           12432
```

B: compensation (add too much, take off)

```
    6467
+   2684
    9467  (6467 + 3000)
    -316  (2684 - 3000)
    9151
```

Standard written methods
Continue to develop an efficient standard method that can be applied generally. For example:

C: using 'carrying'

```
    7648            6584
+   1486       +    5848
    9134           12432
     111             111
```

Extend method to numbers with any number of digits.

Using similar methods, add several numbers with different numbers of digits. For example, find the total of:

42, 6432, 786, 3, 4681.

```
   42
 6432
  786
    3
 4681
11944
```

Extend to decimals
Using the chosen method, add two or more decimal fractions with up to four digits and either one or two decimal places. Know that decimal points should line up under each other, particularly when adding or subtracting mixed amounts such as 14.5 kg ± 750 g. For example:

124.9 + 7.25
401.2 + 26.85 + 0.71

Pupils should be taught to:

Develop and refine written methods for subtraction, building on mental methods

As outcomes, Year 4 pupils should, for example:

Informal written methods
Use pencil and paper methods to support, record or explain calculations, achieving consistent accuracy.
Discuss, explain and compare methods.

Where calculations are set out in columns, know that units should line up under units, tens under tens, and so on...

HTU – TU, then HTU – HTU
Do this crossing the tens or the hundreds boundary, or both.

A: counting up (complementary addition)

```
    754
-    86
      4   to make 90
     10   to make 100
    600   to make 700
     50   to make 750
      4   to make 754
    668
```

B: compensation (take too much, add back)

```
    754
-    86
    654   (754 - 100)
    +14   (since 100 - 86 = 14)
    668
```

Standard written methods
Develop an efficient standard method that can be applied generally. For example:

C: decomposition — leading to

```
   754  =   700 + 50 + 4
-   86  -         80 + 6

        =   700 + 40 + 14   adjust from T to U     744 (1)
        -         80 +  6                        -  86

        =   600 + 140 + 14  adjust from H to T     644 (1 1)
        -          80 +  6                       -  86
            600 +  60 +  8 = 668
```

Subtract numbers with different numbers of digits.
For example, find the difference between:

671 and 58, 46 and 518.

Extend to decimals
Using methods similar to those above, begin to find the difference between two three-digit sums of money, with or without 'adjustment' from the pence to the pounds. Know that decimal points should line up under each other. For example:

£8.95 – £4.38
£7.50 – £2.84

As outcomes, Year 5 pupils should, for example:

Informal written methods
Use pencil and paper methods to support, record or explain calculations, achieving consistent accuracy. Discuss, explain and compare methods.

Where calculations are set out in columns, know that units should line up under units, and so on...

HTU – HTU, then ThHTU – ThHTU
For example:

A: counting up — leading to

```
    754                         754
-   286                     -   286
     14  to make 300             14  (300)
    400  to make 700            454  (754)
     54  to make 754            468
    468
```

B: compensation (take too much, add back)

```
    754
-   286
    454  (754 - 300)
    +14  (since 300 - 286 = 14)
    468
```

Standard written methods
Continue to develop an efficient standard method that can be applied generally. For example:

C: decomposition

```
   754   =  700 + 50 + 4
-  286      200 + 80 + 6              leading to

                                      1
         =  700 +  40 + 14          744
            200 +  80 +  6        - 286

                                   1 1     6 14 14
         =  600 + 140 + 14         644     754
            200 +  80 +  6       - 286    -286
            400 +  60 +  8         468     468
```

Subtract numbers with different numbers of digits. For example, find the difference between:

764 and 5821, 4567 and 893.

Extend to decimals
Using the chosen method, find the difference between two decimal fractions with up to three digits and the same number of decimal places. Know that decimal points should line up under each other. For example:

£9.42 – £6.78
72.5 km – 4.6 km

As outcomes, Year 6 pupils should, for example:

Informal written methods
Use pencil and paper methods to support, record or explain calculations, achieving consistent accuracy. Discuss, explain and compare methods.

Where calculations are set out in columns, know that units should line up under units, and so on...

ThHTU – ThHTU, then with any number of digits
For example:

A: counting up (complementary addition)

```
   6467                or      6467
-  2684                      - 2684
     16  (2700)                  16  (2700)
    300  (3000)                 300  (3000)
   3467  (6467)                3467  (6467)
   3000                        3783
    700
     70
     13
   3783
```

B: compensation (take too much, add back)

```
   6467
-  2684
   3467  (6467 - 3000)
   +316  (since 3000 - 2684 = 316)
   3783
```

Standard written methods
Continue to develop an efficient standard method that can be applied generally. For example:

C: decomposition

```
   5 13 16
   6467
-  2684
   3783
```

Subtract numbers with different numbers of digits. For example, find the difference between:

782 175 and 4387.

Extend to decimals
Using the chosen method, subtract two or more decimal fractions with up to three digits and either one or two decimal places. Know that decimal points should line up under each other. For example:

324.9 – 7.25
14.24 – 8.7

Pupils should be taught to:

As outcomes, Year 4 pupils should, for example:

Understand the operation of multiplication and the associated vocabulary, and its relationship to addition and division

Use, read and write:
times, multiply, multiplied by, product, multiple, inverse...
and the × sign.

Understand and use when appropriate the principles (but not the names) of the commutative, associative and distributive laws as they apply to multiplication:
Example of commutative law
$8 \times 15 = 15 \times 8$
Example of associative law
$6 \times 15 = 6 \times (5 \times 3) = (6 \times 5) \times 3 = 30 \times 3 = 90$
Example of distributive law
$18 \times 5 = (10 + 8) \times 5 = (10 \times 5) + (8 \times 5) = 50 + 40 = 90$

Understand that:
- 86 + 86 + 86 is equivalent to 86 × 3 or 3 × 86;
- multiplication by 1 leaves a number unchanged;
- multiplication of zero results in zero.

Understand that multiplication is the inverse of division (multiplication reverses division and vice versa) and use this to check results.

See also mental calculation strategies (pages 60–65) and checking results of calculations (page 72).

Respond rapidly to oral or written questions, explaining the strategy used. For example:
- Two elevens.
- Double 16.
- 7 times 4... 9 multiplied by 3.
- Multiply 15 by 6... by zero... by 1.
- Is 40 a multiple of 5? How do you know?
- What is the product of 15 and 6?
- Find all the different products you can make by using two of these five numbers: 2, 3, 4, 5, 10.

Complete written questions, for example:
- working rapidly, using known facts:
  - $7 \times 2 = \square$ $\quad 10 \times \square = 80$ $\quad \square \times 5 = 35$
  - $4 \times 9 = \square$ $\quad 3 \times \square = 24$ $\quad \square \times 4 = 20$
- using pencil and paper jottings and/or mental strategies:
  - $90 \times 6 = \square$ $\quad 8 \times \square = 560$ $\quad \square \times 90 = 720$
  - $4 \times \square + 8 = 24$

  progressing to:
  - $36 \times 18 = \square$ $\quad \square \times \triangle = 720$
  - $5 \times 35 + \square = 180$

As outcomes, Year 5 pupils should, for example:

Use, read and write, spelling correctly:
times, multiply, multiplied by, product, multiple, inverse... and the × sign.

Understand and use as appropriate the principles (but not the names) of the commutative, associative and distributive laws as they apply to multiplication:

Example of commutative law

$8 \times 65 = 65 \times 8$

Example of associative law

$14 \times 12 = (2 \times 7) \times 12 = 2 \times (7 \times 12) = 2 \times 84 = 168$

Examples of distributive law

$26 \times 7 = (20 + 6) \times 7 = (20 \times 7) + (6 \times 7) = 182$

$(6 \times 15) + (4 \times 15) = 10 \times 15 = 150$

Understand that, with positive whole numbers, multiplying makes a number larger.

Understand that multiplication is the inverse of division and use this to check results.

See also mental calculation strategies (pages 60–65) and checking results of calculations (page 73).

Start to use brackets: know that they determine the order of operations, and that their contents are worked out first. For example:

$3 + (6 \times 5) = 33$, whereas $(3 + 6) \times 5 = 45$.

Respond rapidly to oral or written questions, explaining the strategy used. For example:

- Two twelves.
- Double 32.
- 7 times 8... 9 multiplied by 7.
- Multiply 31 by 8... by zero... by 1.
- Is 81 a multiple of 3? How do you know?
- What is the product of 25 and 4?
- Find all the different products you can make by using three of these: 6, 7, 8, 9, 11.

Complete written questions, for example:

- working rapidly, using pencil and paper jottings and/or mental strategies:

  $70 \times 6 = \square$ $\quad 11 \times \square = 88$ $\quad \square \times 9 = 0.36$

  $80 \times 9 = \square$ $\quad 6 \times \square = 4.8$ $\quad \square \times 7 = 0.49$

- using informal or standard written methods:

  $72 \times 6 = \square$ $\quad 180 \times \square = 540$ $\quad \square \times 9 = 189$

  $14 \times \square + 8 = 50$ $\quad 46 \times 28 = \square$

Use written methods or a calculator to work out:

$132 \times 46 = \square$ $\quad \square \times \triangle = 162$

$2.7 \times 8 = \square$ $\quad (14 \times 60) + \square = 850$

As outcomes, Year 6 pupils should, for example:

Use, read and write, spelling correctly:
times, multiply, multiplied by, product, multiple, inverse... and the × sign.

Understand and use when appropriate the principles (but not the names) of the commutative, associative and distributive laws as they apply to multiplication:

Example of commutative law

$95 \times 78 = 78 \times 95$

Example of associative law

$10.4 \times 40 = 10.4 \times (10 \times 4)$ or $(10.4 \times 10) \times 4$

Example of distributive law

$46 \times 98 = 46 \times (100 - 2)$

$= (46 \times 100) - (46 \times 2)$

$= 4600 - 92 = 4508$

Understand that multiplication is the inverse of division and use this to check results.

See also mental calculation strategies (pages 60–65) and checking results of calculations (page 73).

Use brackets: know that they determine the order of operations, and that their contents are worked out first.

Respond rapidly to oral or written questions, explaining the strategy used. For example:

- Two nineteens.
- Double 75.
- 11 times 8... 9 multiplied by 8.
- Multiply 25 by 8... by zero... by 1.
- Is 210 a multiple of 6? How do you know?
- What is the product of 125 and 4?
- Find all the different products you can make using two of these: 0.2, 1.4, 0.03, 1.5, 0.5.

Complete written questions, for example:

- working rapidly, using pencil and paper jottings and/or mental strategies:

  $0.7 \times 20 = \square$ $\quad 20 \times \square = 8000$ $\quad \square \times 5 = 3.5$

  $4 \times 0.9 = \square$ $\quad 0.3 \times \square = 2.4$ $\quad \square \times 0.4 = 2$

- using informal or standard written methods:

  $132 \times 46 = \square$ $\quad \square \times 9 = 18.9$

  $24 \times \square + 8 = 3008$ $\quad 38 \times \square = 190$

Use written methods or a calculator to work out:

$738 \times 639 = \square$ $\quad \square \times \triangle = 9506$

$(41 \times 76) + \square = 4000$ $\quad 78 \times (97 - 42) = \square$

Pupils should be taught to:	As outcomes, Year 4 pupils should, for example:

Understand the operation of division and the associated vocabulary, and its relationship to subtraction and multiplication

Use, read and write:
share, group, divide, divided by, divided into, divisible by, factor, quotient, remainder, inverse...
and the division signs ÷ or /.

Understand the operation of division either as sharing equally or as grouping (that is, repeated subtraction). For example, 30 ÷ 6 can be modelled as:

- sharing among 6 and the number given to one person counted; or
- groups or lots of 6 being taken and the number of groups or lots counted.

Understand that:

- division by 1 leaves a number unchanged.

Understand that division is the inverse of multiplication (division reverses multiplication and vice versa) and use this to check results.

See also mental calculation strategies (pages 60–65) and checking results of calculations (page 72).

Respond to oral or written questions, explaining the strategy used. For example:

- Share 44 between 4.
- Divide 69 by 3. 69 divided by 3. Divide 3 into 69.
- How many groups of 6 can be made from 48?
- How many lengths of 10 cm can you cut from 183 cm?
- Is 72 divisible by 3? How do you know?
- What are the factors of 12?
- Tell me two numbers with a quotient of 5.
  Are there any other possibilities?

Begin to relate division and fractions. Understand that:

- ½ of 10 is the same as 10 ÷ 2;
- ¼ of 3 is the same as 3 ÷ 4.

Complete written questions, for example:

- with rapid mental recall:
  36 ÷ 4 = □ 60 ÷ □ = 6 □ ÷ 3 = 7
- using pencil and paper jottings and/or mental strategies:
  320 ÷ 4 = □ 240 ÷ □ = 60 □ ÷ 30 = 8
  (25 ÷ □) + 2 = 7 (□ ÷ 5) – 2 = 3
  progressing to:
  1456 ÷ 4 = □ 156 ÷ □ = 26 □ ÷ 9 = 460

As outcomes, Year 5 pupils should, for example:

Use, read and write, spelling correctly:
share, group, divide, divided by, divided into, divisible by, factor, quotient, remainder, inverse...
and the division signs ÷ or /.

Understand the operation of division as either sharing equally or repeated subtraction (grouping):
- sharing is better for dividing by small numbers;
- grouping is better for dividing by larger numbers.

Understand that:
- with positive whole numbers, division makes a number smaller;
- division is non-commutative: that is, 72 ÷ 9 is not the same as 9 ÷ 72;
- a number cannot be divided by zero.

Understand that division is the inverse of multiplication and use this to check results.

See also mental calculation strategies (pages 60–65) and checking results of calculations (page 73).

Respond to oral or written questions, explaining the strategy used. For example:
- Share 48 between 8.
- Divide 56 by 7. Divide 3 into 72.
- How many groups of 8 can be made from 73?
- What is the remainder when 74 is divided by 8?
- How many lengths of 20 cm can you cut from 270 cm?
- Is 156 divisible by 6? How do you know?
- What are the factors of 36?
- Tell me two numbers with a quotient of 100.

Relate division and fractions. Understand that:
- $\frac{1}{3}$ of 24 is equivalent to 24 ÷ 3 or $\frac{24}{3}$;
- 16 ÷ 5 is equivalent to $\frac{16}{5}$ or $3\frac{1}{5}$.

Complete written questions, for example:
- with rapid mental recall:
  $\frac{63}{7} = \square$ $\quad$ $56 \div \square = 8$ $\quad$ $\square \div 9 = 8$
- using pencil and paper jottings and/or mental strategies:
  $172 \div 4 = \square$ $\quad$ $\frac{54}{\square} = 18$ $\quad$ $\square \div 21 = 90$

Use written methods or a calculator to work out:

$(125 \div \square) + 2 = 27$ $\quad$ $(\square \div 5) - 22 = 30$

$900 \div 36 = \square$ $\quad$ $1560 \div \square = 120$

$\frac{\square}{28} = 46$

As outcomes, Year 6 pupils should, for example:

Use, read and write, spelling correctly:
share, group, divide, divided by, divided into, divisible by, factor, quotient, remainder, inverse...
and the division signs ÷ or /.

Continue to understand the operation of division as either sharing or repeated subtraction (grouping):
- sharing is better for dividing by small numbers;
- grouping is better for dividing by larger numbers.

Understand that division is the inverse of multiplication and use this to check results.

See also mental calculation strategies (pages 60–65) and checking results of calculations (page 73).

Respond to oral or written questions, explaining the strategy used. For example:
- Share 108 between 9.
- Divide 112 by 7. Divide 15 into 225.
- How many groups of 16 can be made from 100?
- What is the remainder when 104 is divided by 12?
- How many lengths of 25 cm can you cut from 625 cm?
- Is 156 divisible by 8? How do you know?
- What are the factors of 98?
- Tell me two numbers with a quotient of 0.5.

Relate division and fractions. Understand that:
- $\frac{1}{8}$ of 72 is equivalent to 72 ÷ 8 or $\frac{72}{8}$;
- 4 ÷ 7 is equivalent to $\frac{4}{7}$;
- 13 ÷ 7 is equivalent to $1\frac{6}{7}$.

Complete written questions, for example:
- with rapid mental recall:
  $6.3 \div 7 = \square$ $\quad$ $9.9 \div \square = 1.1$ $\quad$ $\square \div 5 = 0.8$
- using pencil and paper jottings and/or mental strategies:
  $17.2 \div 4 = \square$ $\quad$ $\frac{\square}{25} = 39$

Use written methods or a calculator to work out:

$4123 \div 365 = \square$ $\quad$ $\square \div 2.8 = 4.6$

$(\square \div 25) - 22 = 30$ $\quad$ $(56 + 97)/(133 - 85)$

$(100 \div \square) + 5 = 7.5$

Pupils should be taught to:

Understand the idea of a remainder, and when to round up or down after division

As outcomes, Year 4 pupils should, for example:

Give a remainder as a **whole number**.
For example:

- 41 ÷ 4 is 10 remainder 1 — 28 = (5 × 5) + □
- 72 ÷ 5 is 14 remainder 2 — 97 = (9 × 10) + □
- 768 ÷ 100 is 7 remainder 68 — 327 = (3 × 100) + □

- There are 64 children in Year 5.
  How many teams of 6 children can be made?
  How many children will be left over?

Divide a whole number of pounds by 2, 4, 5 or 10. For example:

- Four children collected £19 for charity.
  They each collected the same amount.
  How much did each one collect? (£4.75)

Decide what to do after division and round up or down accordingly

Make sensible decisions about rounding up or down after division. For example, 62 ÷ 8 is 7 remainder 6, but whether the answer should be rounded up to 8 or rounded down to 7 depends on the context.

Examples of rounding down

- I have £62. Tickets cost £8 each.
  62 ÷ 8 = 7 remainder 6.
  I can buy only 7 tickets.

- I have 62 cakes. One box holds 8 cakes.
  I could fill only 7 boxes of cakes.

Examples of rounding up

- I have 62 cakes. One box holds 8 cakes.
  I will need 8 boxes to hold all 62 cakes.

- There are 62 people. There are 8 seats in a row.
  8 rows of seats are needed to seat everyone.

See also rounding whole numbers (page 12).

As outcomes, Year 5 pupils should, for example:

Begin to give a quotient as a **fraction** when dividing by a whole number. For example:

$43 \div 9 = 4\frac{7}{9}$

Begin to give a quotient as a **decimal fraction**:

- when dividing by 10, 5, 4 or 2, for example:
  $351 \div 10 = 35.1$ $61 \div 4 = 15.25$
- when dividing pounds and pence by a small whole number, for example:
  It cost 4 children a total of £5.40 to swim. What did it cost each child? (£1.35)

When dividing with a calculator, interpret the quotient displayed. For example:

- interpret 8.4 as £8.40 in the context of money;
- round other decimals to the nearest whole number, recognising, say, 9.714 285 after dividing 68 by 7 as 'between 9 and 10'.

Decide what to do after division, and round up or down accordingly

Make sensible decisions about rounding down or up after division. For example, 240 ÷ 52 is 4 remainder 32, but whether the answer should be rounded up to 5 or rounded down to 4 depends on the context.

Examples of rounding down

- I have saved £240. A train ticket to Durham is £52.
  240 ÷ 52 is 4.615 384 on my calculator.
  I can buy only 4 tickets.
- I have 240 cakes. One box holds 52 cakes.
  I could fill only 4 boxes of cakes.

Examples of rounding up

- I have 240 cakes. One box holds 52 cakes.
  I will need 5 boxes to hold all 240 cakes.
- There are 240 people. One bus holds 52 people.
  5 buses are needed to hold them all.

See also rounding whole numbers (page 13) and rounding decimals (page 31).

As outcomes, Year 6 pupils should, for example:

Give a quotient as a **fraction** when dividing by a whole number. For example:

$90 \div 7 = 12\frac{6}{7}$

Give a quotient as a **decimal fraction**:

- when dividing by a whole number, for example:
  $676 \div 8 = 84.5$ $612 \div 100 = 6.12$
  rounding where appropriate to 1 decimal place:
  $85 \div 7 = 12.1$ to 1 decimal place
- when dividing pounds and pence, for example:
  It cost 15 people a total of £78.75 for a theatre trip. What did it cost each one? (£5.25)

When dividing with a calculator, interpret the quotient displayed. For example:

- interpret halves, quarters, tenths and hundredths as either decimals or fractions;
- recognise one third, two thirds and one ninth;
- round decimals to the nearest whole number or the nearest tenth.

Decide what to do after division, and round up or down accordingly

Make sensible decisions about rounding down or up after division. For example: 1000 ÷ 265 3.8, but whether the answer should be rounded up to 4 or rounded down to 3 depends on the context.

Examples of rounding down

- Dad has saved £5000. An air fare to Sydney is £865.
  5000 ÷ 865 is 5.780 346 on my calculator.
  He can buy 5 tickets.
- I have 5 metres of rope. I need lengths of 865 cm.
  I can cut off 5 lengths.

Examples of rounding up

- I have 5000 sheets of paper. A box holds 865 sheets. I will need 6 boxes to hold all 5000 sheets.
- 5000 football fans have tickets for a match. Each stand seats 865 people. They can all sit in 6 stands.

See also rounding whole numbers (page 13) and rounding decimals (page 31).

Pupils should be taught to:	As outcomes, Year 4 pupils should, for example:
Know multiplication facts by heart and derive quickly the corresponding division facts	Know by heart multiplication facts for the 2, 3, 4, 5 and 10 times-tables, up to ×10, including multiplication by 0 and 1, and begin to know them for the 6, 7, 8 and 9 times-tables. Derive quickly the corresponding division facts. Respond rapidly to oral or written questions like: • Nine fives. • 3 times 7... times 0. • 4 multiplied by 8... by 0. • Multiply 9 by 5... by 1. Respond quickly to questions like: • Divide 36 by 4. • What is 24 shared between 3? • How many fives in 55? • Half of 17. • One quarter of 3.
Know by heart or derive rapidly doubles and halves	Use, read and write: *double, twice, half, halve, whole, divide by 2, divide into 2...* and ½ as one half. Understand that halving is the inverse of doubling: for example, if half of 18 is 9, then double 9 is 18. Know by heart or derive quickly: • doubles of all numbers 1 to 50; • doubles of multiples of 10 up to 500; • doubles of multiples of 100 up to 5000; and all the corresponding halves. Respond rapidly to oral or written questions like: • Double 19... 75... 350... 4200... • Half of 38... of 150... of 700... of 8400... • ½ of 700... of 34... • Twice 95. • Jo spent half of her £21.60 savings. How much did she spend? • How many metres is half a kilometre? Complete written questions, for example: • working quickly, using known facts: $60 \times 2 = \square$ $160 \div \square = 80$ • using cubes or a number line, then mental strategies: $74 \times 2 = \square$ $72 \div 2 = \square$ $\square \times 2 = 126$ $\square \div 2 = 37$

As outcomes, Year 5 pupils should, for example:

Know by heart all multiplication facts up to 10 × 10, including multiplication by 0 and 1.

Derive quickly the corresponding division facts.

Know by heart the squares of all numbers from 1 × 1 to 10 × 10.

Respond rapidly to oral or written questions like:

- Nine sevens.
- How many eights in 48?
- 6 times 7.
- 5 multiplied by 9.
- Multiply 9 by 6.
- 7 multiplied by 0.

Respond quickly to questions like:

- Divide 38 by 9.
- What is 48 shared between 8?
- Three divided by 5.
- One seventh of 35.

Use, read and write, spelling correctly:
double, twice, half, halve, whole, divide by 2, divide into 2... and ½ as one half.

Understand that halving is the inverse of doubling: for example, if half of 72 is 36, then double 36 is 72.

Know by heart or derive quickly:

- doubles of all numbers 1 to 100;
- doubles of multiples of 10 up to 1000;
- doubles of multiples of 100 up to 10 000;

and all the corresponding halves.

Respond rapidly to oral or written questions like:

- Double 7½... 98... 680... 8500...
- Half of 154... of 820... of 5600...
- Twice 85.
- ½ of 920.
- Half of one half.
- What is half of £71.30?
- How many millimetres is half a metre?

Complete written questions, for example:

- working quickly, using mental strategies:

160 × 2 = □	1600 ÷ □ = 800	16/2 = □
134 × 2 = □	430 ÷ 2 = □	□/2 = 65
□ × 2 = 290	□ ÷ 2 = 330	

As outcomes, Year 6 pupils should, for example:

Continue to know by heart all multiplication facts up to 10 × 10, including multiplication by 0 and 1.

Derive quickly the corresponding division facts.

Know by heart the squares of all numbers from 1 × 1 to 12 × 12.

Derive quickly squares of multiples of 10 to 100, such as 20^2, 80^2.

Respond rapidly to oral or written questions like:

- Nine eights.
- How many sevens in 35?
- 8 times 8.
- 6 multiplied by 7.
- Multiply 11 by 8.

Respond quickly to questions like:

- 7 multiplied by 0.8... by 0.
- Multiply 0.9 by 0.6... by 0.
- Divide 3.6 by 9... by 1.
- What is 88 shared between 8?
- Divide 6 into 39.
- 9 divided by 4.
- 0.6 times 7... times 2.
- One twentieth of 360.

Use, read and write, spelling correctly:
double, twice, half, halve, whole, divide by 2, divide into 2... and ½ as one half.

Understand that halving is the inverse of doubling: for example, if half of 0.3 is 0.15, then double 0.15 is 0.3.

Know by heart or derive quickly:

- doubles of two-digit whole numbers or decimals;
- doubles of multiples of 10 up to 1000;
- doubles of multiples of 100 up to 10 000;

and all the corresponding halves.

Respond rapidly to oral or written questions like:

- Double 37½... 3.7... 0.59...
- Twice 2.6.
- ½ of 9.5.
- Half of one eighth.
- What is half of £581?
- What fraction of 1 cm is half a millimetre?

Complete written questions, for example:

- working quickly, using mental strategies:

370 × 2 = □	1750 ÷ □ = 875	190/2 = □
176 × 2 = □	570 ÷ 2 = □	□/2 = 165
□ × 2 = 3.9	□ ÷ 2 = 0.87	

Pupils should be taught to:	As outcomes, Year 4 pupils should, for example:

Use related facts and doubling or halving

Use related facts and doubling or halving. For example:

- double 34 is double 30 add double 4, or 60 + 8 = 68;
- half of 56 is half of 50 plus half of 6.

For example:

- To multiply by 4, double and double again. For example, to work out 12 × 4, say 12, 24, 48.
- To multiply by 5, multiply by 10 and halve. For example:
  14 × 5 = 14 × (10 ÷ 2)
  = (14 × 10) ÷ 2
  = 140 ÷ 2
  = 70
- To multiply by 20, multiply by 10 and then double. For example:
  14 × 20 = 14 × (10 × 2)
  = (14 × 10) × 2
  = 140 × 2
  = 280
- Work out the 8 times-table facts by doubling the 4 times-table facts.
- Work out some multiples of 15 by doubling:
  1 × 15 = 15 so
  2 × 15 = 30
  4 × 15 = 60
  8 × 15 = 120
  16 × 15 = 240 …

  Use combinations of these facts to work out, say,
  11 × 15 = (8 × 15) + (2 × 15) + (1 × 15) = 165.

Explain how to find quarters and eighths by halving. For example, work out mentally that:

- one eighth of 64 is 8
  (half of 64 is 32, half again is 16, half again is 8);
- one quarter of 600 is 150
  (because one half of 600 is 300 and half again is 150).

Use factors

As outcomes, Year 5 pupils should, for example:

Use related facts and doubling/halving. For example:
- double 78 = double 70 + double 8
  $= 140 + 16 = 156$;
- half of 256 = half of 200 + half of 50 + half of 6
  $= 128$.

For example:
- Double a number ending in 5, and halve the other number. For example:
  16×5 is equivalent to $8 \times 10 = 80$
  35×14 is equivalent to $70 \times 7 = 490$
- Halve an even number in the calculation, find the product, then double it. For example:
  13×14 $\quad 13 \times 7 = 91$ $\quad 91 \times 2 = 182$
  16×51 $\quad 8 \times 51 = 408$ $\quad 408 \times 2 = 816$
- To multiply by 50, multiply by 100, then halve. For example:
  36×50 $\quad 36 \times 100 = 3600$ $\quad 3600 \div 2 = 1800$
- Work out the 16 times-table facts by doubling the 8 times-table facts.
- Work out:
  $1 \times 25 = 25$ and so deduce that
  $2 \times 25 = 50$
  $4 \times 25 = 100$
  $8 \times 25 = 200$
  $16 \times 25 = 400$ ...

  Use combinations of these facts to work out, say, $25 \times 25 = (16 \times 25) + (8 \times 25) + (1 \times 25) = 625$.

Explain how to find sixths by halving thirds, or twentieths by halving tenths.
For example, work out mentally that:
- one sixth of 300 is 50
  (one third of 300 is 100, half of that is 50);
- one twentieth of 900 is 45
  (one tenth is 90, and half of that is 45).

Use factors. For example:

15×6 $\quad 15 \times 3 = 45$
$\quad 45 \times 2 = 90$ $\quad 15 \times 6 = 90$

$90 \div 6$ $\quad 90 \div 3 = 30$
$\quad 30 \div 2 = 15$ $\quad 90 \div 6 = 15$

As outcomes, Year 6 pupils should, for example:

Use related facts and doubling/halving. For example:
- double $176 = 200 + 140 + 12 = 352$;
- half of 948 = half of 900 + half of 40 + half of 8
  $= 474$.

For example:
- Double a number ending in 5, and halve the other number.
- Halve/double one number in the calculation, find the product, then double/halve it.
- To multiply by 15, multiply by 10, halve the result, then add the two parts together. For example:
  14×15 $\quad 14 \times 10 = 140$
  $\quad 140 \div 2 = 70$
  $\quad 14 \times 15 = 210$

  Alternatively, multiply by 30, then divide by 2.
- To multiply by 25, multiply by 100, then divide by 4. For example:
  39×25 $\quad 39 \times 100 = 3900$ $\quad 3900 \div 4 = 975$
- Work out the 24 times-table facts by doubling the 6 times-table facts and doubling again.
- Work out:
  $1 \times 32 = 32$ and so deduce that
  $2 \times 32 = 64$
  $4 \times 32 = 128$
  $8 \times 32 = 256$
  $16 \times 32 = 512$ ...

  Use combinations of these facts to work out other multiples of 32.

Explain how to find sixths and twelfths by halving thirds, or twentieths by halving tenths.
For example, work out mentally that:
- one twelfth of 300 is 25
  (one third of 300 is 100, half is 50, half again is 25);
- one twentieth of 150 is $7\frac{1}{2}$
  (one tenth is 15, and half of that is $7\frac{1}{2}$).

Use factors. For example:

35×18 $\quad 35 \times 6 = 210$
$\quad 210 \times 3 = 630$ $\quad 35 \times 18 = 630$

$378 \div 21$ $\quad 378 \div 3 = 126$
$\quad 126 \div 7 = 18$ $\quad 378 \div 21 = 18$

Pupils should be taught to:	As outcomes, Year 4 pupils should, for example:
Use closely related facts already known	Work out the 6 times-table by adding 2 times-table facts to 4 times-table facts. To multiply a number by 9 or 11, multiply it by 10 and add or subtract the number. For example: $13 \times 11 = (13 \times 10) + 13 = 130 + 13 = 143$ $13 \times 9 = (13 \times 10) - 13 = 130 - 13 = 117$
Partition and use the distributive law	Begin to multiply a two-digit number by a single-digit number, multiplying the tens first. For example: $32 \times 3 = (30 \times 3) + (2 \times 3) = 90 + 6 = 96$
Use the relationship between multiplication and addition, or multiplication and division	Continue to recognise that knowing one of: $12 \times 9 = 108$ $9 \times 12 = 108$ $108 \div 9 = 12$ $108 \div 12 = 9$ means that you also know the other three. Recognise and use, for example, $25 \times 4 = 25 + 25 + 25 + 25$. Answer oral or written questions like: • Given that $14 \times 6 = 84$, what is 6×14, or $84 \div 6$, or $84 \div 14$? • Given that $400 \div 5 = 80$, what is $400 \div 80$, or 5×80, or 80×5? • Use the numbers 2, 15 and 30. Say or write four different multiplication or division statements relating the numbers.

As outcomes, Year 5 pupils should, for example:

Work out the 12 times-table by adding 2 times-table facts to 10 times-table facts.

To multiply a number by 19 or 21, multiply it by 20 and add or subtract the number. For example:

$$13 \times 21 = (13 \times 20) + 13 = 260 + 13 = 273$$
$$13 \times 19 = (13 \times 20) - 13 = 260 - 13 = 247$$

Multiply a two-digit number by a single-digit number, multiplying the tens first. For example:

$$47 \times 5 = (40 \times 5) + (7 \times 5) = 200 + 35 = 235$$

Continue to recognise that knowing one of:

$23 \times 3 = 69$ $\quad 3 \times 23 = 69$
$69 \div 3 = 23$ $\quad 69 \div 23 = 3$

means that you also know the other three.

Recognise, for example, that:

- if $12 \times 6 = 72$, then $\frac{1}{6}$ of 72 = 12 and $\frac{1}{12}$ of 72 = 6.

Answer oral or written questions like:

- Given that $14 \times 11 = 154$, what is 11×14, or $154 \div 11$, or $154 \div 14$?
- Given that $315 \div 15 = 21$, what is $315 \div 21$, or 15×21 or 21×15?
- Use the numbers 20, 15 and 300. Say or write four different multiplication or division statements relating the numbers.

As outcomes, Year 6 pupils should, for example:

Work out the 17 times-table by adding 7 times-table facts to 10 times-table facts.

To multiply a number by 49 or 51, multiply it by 50 and add or subtract the number. For example:

$$13 \times 51 = (13 \times 50) + 13 = 650 + 13 = 663$$
$$13 \times 49 = (13 \times 50) - 13 = 650 - 13 = 637$$

To multiply a number by 99 or 101, multiply it by 100 and add or subtract the number. For example:

$$13 \times 101 = (13 \times 100) + 13 = 1300 + 13 = 1313$$
$$13 \times 99 = (13 \times 100) - 13 = 1300 - 13 = 1287$$

Continue to multiply a two-digit number by a single-digit number, multiplying the tens first. For example:

$$86 \times 7 = (80 \times 7) + (6 \times 7) = 560 + 42 = 602$$

Multiply a whole number and tenths by a single-digit number, multiplying the units first. For example:

$$8.6 \times 7 = (8 \times 7) + (0.6 \times 7) = 56 + 4.2 = 60.2$$

Continue to recognise that knowing one of:

$0.75 \times 4 = 3$ $\quad 4 \times 0.75 = 3$
$3 \div 4 = 0.75$ $\quad 3 \div 0.75 = 4$

means that you also know the other three.

Recognise, for example, that:

- if $5 \times 60 = 300$, then $\frac{1}{5}$ of 300 = 60 and $\frac{1}{6}$ of 300 = 50;
- if $\frac{3}{4}$ of 4 = 3, then $4 \times \frac{3}{4} = 3$.

Answer oral or written questions like:

- Given that $1.4 \times 1.1 = 1.54$, what is 1.1×1.4, or $1.54 \div 1.1$, or $1.54 \div 1.4$?
- Given that $31.5 \div 15 = 2.1$, what is $31.5 \div 2.1$, or 15×2.1 or 2.1×15?
- Use the numbers 0.2, 0.3 and 0.06. Say or write four different multiplication or division statements relating the numbers.

Pupils should be taught to:	As outcomes, Year 4 pupils should, for example:

Use known number facts and place value to multiply or divide mentally

Multiply a two- or three-digit number by 10 or 100

For example:

327×10 54×100

Work mentally to complete written questions like:

$96 \times 100 = \square$ $82 \times \square = 8200$

Divide a four-digit multiple of 1000 by 10 or 100

For example:

$8000 \div 100$ $3000 \div 10$

Respond to oral questions like:

- Find one tenth of 6000…
- Find one hundredth of 4000…

Work mentally to complete written questions like:

$\square \div 100 = 60$ $9000 \div 100 = \square$ $6000 \div \square = 60$

Double any multiple of 5 up to 100

Respond to oral questions such as double 30 or double 45, and explain method.

Work mentally to complete written questions like:

$55 \times 2 = \square$ $\square \times 2 = 150$

then explain method in writing.

Halve any multiple of 10 to 200

Respond to oral questions such as half of 70, halve 150, and explain method.

Work mentally to complete written questions like:

$150 \div 2 = \square$ $\square \div 2 = 65$ $\frac{1}{2}$ of $80 = \square$

then explain method in writing.

Consolidate multiplying a two-digit multiple of 10 by 2, 3, 4, 5 or 10 and begin to multiply by 6, 7, 8 or 9

Respond to oral questions like:

20×3 40×5 90×10 70×6

and explain method.

Work mentally to complete written questions like:

$70 \times 2 = \square$ $20 \times \square = 100$ $\square \times 10 = 500$

$500 = 10 \times \square$ $121 = 60 \times \square + 1$

then explain method in writing.

Multiply a two-digit number by 2, 3, 4 or 5, crossing the tens boundary

Work mentally to complete written questions like:

$13 \times 5 = \square$ $18 \times \square = 54$

$70 = 10 \times \square$ $22 = 5 \times \square + 2$

then explain method in writing.

Use and apply these skills in a variety of contexts, in mathematics and other subjects.

As outcomes, Year 5 pupils should, for example:

Multiply a two-digit multiple of 10 by a three-digit multiple of 100

For example:

30×400 40×700

Work mentally to complete written questions like:

$50 \times 900 = \square$ $60 \times \square = 42\,000$

Divide a four-digit multiple of 100 by 1000, 100 or 10

For example:

$8200 \div 100$ $3600 \div 10$

Respond to oral questions like:

- Find one thousandth of 4000…
- Find one hundredth of 9000… of 5400…
- Find one tenth of 5000… of 6400…

Work mentally to complete written questions like:

$\square \div 1000 = 6$ $3900 \div 10 = \square$ $6200 \div \square = 62$

Double any multiple of 5 up to 500

Respond to oral questions such as double 420 or double 345, and explain method.

Work mentally to complete written questions like:

$135 \times 2 = \square$ $\square \times 2 = 630$

then explain method in writing.

Halve any three-digit multiple of 10

Respond to oral questions such as half of 700, half of 650, and explain method.

Work mentally to complete written questions like:

$150 \div 2 = \square$ $\square \div 2 = 185$

$150 \times \frac{1}{2} = \square$ $\square \times \frac{1}{2} = 75$

then explain method in writing.

Multiply a two-digit multiple of 10 or a three-digit multiple of 100 by a single-digit number

Respond to oral questions like:

400×9 60×8

and explain method.

Work mentally to complete written questions like:

$700 \times 5 = \square$ $20 \times \square = 180$

$2000 = 900 \times \square + 200$

then explain method in writing.

Multiply a two-digit whole number by any single-digit number, crossing the tens boundary

Respond to oral questions like:

24×3 17×4

and explain method.

Work mentally to complete written questions like:

$49 \times 6 = \square$ $28 \times \square = 140$

then explain method in writing.

Use and apply these skills in a variety of contexts, in mathematics and other subjects.

As outcomes, Year 6 pupils should, for example:

Multiply a decimal fraction with one or two decimal places by 10 or 100

For example:

3.27×10 5.4×100

Work mentally to complete written questions like:

$9.6 \times 100 = \square$ $0.82 \times \square = 82$

Divide a one- or two-digit whole number by 100 or 10

For example:

$84 \div 100$ $3 \div 10$ $7 \div 100$

Respond to oral questions like:

- Find one hundredth of 91… of 5…
- Find one tenth of 52… of 6…

Work mentally to complete written questions like:

$\square \div 100 = 0.6$ $39 \div 10 = \square$ $62 \div \square = 0.62$

Double a decimal fraction less than 1 with one or two decimal places

Respond to oral questions such as double 0.75 or double 0.9, and explain method.

Work mentally to complete written questions like:

$0.65 \times 2 = \square$ $\square \times 2 = 1.6$

then explain method in writing.

Halve a decimal fraction less than 1 with one or two decimal places

Respond to oral questions such as half of 0.7, half of 0.62, half of one quarter, and explain method.

Work mentally to complete written questions like:

$0.15 \div 2 = \square$ $\square \div 2 = 0.85$

$0.15 \times 0.5 = \square$

then explain method in writing.

Multiply a decimal fraction such as 0.6 by a single-digit number

Respond to oral questions like:

0.4×9 0.7×8

and explain method.

Work mentally to complete written questions like:

$0.7 \times 5 = \square$ $0.2 \times \square = 1.8$ $\square \times 9 = 5.4$

then explain method in writing.

Multiply a two-digit whole number or decimal fraction by any single-digit number

Respond to oral questions like:

83×7 39×6

and explain method.

Work mentally to complete written questions like:

$3.7 \times 5 = \square$ $4.2 \times \square = 16.8$ $\square \times 9 = 14.4$

then explain method in writing.

Use and apply these skills in a variety of contexts, in mathematics and other subjects.

Pupils should be taught to:

Develop and refine written methods for multiplication

As outcomes, Year 4 pupils should, for example:

Informal written methods

Use pencil and paper methods to support, record or explain calculations, achieving consistent accuracy.
Discuss, explain and compare methods.

Approximate first. Explain orally how method works.

A: grid method (TU × U)

For example, 23 × 8 is approximately 20 × 10 = 200.

×	20	3	
8	160	24	= 184

Standard written methods

Develop an efficient standard method that can be applied generally, approximating first. Where calculations are set out in columns, know that units should line up under units, tens under tens...

B: partitioning

Short multiplication: TU × U
For example, 23 × 7 is approximately 20 × 10 = 200.

```
                23                      23
              × _7     leading to     × _7
20 × 7         140                     161
 3 × 7         _21                      2
               161
```

As outcomes, Year 5 pupils should, for example:

Informal written methods
Use pencil and paper methods to support, record or explain calculations, achieving consistent accuracy. Discuss, explain and compare methods.

Approximate first. Explain orally how method works.

A: grid method (HTU × U and TU × TU)

346 × 9 is approximately 350 × 10 = 3500.

346 × 9

×	300	40	6	
9	2700	360	54	= 3114

72 × 38 is approximately 70 × 40 = 2800.

72 × 38

×	70	2	
30	2100	60	2160
8	560	16	+ 576
			2732

Standard written methods
Continue to develop an efficient standard method that can be applied generally, approximating first. Where calculations are set out in columns, know that units should line up under units, tens under tens…

B: partitioning

Short multiplication: HTU × U
346 × 9 is approximately 350 × 10 = 3500.

```
              346                    346
          ×     9               ×      9
300 × 9      2700   leading to      3114
 40 × 9       360                     45
  6 × 9        54
             3114
```

Long multiplication: TU × TU
72 × 38 is approximately 70 × 40 = 2800.

```
              72
            × 38
72 × 30     2160
72 ×  8      576
            2736
              1
```

Extend to simple decimals with one decimal place
Multiply by a single digit, approximating first. Know that decimal points should line up under each other.

4.9 × 3 is approximately 5 × 3 = 15.

```
4.9 × 3     4.0 × 3 = 12.0
            0.9 × 3 =  2.7
                      14.7
```

As outcomes, Year 6 pupils should, for example:

Informal written methods
Use pencil and paper methods to support, record or explain calculations, achieving consistent accuracy. Discuss, explain and compare methods.

Approximate first. Explain orally how method works.

A: grid method (ThHTU × U and HTU × TU)

4346 × 8 is approximately 4500 × 10 = 45 000.

4346 × 8

×	4000	300	40	6	
8	32000	2400	320	48	= 34768

372 × 24 is approximately 400 × 20 = 8000.

372 × 24

×	300	70	2	
20	6000	1400	40	7440
4	1200	280	8	+ 1488
				8928

Standard written methods
Continue to develop an efficient standard method that can be applied generally, approximating first. Where calculations are set out in columns, know that units should line up under units, tens under tens…

B: partitioning

Short multiplication: ThHTU × U
4346 × 8 is approximately 4500 × 10 = 45 000.

```
               4346                    4346
           ×      8               ×       8
4000 × 8      32000   leading to      34768
 300 × 8       2400                     234
  40 × 8        320
   6 × 8         48
              34768
```

Long multiplication: HTU × TU
352 × 27 is approximately 350 × 30 = 10 500.

```
              352
            ×  27
352 × 20     7040
352 ×  7     2464
             9504
             1
```

Extend to decimals with up to two decimal places
Multiply by a single digit, approximating first. Know that decimal points should line up under each other.

4.92 × 3 is about 5 × 3 = 15.

```
4.92 × 3     4.00 × 3 = 12.00
             0.90 × 3 =  2.70
             0.02 × 3 =  0.06
                        14.76
```

Begin to extend to multiplying by two-digit numbers: for example, 4.92 × 73 is about 5 × 70 = 350.

Pupils should be taught to:	As outcomes, Year 4 pupils should, for example:

Develop and refine written methods for division

Informal written methods
Use pencil and paper methods to support, record or explain calculations, achieving consistent accuracy.
Discuss, explain and compare methods.

Approximate first. Explain orally how method works.

A: using multiples of the divisor

TU ÷ U

For example, 72 ÷ 5 lies between 50 ÷ 5 = 10 and 100 ÷ 5 = 20.

```
72 ÷ 5          = (50 + 22) ÷ 5
                =  10 + 4 remainder 2
                or 14 remainder 2
or:
72 ÷ 5             72
                -  50        10 × 5
                   22
                -  20         4 × 5
                    2

            Answer:      14 remainder 2
```

Standard written methods
Develop an efficient standard method that can be applied generally, approximating first. Where calculations are set out in columns, know that units should line up under units, tens under tens, and so on...

B: short division TU ÷ U

For example, 96 ÷ 6 is approximately 100 ÷ 5 = 20.

```
96 ÷ 6
                   ____
                6) 96
                  -60        10 × 6
                   36
                  -36         6 × 6
                    0

            Answer:      16
```

See also understanding remainders (page 56).

As outcomes, Year 5 pupils should, for example:

Informal written methods
Use pencil and paper methods to support, record or explain calculations, achieving consistent accuracy.
Discuss, explain and compare methods.

Approximate first. Explain orally how method works.

A: using multiples of the divisor

HTU ÷ U

256 ÷ 7 lies between 210 ÷ 7 = 30 and 280 ÷ 7 = 40.

```
256 ÷ 7      256
           -  70      10 × 7
             186
           - 140      20 × 7
              46
           -  42       6 × 7
               4
       Answer:        36 remainder 4
```

Standard written methods
Continue to develop an efficient standard method that can be applied generally, approximating first.
Where calculations are set out in columns, know that units should line up under units, tens under tens…

B: short division HTU ÷ U

196 ÷ 6 is approximately 200 ÷ 5 = 40.

```
                              32 R 4
 6) 196                     6)196
   - 180   30 × 6             18
      16                      16
    - 12    2 × 6             12
       4                       4

Answer:  32 R 4
```

See also understanding remainders (page 57).

As outcomes, Year 6 pupils should, for example:

Informal written methods
Use pencil and paper methods to support, record or explain calculations, achieving consistent accuracy.
Discuss, explain and compare methods.

Approximate first. Explain orally how method works.

A: using multiples of the divisor

HTU ÷ TU

977 ÷ 36 is approximately 1000 ÷ 40 = 25.

```
977 ÷ 36      977
            - 360      10 × 36
              617
            - 360      10 × 36
              257
            - 180       5 × 36
               77
               72       2 × 36
                5
        Answer:        27 5/36
```

Standard written methods
Continue to develop an efficient standard method that can be applied generally, approximating first.
Where calculations are set out in columns, know that units should line up under units, tens under tens…

B: long division HTU ÷ TU

972 ÷ 36 is approximately 1000 ÷ 40 = 25.

```
                                      27
36) 972                          36) 972
   - 720    20 × 36                 - 72
     252                             252
   - 252     7 × 36                - 252
       0                               0
Answer:     27
```

Extend to decimals with up to two decimal places
Approximate first. Know that decimal points should line up under each other.

87.5 ÷ 7 is approximately 80 ÷ 8 = 10.

```
7) 87.5
 - 70.0     10 × 7
   17.5
   14.0      2 × 7
    3.5
    3.5      0.5 × 7
    0.0
Answer:    12.5
```

See also understanding remainders (page 57).

Pupils should be taught to:	As outcomes, Year 4 pupils should, for example:
Develop calculator skills and use a calculator effectively	

As outcomes, Year 5 pupils should, for example:

Use, read and write, spelling correctly:
calculator, display, key, enter, clear, constant...

Know how to:

- clear the display before starting a calculation;
- use the [+], [–], [×] and [÷] keys, the [=] key and decimal point to calculate with realistic data;
- change an accidental wrong entry by using the [clear entry] key;
- recognise a negative number output;
- key in and interpret money calculations: for example, key in £4.35 + £3.85 as 4.35 [+] 3.85 [=], and interpret the outcome of 8.2 as £8.20; key in £6.30 + 85p as 6.3 [+] 0.85 [=], recognising that '0.' signals no pounds and only pence (alternatively, change money to pence and divide final answer by 100 to convert back to pounds);
- begin to select the correct key sequence to carry out calculations involving more than one step: for example, 8 × (37 + 58);
- know, for example, that a number such as 81.75 lies between 81 and 82;
- interpret a rounding error such as 6.9999999 as 7;
- have a feel for the approximate size of an answer, and check it by performing the inverse calculation or by clearing and repeating the calculation.

Use a calculator to respond to questions such as:

- The perimeter of a square is 274 cm. What is the length of each side?
- Julie is 92 cm tall. Tom is 184 cm tall. Lisa's height is half way between Julie's height and Tom's height. Calculate Lisa's height.
- Write the missing number: 3.42 + □ = 12.1.
- Emma saves £3.50 each week. How much has she saved after 16 weeks?
- Rupert saves the same amount of money each month. He saved £149.40 in a year. How much money does he save each month?
- There are 75 grams of rice in one portion. How many portions are there in a 3 kg bag of rice?
- Find three consecutive numbers which add up to 171.

As outcomes, Year 6 pupils should, for example:

Use, read and write, spelling correctly:
calculator, display, key, enter, clear, constant...
recurring

Know how to:

- use the [clear] and [clear entry] keys, all operation keys, the [=] key and decimal point, to calculate with realistic data;
- recognise a negative number output and use the [sign change] key where appropriate;
- key in and interpret the outcome of calculations involving sums of money;
- key in fractions, recognise the equivalent decimal form, and use this to compare and order fractions;
- read the display of, say, 0.3333333 as 'point three recurring', know that it represents one third, and that 0.6666666 represents two thirds;
- start to use the memory and select the correct key sequence to carry out calculations involving more than one operation including brackets: for example, (23 + 41) × (87 + 48);
- have a feel for the approximate size of an answer after a calculation, and check it appropriately.

Use a calculator to respond to questions such as:

- The area of a square is 256 cm^2. What is the length of each side?
- Every day a machine makes 100 000 paper clips which go into boxes. A full box has 120 paper clips. How many full boxes can be made from 100 000 paper clips?

  Each paper clip is made from 9.2 cm of wire. What is the greatest number of paper clips that can be made from 10 metres of wire?
- 2753 people go to a sports event. Each person pays £2.30 for a ticket. What is the total amount of ticket money collected?
- Programmes cost 65p each. The total money from programme sales is £612.95. How many programmes are sold?
- Calculate 24% of 525.
- Write the missing number: 568.1 ÷ □ = 24.7.
- Find two consecutive numbers with a product of 1332.

Pupils should be taught to:	As outcomes, Year 4 pupils should, for example:
Check by doing the inverse operation	For example, check: • 625 – 87 = 538 with 538 + 87 = 625; • 160 ÷ 4 = 40 with 40 × 4 = 160. • half of 36 = 18 with double 18.
Check the sum of several numbers by adding them in reverse order	Check the total of several numbers by adding them in reverse order.
Do an equivalent calculation	For example, check: • 140 + 136 with 140 + 130 + 6, or double 140 minus 4; • 35 × 4 with 30 × 4 plus 5 × 4, or four 40s minus four 5s, or 35 + 35 + 35 + 35.
Approximate by rounding	Use rounding to approximate. For example: • 297 + 406 is about 300 + 400 (rounding to the nearest hundred).
Use knowledge of sums or products of odd or even numbers	Recognise that the sum of: • two or more even numbers is even: for example, 78 + 26 is even; • two odd numbers is even: for example, 73 + 57 is even; • three odd numbers is odd: for example, 23 + 13 + 59 is odd; • one odd and one even number is odd: for example, 47 + 36 is odd. Recognise that the difference between: • two even numbers is even: for example, 78 – 26 is even; • two odd numbers is even: for example, 73 – 57 is even; • one odd and one even number is odd: for example, 68 – 49 is odd.
Use tests of divisibility	

As outcomes, Year 5 pupils should, for example:

For example, use a calculator to check:

- 3685 – 987 = 2698 with 2698 + 987 = 3685;
- 1650 ÷ 50 = 33 with 33 × 50 = 1650;
- half of 920 = 460 with double 460;
- ⅕ of 300 = 60 with 60 × 5 = 300.

Check the total of several numbers by adding them in reverse order.

For example, check:

- 2400 + 1365 with 3000 + 765, or 1765 + 2000;
- 86 × 9 with (80 × 9) + (6 × 9), or (86 × 10) – 86.

Use rounding to approximate. For example:

- 523 + 228 is more than 500 + 200;
- 605 – 197 is about 600 – 200;
- 24 × 19 is approximately 25 × 20;
- 520 ÷ 11 is about 500 ÷ 10.

Recognise that the sum of:

- two or more even numbers is even: for example, 132 + 512 is even;
- two odd numbers is even: for example, 423 + 617 is even;
- three odd numbers is odd: for example, 523 + 13 + 259 is odd;
- one odd and one even number is odd: for example, 917 + 226 is odd.

Recognise that the difference between:

- two even numbers is even: for example, 178 – 426 is even;
- two odd numbers is even: for example, 673 – 257 is even;
- one odd and one even number is odd: for example, 568 – 349 is odd.

As outcomes, Year 6 pupils should, for example:

For example, use a calculator to check:

- 6.5 – 9.8 = –3.3 with –3.3 + 9.8 = 6.5;
- 4.8 ÷ 5 = 0.96 with 0.96 × 5 = 4.8;
- half of 8.1 = 4.05 with double 4.05;
- ⅛ of 320 = 40 with 40 × 8 = 320.

Check the total of several numbers by adding them in reverse order.

For example, check:

- 24.5 – 3.35 with 21 + 0.5 – 0.35, or 24.5 – 3.5 + 0.15;
- 486 × 8 with (486 × 10) – 972, or (500 × 8) – (14 × 8).

Use rounding to approximate. For example:

- 2593 + 6278 is more than 2500 + 6200;
- 2605 – 1997 is about 2600 – 2000;
- 245 × 19 is approximately 250 × 20;
- 786 ÷ 38 is about 800 ÷ 40.

Recognise that the sum of:

- two or more even numbers is even: for example, 4132 + 512 is even;
- an even number of odd numbers is even: for example, 8423 + 5617 is even;
- an odd number of odd numbers is odd: for example, 1523 + 9013 + 2259 is odd.

Recognise that the difference between:

- two even numbers is even: for example, 7982 – 268 is even;
- two odd numbers is even: for example, 4735 – 1579 is even;
- one odd and one even number is odd: for example, 3687 – 49 is odd.

Recognise that the product of:

- two or more even numbers is even: for example, 74 × 36 is even;
- two odd numbers is odd: for example, 93 × 27 is odd;
- one odd and one even number is even: for example, 59 × 42 is even.

Use knowledge that in exact multiples of:

100	the last two digits are 00;
25	the last two digits are 00, 25, 50 or 75;
10	the last digit is 0;
2	the last digit is 0, 2, 4, 6 or 8;
3	the sum of the digits is divisible by 3;
4	the last two digits are divisible by 4;
5	the last digit is 0 or 5;
6	the number is even **and** divisible by 3;
8	the last 3 digits are divisible by 8;
9	the sum of the digits is divisible by 9.

Pupils should be taught to:

Choose and use appropriate number operations and appropriate ways of calculating (mental, mental with jottings, written methods, calculator) to solve problems

As outcomes, Year 4 pupils should, for example:

Use, read and write:
operation, sign, symbol, number sentence, equation...

Make and justify decisions:

- choose the appropriate operation(s) to solve word problems and number puzzles;
- decide whether calculations can be done mentally or with pencil and paper;
- explain and record how the problem was solved.

For examples of problems see sections on: puzzles (page 78), 'real life' (page 82), money (page 84), measures (page 86) and time (pages 88 and 100).

Make up 'number stories' to reflect statements like:

$435 + 245 = 680$ $\quad 90 \times 4 = 360$

$72 - 25 = 47$ $\quad 93 \div 3 = 31$

For example:

Four portions of fries at 90p each cost 360p or £3.60 altogether.

Recognise the operation represented by the ∗ in examples such as:

$19 * 21 = 40$ $\quad 72 * 29 = 43$

$80 * 6 = 480$ $\quad 28 * 2 = 14$

Look at a set of subtractions of different pairs of numbers. Discuss which is easiest/hardest to do and justify why.

As outcomes, Year 5 pupils should, for example:

Use, read and write, spelling correctly:
operation, sign, symbol, number sentence, equation...

Make and justify decisions:

- choose the appropriate operation(s) to solve word problems and number puzzles;
- decide whether calculations can be done mentally or with pencil and paper or a calculator;
- explain and record how the problem was solved.

For examples of problems see sections on: puzzles (page 79), 'real life' (page 83), money (page 85), measures (page 87) and time (pages 89 and 101).

Make up 'number stories' to reflect statements like:

1435 + 3245 = 4680   38.7 × 24 = 928.8
572 − 25 = 547   564 ÷ 8 = 70.5

For example:
If 8 equal pieces are cut from 564 mm of string, each piece is 70.5 mm long.

Recognise the operation represented by the ⁎ in examples such as:

319 ⁎ 274 = 593   572 ⁎ 291 = 281
18 ⁎ 6 = 108   228 ⁎ 38 = 6

Look at multiplications of different pairs of numbers. Discuss which is easiest/hardest to do and justify why.

As outcomes, Year 6 pupils should, for example:

Use, read and write, spelling correctly:
operation, sign, symbol, number sentence, equation...

Make decisions:

- choose the appropriate operation(s) to solve word problems and number puzzles;
- decide whether calculations can be done mentally or with pencil and paper or a calculator;
- explain and record how the problem was solved.

For examples of problems see sections on: puzzles (page 79), 'real life' (page 83), money (page 85), measures (page 87) and time (pages 89 and 101).

Make up 'number stories' to reflect statements like:

143.5 + 32.45 = 175.95   6.83 × 27 = 184.41
57.2 − 2.56 = 54.64   448.91 ÷ 53 = 8.47

For example:
27 compact discs at £6.83 each will cost £184.41.

Recognise the operation represented by the ⁎ in examples such as:

377 ⁎ 58 = 435   377 ⁎ 58 = 319
377 ⁎ 58 = 6.5   377 ⁎ 58 = 21 866

Look at divisions of different pairs of numbers. Discuss which is easiest/hardest to do and justify why.

Pupils should be taught to:

Explain methods and reasoning about numbers orally and in writing

As outcomes, Year 4 pupils should, for example:

Explain calculations that have wholly or partly been done mentally, beginning to use conventional notation and vocabulary to record the explanation.

For example:

23 +17	Add 17 and 3 to get 20, then 20 more to get 40.
32 – 15	16 + 16 = 32, so 15 + 17 is the same, so 32 – 15 is 17.
24 × 2	24 × 2 is 24 + 24 = 20 + 20 + 4 + 4 = 40 + 8 = 48.
49 + 57	9 + 7 = 16 and 40 + 50 = 90, so 90 + 16 is 90, 100, 106.
65 – 28	65 – 30 is 35, but this takes away 2 too many, so add back 2 to make 37.
102 + 295	There are three hundreds and 90 and 7, that's 397.
500 – 180	Take away 200, that's 300, add 20 is 320.
87 ÷ 2	Half of 80 is 40, and half of 7 is 3.5, so it's 43.5.

Extend to calculations that cannot entirely be done mentally. For example:

447 + 165	447 + 100 = 547
	547 + 60 = 607
	607 + 5 = 612

See also pencil and paper procedures for: addition (page 48), subtraction (page 50), multiplication (page 66) and division (page 68).

As outcomes, Year 5 pupils should, for example:

Explain calculations that have wholly or partly been done mentally, and develop the use of conventional notation and vocabulary to record the explanation.

For example:

7003 – 6994	6994 + 6 = 7000, add 3 more is 7003. Answer: 9.
15 × 12	This is 15 × 4 × 3 = 60 × 3 = 180.
400 × 80	This is the same as 4000 × 8 = 32 000.
49 × 30	50 × 30 = 1500, subtract 30 is 1470.
109 ÷ 21	21 × 5 = 105, plus 4 more is 109. Answer: $5\frac{4}{21}$
$\frac{1}{8}$ of 424	$\frac{1}{2}$ of 424 = 212, and $\frac{1}{2}$ of 212 = 106, and $\frac{1}{2}$ of 106 = 53, so $\frac{1}{8}$ of 424 = 53.

Extend to calculations that cannot entirely be done mentally. For example:

447	round up to	450	– 3
+ 165	round down to	150	+ 15
		600	+ 12 = 612

4785 + 3296
7000 + 900 + 170 + 11 =
8000 + 81 =
8081

49 × 30
(40 × 30) + (9 × 30) =
1200 + 270 =
1470

Compare ways of recording and understand that different ways of recording are equivalent: for example, that 176 ÷ 28 is equivalent to 176/28 and to $28\overline{)176}$.

Work towards more efficient methods of recording to support and/or explain calculations that are too difficult to do mentally.

See also pencil and paper procedures for: addition (page 49), subtraction (page 51), multiplication (page 67) and division (page 69).

As outcomes, Year 6 pupils should, for example:

Explain calculations that have wholly or partly been done mentally, using conventional notation and vocabulary to record the explanation.

For example:

42 × 15
42 × 10 = 420
42 × 5 = 210
42 × 15 = 630

387 ÷ 9
387 ÷ 3 = 129
129 ÷ 3 = 43

17.5% of £30 000
10% = £3000
5% = £1500
2.5% = £ 750
17.5% = £5250

$\frac{1}{20}$ of 400
$\frac{1}{10}$ of 400 = 40, and $\frac{1}{2}$ of 40 = 20, so $\frac{1}{20}$ of 400 = 20.

Extend to calculations that cannot entirely be done mentally. For example:

42 × 35
(42 × 30) + (42 × 5)
1260 + (42 × 5) =
1260 + 200 + 10 =
1470

612 ÷ 27
612
540   20 × 27
72
54   2 × 27
18
Answer: $22\frac{18}{27} = 22\frac{2}{3}$ or 22.67

17.5% of £40 000
$\frac{17.5}{100} \times 40\,000 =$
17.5 × 400 =
1750 × 4 =
4000 + 2800 + 200 = 7000
Answer: £7000

Develop efficient methods of recording calculations, including generally applicable or standard written methods for:

- addition and subtraction of whole numbers (three or more digits, including decimals with up to two decimal places);
- long multiplication and division (three digits by two digits).

See also pencil and paper procedures for: addition (page 49), subtraction (page 51), multiplication (page 67) and division (page 69).

Pupils should be taught to:

Solve mathematical problems or puzzles, recognise and explain patterns and relationships, generalise and predict. Suggest extensions by asking 'What if...?'

As outcomes, Year 4 pupils should, for example:

Solve puzzles and problems such as:

- Find three consecutive numbers which add up to 39. What other numbers up to 50 can you make by adding three consecutive numbers?
- Find a pair of numbers with:
  a sum of 11 and a product of 24;
  a sum of 40 and a product of 400;
  a sum of 15 and a product of 54.
- 72 cubes can be arranged to make a $2 \times 3 \times 12$ cuboid. What other cuboids can you make with 72 cubes?
- You can make 6 by using each of the digits 1, 2, 3 and 4 once, and any operation: for example,
  $6 = (21 + 3) \div 4$ or $6 = (3 \times 4) \div (1 \times 2)$
  Use each of the digits 1, 2, 3 and 4 and any operation to make each number from 1 to 40. Can you go further?
- Arrange the numbers 1, 2, 3... to 9 in the circles so that each side of the square adds up to 12.

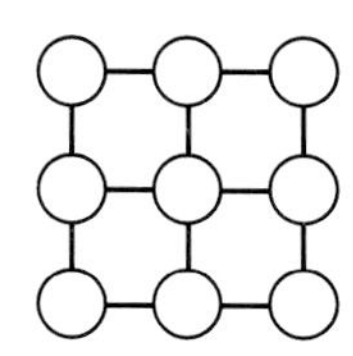

- Draw three rings.
  Use each of the numbers from 1 to 9.
  Write them in the rings so that each ring has a total of 15.
  Find different ways to do it.
- Use a computer program to solve number puzzles: for example, to fill a given number of carriages on a train with given numbers of people.
- Each ◆ represents a missing digit.

  a. Choose three digits from this set: 1, 3, 4, 8.
     Replace each ◆ to make this statement true:
     ◆◆ – ◆ = 38

  b. Find the missing digits.
     4◆ + ◆8 = 74   3◆ – ◆9 = 9   3◆ + ◆7 = 120

  c. Find different ways of completing:
     ◆◆ × ◆ = 252

- Count all the triangles in this diagram (11).

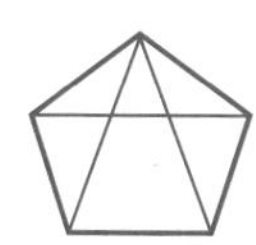

- Start with a rectangular sheet of paper.
  By folding, making one straight cut, and then unfolding, make this hexagon.

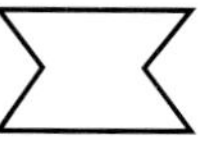

As outcomes, Year 5 pupils should, for example:

Solve puzzles and problems such as:

- Find:
  two consecutive numbers with a product of 182;
  three consecutive numbers with a total of 333.

- Choose any four numbers from the grid.
  Add them up.
  Find as many ways as possible of making 1000.

275	382	81	174
206	117	414	262
483	173	239	138
331	230	325	170

- Use a 'binary tree' computer program to sort a set of numbers according to their properties.

- Write a number in each circle so that the number in each square box equals the sum of the two numbers on either side of it.

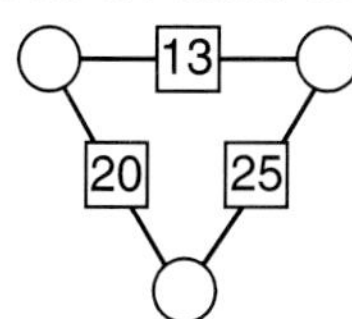

- With 12 squares you can make 3 different rectangles.

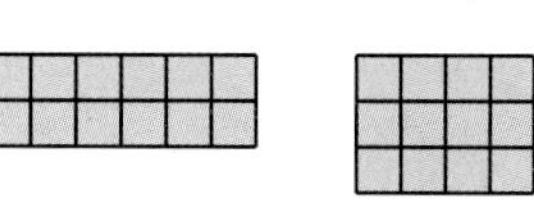

  Find how many squares can be rearranged to make exactly 5 different rectangles.

- A two-digit number is an odd multiple of 9. When its digits are multiplied, the result is also a multiple of 9. What is the number?

- Find ways to complete: 

- Each ◆ represents a missing digit.
  Use your calculator to solve:
  ◆◆ × 6◆ = 6272

- A pentomino is a shape made from five identical squares touching edge to edge.

  Divide this shape into two pentominoes.
  Do it in four different ways.

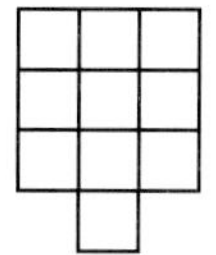

- Count all the rectangles in this diagram (26).

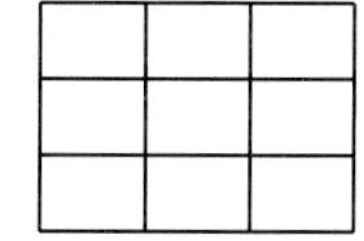

As outcomes, Year 6 pupils should, for example:

Solve puzzles and problems such as:

- Find:
  two consecutive numbers with a product of 1332;
  two numbers with a product of 899.

- Complete this multiplication table.

×		4	9	
		8	18	
3		12		
	35			14
				2

- Each ◆ represents one of the digits 1 to 6.
  Use each of the digits 1 to 6 once.
  Replace each ◆ to make a correct product.

- A number sequence is made from counters.
  There are 7 counters in the third number.

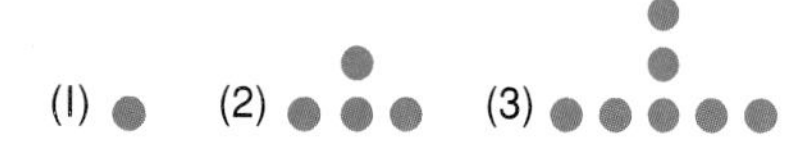

  How many counters in the 6th number? the 20th...?
  Write a formula for the number of counters in the *n*th number in the sequence.

- For how many three-digit numbers does the sum of the digits equal 25?

- Each letter from A to G is a code for one of these digits: 1, 3, 4, 5, 6, 8, 9. Crack the code.

A + A = B	A × A = DF	A + C = DE
C + C = DB	C × C = BD	A × C = EF

- Use a computer program to investigate and generalise a number relationship: for example, the number of times a bouncing ball will touch the sides of a billiard table.

- Use a calculator to solve these.

  a. Each ◆ represents a missing digit. Solve:
  ◆2◆ × ◆◆ = 11 316

  b. One whole number divided by another gives 1.1818181. What are the two numbers?

- This is half a shape.

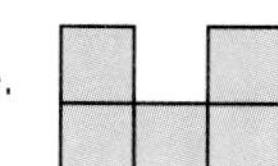

  Sketch some of the different whole shapes the original could have been. Mark any lines of symmetry of these shapes.

- Using straight cuts, divide a square into 6 smaller squares.

Pupils should be taught to:	As outcomes, Year 4 pupils should, for example:

Make and investigate a general statement about familiar numbers or shapes by finding examples that satisfy it

Find examples that match a general statement. For example, explain and start to make general statements like:

- *The sum of three odd numbers is odd.*
  Examples: 3 + 5 + 7 = 15   137 + 31 + 465 = 633
- *If 14 < □ < 17, then any number between 14 and 17 can go in the box.*
  Examples: 16, 14.5, 16.99
- *Half way between any two multiples of 10 is a multiple of 5.*
  Examples: 90 and 120 are both multiples of 10;
  half way between them is 105, which is a multiple of 5.
- *Multiples of 4 end in 0, 2, 4, 6 or 8.*
  Examples: 12, 64, 96, 108, 6760
- *Any odd number is double a number add 1.*
  Example: 63 = 2 × 31 + 1
- *If I multiply a whole number by 10, every digit moves one place to the left.*
  Examples: 63 × 10 = 630   5 × 10 = 50   366 × 10 = 3660
- *The perimeter of a rectangle is twice the length plus twice the breadth.*
  Example: The perimeter of a 5 cm × 3 cm rectangle is:
  5 cm + 3 cm + 5 cm + 3 cm = 16 cm.
  This is the same as 5 cm × 2 add 3 cm × 2.
- *The number of lines of reflective symmetry in a regular polygon is equal to the number of sides of the polygon.*
  Example: a regular hexagon has 6 sides and 6 lines of symmetry.

Start to express a relationship orally in words.
For example:

- Explain how to find the number of days in any number of weeks.
- Explain how to find the change from £1 after buying two first class stamps.
- Describe a short way to work out the perimeter of a rectangle.
- The rule is add 4. Start with 0. Explain how to find the first five numbers in the sequence. What would the 10th number be?
- A sequence starts 1, 4, 7, 10, 13...
  Explain in words the rule for the sequence.

As outcomes, Year 5 pupils should, for example:

Find examples that match a general statement. For example, explain and make general statements like:

- *A multiple of 6 is both a multiple of 2 and a multiple of 3.*
  Example: $48 = 6 \times 8$ or 3×16 or 2×24
- *A multiple of 6 is always twice a multiple of 3.*
  Examples: $24 = 2 \times 12$, and 12 is a multiple of 3; $60 = 2 \times 30$, and 30 is a multiple of 3.
- *A number is not a multiple of 9 if its digits do not add up to a multiple of 9.*
  Example: 58 is not a multiple of 9, since $5 + 8 = 13$, and $1 + 3 = 4$, which is not a multiple of 9.
- *The product of two consecutive numbers is even.*
  Example: $15 \times 16 = 240$, which is even.
- *If you divide two different numbers the other way round, the answer is not the same.*
  Example: $15 \div 3 = 5$ $\quad 3 \div 15 = 0.2$
- *The perimeter of a regular polygon is length of side × number of sides.*
  Example: The perimeter of a 9 cm × 9 cm square is 9 cm × 4 = 36 cm.
- *Angles on a straight line add up to 180°.*
  Example:
  $58° + 122° = 180°$

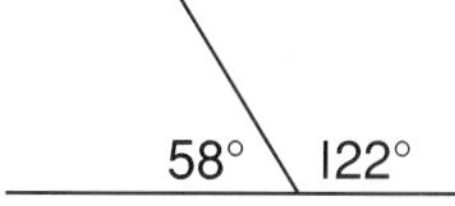

Express a relationship in words, orally and in writing. For example:

- Explain how to find the number of months in any number of years.
- Explain how to find the change from 50p for a number of chews at 4p each.
- Describe a way to calculate the area of a rectangle.
- The rule is double the previous number, add 1. Start with 1. Write the next six numbers in the sequence.
- A sequence starts 1, 4, 9, 16, 25...
  Explain in words the rule for the sequence.

As outcomes, Year 6 pupils should, for example:

Find examples that match a general statement. For example, explain and make general statements like:

- *If 0.24 < □ < 0.27, then any number between 0.24 and 0.27 can go in the box.*
  Examples: 0.25, 0.26, 0.251, 0.267
- *If you add three consecutive numbers, the sum is three times the middle number.*
  Example: $4 + 5 + 6 = 15 = 3 \times 5$
- *To multiply by 25, multiply by 100 and divide by 4.*
  Example: $12 \times 25 = 12 \times 100 \div 4 = 1200 \div 4 = 300$
- *Any square number is the sum of two consecutive triangular numbers.*
  Examples: $4 = 1 + 3$ $\quad 25 = 10 + 15$ $\quad 64 = 28 + 36$
- *Dividing a whole number by one half makes the answer twice as big.*
  Example: $34 \div 0.5 = 68 = 2 \times 34$
- *If I multiply a decimal number by 10, every digit moves one place to the left.*
  Examples: $6.3 \times 10 = 63$ $\quad 0.25 \times 10 = 2.5$
- *A trapezium is a quadrilateral with one pair of parallel sides.*
- *The sum of the angles of a triangle is 180°.*
  Example:
  $67° + 42° + 71° = 180°$

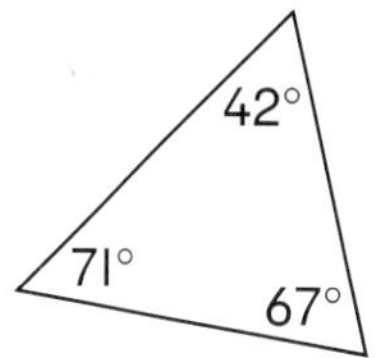

Express a relationship in symbols, and start to use simple formulae. For example:

- Use symbols to write a formula for the number of months m in y years.
- Write a formula for the cost of c chews at 4p each.
- Write a formula for the nth term of this sequence:
  3, 6, 9, 12, 15...
- The perimeter of a rectangle is $2 \times (l + b)$, where l is the length and b is the breadth of the rectangle. What is the perimeter if $l = 8$ cm and $b = 5$ cm?
- The number of bean sticks needed for a row which is m metres long is $2m + 1$. How many bean sticks do you need for a row which is 60 metres long?
- Plot the points which show pairs of numbers with a sum of 9.

Pupils should be taught to:

Use all four operations to solve word problems involving numbers in 'real life'

As outcomes, Year 4 pupils should, for example:

Solve 'story' problems about numbers in real life, choosing the appropriate operation and method of calculation.

Explain and record using numbers, signs and symbols how the problem was solved.

Examples of problems

Single-step operations

- I think of a number, then subtract 18.
  The answer is 26.
  What was my number?

- A beetle has 6 legs.
  How many legs have 9 beetles?
  How many legs have 15 beetles?

- Kate has 38 toy cars.
  John has half as many.
  How many toy cars has John?

- A box holds 70 biscuits.
  How many biscuits are left if you eat 17 biscuits?
  How many people can have 5 biscuits each?
  How many biscuits are there in 6 boxes?
  How many boxes are needed to hold 200 biscuits?

- To cook rice, you need 5 cups of water for every cup of rice.
  You cook 3 cups of rice.
  How many cups of water do you need?

Multi-step operations

- There are 129 books on the top shelf.
  There are 87 books on the bottom shelf.
  I remove 60 of the books.
  How many books are left on the shelves?

- There are 4 stacks of plates.
  3 stacks have 15 plates each.
  1 stack has 5 plates.
  How many plates altogether?

- I think of a number, add 2, then multiply by 3.
  The answer is 15.
  What was my number?

- There are 36 children in the class.
  Half of them have flavoured crisps.
  One third of them have plain crisps.
  How many children have crisps?

See also problems involving money (page 84), measures (page 86), time (pages 88 and 100), and puzzles (page 78).

As outcomes, Year 5 pupils should, for example:

Solve 'story' problems about numbers in real life, choosing the appropriate operation and method of calculation.

Explain and record using numbers, signs and symbols how the problem was solved.

Examples of problems

Single-step operations

- Three children play Tiddlywinks.
  What was each child's score?
  Yasmin 258 + 103
  Steven 177 + 92
  Micky 304 + 121

- I think of a number, then divide it by 15.
  The answer is 20.
  What was my number?

- There are 12 eggs in a box.
  How many eggs in 9 boxes?
  How many boxes will 192 eggs fill?

- A bus seats 52 people. No standing is allowed.
  17 people got off a full bus. How many were left on?
  How many seats for two people are there?
  How many people can sit on 6 buses?
  How many buses are needed to seat 327 people?

Multi-step operations

- I have read 134 of the 512 pages of my book.
  How many more pages must I read to reach the middle?

- There are 8 shelves of books.
  6 of the shelves hold 25 books each.
  2 of the shelves have 35 books each.
  How many books altogether are on the shelves?

- I think of a number, subtract 17, and divide by 6.
  The answer is 20. What was my number?

- You start to read a book on Thursday.
  On Friday you read 10 more pages than on Thursday.
  You reach page 60.
  How many pages did you read on Thursday?

- Ravi bought a pack of 30 biscuits.
  He ate one fifth of them on Thursday.
  He ate one eighth of the remaining biscuits on Friday.
  How many biscuits did he have left?

See also problems involving money (page 85), measures (page 87), time (pages 89 and 101), and puzzles (page 79).

As outcomes, Year 6 pupils should, for example:

Solve 'story' problems about numbers in real life, choosing the appropriate operation and method of calculation.

Explain and record using numbers, signs and symbols how the problem was solved.

Examples of problems

Single-step operations

- 12 500 people visited the museum this year.
  This is 2568 more than last year.
  How many people visited the museum last year?

- There are 35 rows of chairs.
  There are 28 chairs in each row.
  How many chairs are there altogether?
  How many rows of chairs do 420 people need?

- A school has 486 pupils and 15 classes.
  What is the average class size?

- Gwen has a box of 250 staples to make kites.
  She uses 16 staples to make each kite.
  How many complete kites can she make?

- Use a calculator or a written method.
  A full box has 180 pins.
  How many full boxes can be made from 100 000 pins?

Multi-step operations

- There is space in the multi-storey car park for 17 rows of 30 cars on each of 4 floors.
  How many cars can park?

- 196 children and 15 adults went on a school trip.
  Buses seat 57 people.
  How many buses were needed?

- 960 marbles are put into 16 bags.
  There is the same number of marbles in each bag.
  How many marbles are there in 3 of these bags?

- In a dance there are 3 boys and 2 girls in every line. 42 boys take part in the dance.
  How many girls take part?

- I think of a number, add 3.7 and multiply by 5.
  The answer is 22.5. What was my number?

- Of the 96 children in Y6, three quarters have pets.
  45 children have a dog. 21 children have a cat.
  How many Y6 children have other kinds of pets?

See also problems involving money (page 85), measures (page 87), time (pages 89 and 101), and puzzles (page 79).

Pupils should be taught to:

Use all four operations to solve word problems involving money

As outcomes, Year 4 pupils should, for example:

Use, read and write:
money, coin, pound, £, pence, note, price, cost, cheaper, more expensive, pay, change, total, value, amount...

Solve problems involving money, choosing the appropriate operation. Explain and record how the problem was solved. For example:

Shopping problems

- What is the total cost of a £4.70 book and a £6.10 game?
- It costs 80p for a child to swim.
  How much does it cost for 6 children to swim?
- A jigsaw costs 65p. How many can you buy for £2?
  How much change do you get?
- A CD costs £4.
  Parveen saves 40p a week.
  How many weeks must she save to buy the CD?
- Lauren has three 50p coins and three 20p coins.
  She pays 90p for a Big Dipper ride.
  How much does she have left?
- Dad bought 3 tins of paint at £5.68 each.
  What was his change from £20?
- Peter offered two silver coins to pay for a 14p pencil.
  Investigate how much change he got.
- A chocolate bar costs 19p.
  How many bars can be bought for £5?
- For her party Asmat spent:

£2.88 on apples	£3.38 on bananas	£3.76 on oranges

  Will a £10 note cover the cost? Explain your reasoning.

Converting pounds to pence and vice versa

- How many pence is: £1.57... £10.50... £31.06...?
- Write in pounds: 356p... 970p... 2040p...

Calculating fractions

- Harry spent one quarter of his savings on a book.
  What did the book cost if he saved: £8... £10... £2.40...?
- Gran gave me £8 of my £10 birthday money.
  What fraction of my birthday money did Gran give me?

As outcomes, Year 5 pupils should, for example:

Use, read and write, spelling correctly, the vocabulary of the previous year, and extend to: *discount...*

Solve problems involving money, choosing the appropriate operation. Explain and record how the problem was solved. For example:

Shopping problems

- Find the total of:
  £9.63, £15.27 and £3.72;
  66p, 98p, 48p and £3.72.
- How much does one of each cost?

4 for £1.00	10 for £2.50	6 for £3.24

- What change do you get from £20 for £13.68?
- Kobi saved 15p a week for one year.
  How many pounds did he save?
- Four people paid £72 for football tickets.
  What was the cost of each ticket?
  How much change did they get from £100?
- Petrol costs 64.2p per litre.
  What do you pay to fill a 5 litre can?
- Which amounts up to £1 cannot be paid exactly with fewer than six coins?
- You have four 35p and four 25p stamps.
  Find all the different amounts you could stick on a parcel.
- Take £1 worth of coins: four 1p, three 2p, four 5p, three 10p and two 20p.
  Find all the different ways of using the coins to pay 50p exactly.

Converting foreign currency

- Exchange rates for £1 are:

1.6 US dollars
8.7 French francs
220 Spanish pesetas

  How many dollars, francs, pesetas do you get for £5?

Calculating fractions and percentages

- The deposit on a £230 chair is 50%.
  How much is the deposit?
- There is 25% off prices in a sale.
  How much do you get off £36... £1.80...?

As outcomes, Year 6 pupils should, for example:

Use, read and write, spelling correctly, the vocabulary of the previous year.

Solve problems involving money, choosing the appropriate operation. Explain and record how the problem was solved. For example:

Shopping problems

- What is the total of £110.12, £3.43 and £11.07?
- How much does one of each cost?

10 for £3.90	100 for £16.00	5 for £1.55

- Find the cost of 145 bottles of lemonade at 21p each. What change do you get from £50?
- Things at half price now cost:
  £36.18 £111 £27.34 £274.30
  What was the original price of each item?
- Three people won £363 630 on the lottery to be shared equally between them.
  How much does each one get?
- Costs of rides are:

Galaxy	£1.65
Laser	£2.80
Big wheel	£1.45
Spaceship	£2.70

  Amy went on two rides.
  She had £5.65 change from £10.
  Which two rides did she go on?
- Use a calculator or a written method.
  4030 people go to a football match.
  Each ticket costs £4.25.
  What is the total cost of all the tickets?

Converting to European or foreign currency

- There are 1.43 euros to £1.
  What is the price in pounds of a car costing 14 300 euros?
- Use a calculator or a written method.
  There are 2560 lira to £1.
  Find the price in lira of a house costing £60 000.

Calculating fractions and percentages

- The agent's fee for selling a house is 5%.
  Calculate the fee on a house sold for £80 000.
- Use a calculator or a written method.
  There is a 15% discount in a sale.
  How much is the discount on £200... £25...?

Pupils should be taught to:

Use all four operations to solve word problems involving length, mass or capacity

As outcomes, Year 4 pupils should, for example:

Solve 'story' problems involving:
- kilometres, metres, centimetres, millimetres...
- kilograms, half kilograms, grams...
- litres, half litres, millilitres...
- miles, pints...

and explain and record how the problem was solved.

For example:

- Measure the lengths of these lines to the nearest mm.

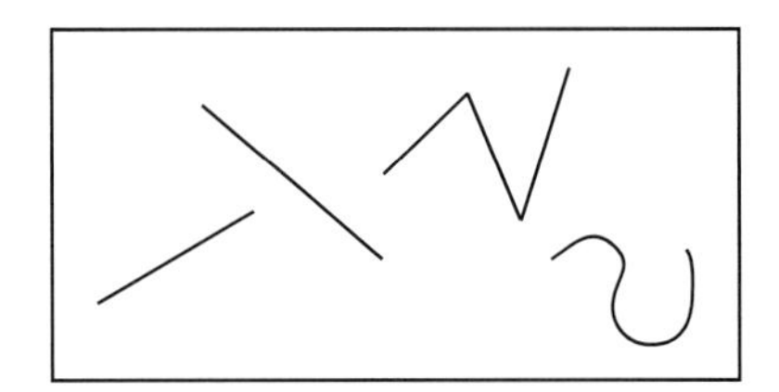

- Two shelves are 75 cm and 87 cm long.
  What is their total length in metres?
  What is the difference in their lengths in centimetres?
- A family sets off to drive 524 miles.
  After 267 miles, how much further do they have to go?
- A potato weighs about 250 g.
  Roughly how much do 10 potatoes weigh?
  How many times heavier is a 1 kg potato?
- A bottle of salad dressing holds 300 millilitres.
  A tablespoon holds 15 millilitres.
  How many tablespoons of dressing are in the bottle?
- A full jug holds 2 litres.
  A full glass holds $\frac{1}{4}$ of a litre.
  How many glasses full of water will the jug fill?
- Change this recipe for ginger nuts for 6 people to a recipe for 12 people for a party.

125 g	flour
50 g	fat
75 g	sugar
30 ml	treacle
1 teaspoon	ground ginger

- Each side of a regular hexagon is 14 centimetres long.
  How long is its perimeter?

See also problems involving numbers in 'real life' (page 82), money (page 84), time (pages 88 and 100), and puzzles (page 78).

As outcomes, Year 5 pupils should, for example:

Solve 'story' problems involving:
- kilometres, metres, centimetres, millimetres…
- kilograms, grams…
- litres, millilitres…
- miles, gallons, pints…

and explain and record how the problem was solved.

For example:

- There is 365 ml of milk in a jug.
  Another 450 ml of milk is added.
  How much milk is in the jug now?
- Dad bought a 2 kg bag of carrots.
  He used 400 grams of carrots to make some soup.
  How many grams of carrots were left?
- The football club has 400 litres of soup for the fans.
  One cup of soup is 250 ml.
  How many fans can have a cup of soup?
- Mum's car holds 40 litres of petrol.
  Dad's van holds two and half times as much.
  How much petrol does the van hold?
- Greg uses 5 tomatoes to make ½ a litre of sauce.
  How much sauce can he make from 15 tomatoes?
- A full bucket hold 5½ litres.
  A full jug holds ½ a litre.
  How many jugs full of water will fill the bucket?
- Change this pancake recipe for 4 people to a recipe for 6 people.

240 g	flour
300 ml	milk
2	eggs

Use a written method or a calculator to solve, for example:

- There is 2.2 kg of sugar in a bag.
  How much sugar is there in 10 bags?

See also problems involving numbers in 'real life' (page 83), money (page 85), time (pages 89 and 101), and puzzles (page 79).

As outcomes, Year 6 pupils should, for example:

Solve 'story' problems involving:
- kilometres, metres, centimetres, millimetres…
- kilograms, grams… newtons…
- litres, millilitres, centilitres…
- miles, gallons, pints, pounds, ounces…

and explain and record how the problem was solved.

For example:

- Sarah travelled 34.24 km by car, 2.7 km by bus and 1000 m on foot. How many kilometres did she travel? How many metres?
- I cut 65 cm off 3.5 metres of rope.
  How much is left?
- How many grams of carrots must be added to 2.76 kg to make 5 kg of carrots altogether?
- Which is more:
  10 lb of potatoes or 10 kg of potatoes?
- There is 300 ml of oil in the small bottle.
  There is six and one quarter times as much in the big bottle.
  How much oil is in the big bottle?
- A full bucket hold 3.2 litres.
  A full jug holds 0.2 of a litre.
  How many jugs full of water will fill the bucket?
- Change this cake recipe to metric units.

half a pint	water
3 oz	butter
4 oz	sugar
10 oz	flour
1 teaspoon	almond essence
2	eggs

Use a written method or a calculator to solve, for example:

- A pin is made from 14 mm of wire.
  How many pins can be made from 1 m of wire?
- There are exactly 2.54 cm to 1 inch.
  1 yard is 36 inches.
  About how many centimetres are there in 1 yard?
- A garage orders 50 000 litres of petrol.
  It sells an average of 1250 litres per day.
  How long does its supply of petrol last?

See also problems involving numbers in 'real life' (page 83), money (page 85), time (pages 89 and 101), and puzzles (page 79).

Pupils should be taught to:	As outcomes, Year 4 pupils should, for example:

Use all four operations to solve word problems involving time

Solve 'story' problems involving units of time, and explain and record how the problem was solved.

For example:

- Raiza got into the pool at 2:26. She swam until 3 o'clock. How long did she swim?
- The cake went in the oven at 1:20.
  It cooked for 75 minutes.
  What time did it come out?
- Lunch takes 40 minutes.
  It ends at 1:10 pm.
  What time does it start?
- Mary got up at 7:35.
  She left for school 45 minutes later.
  Her journey took 15 minutes.
  What time did she arrive at school?
- The football team kicked off at 1:30 pm.
  They played 45 minutes each way.
  They had a 10 minute break at half time.
  At what time did the game finish?
- Jan went swimming on Wednesday, 14 January.
  She went swimming again 4 weeks later.
  On what date did she go swimming the second time?
- The swimming pool shut for repairs on Friday, 20 March.
  It opened again on Friday, 10 April.
  For how many weeks was the swimming pool shut?

See also using timetables (page 100), problems involving numbers in 'real life' (page 82), money (page 84), measures (page 86), and puzzles (page 78).

As outcomes, Year 5 pupils should, for example:

Solve 'story' problems involving units of time, and explain and record how the problem was solved.

For example:

- The car race began at 08:45 and finished at 14:35. How long did the race last?
- The sun sets at 19:30 and rises again at 06:30. How many hours of darkness? Of daylight?
- A train leaves at 09:45 h and arrives at 15:46 h. How long does the journey last?
- These are the start and stop times on a video cassette recorder.

  START 14:45
  STOP 17:25

  For how long was the video recording?
- Four children in a relay team swim in a race. Here are their times for each lap.

LAP 1	Craig	92.4 seconds
LAP 2	Fiona	86.3 seconds
LAP 3	Harun	85.1 seconds
LAP 4	Jenny	91.8 seconds

  What is their total time for the four laps?

See also using timetables (page 101), problems involving numbers in 'real life' (page 83), money (page 85), measures (page 87), and puzzles (page 79).

As outcomes, Year 6 pupils should, for example:

Solve 'story' problems involving units of time, and explain and record how the problem was solved.

For example:

- Lamb must be cooked for 60 minutes for every kg. Chicken must be cooked for 50 minutes for every kg. Complete this table of cooking times.

kilograms	1	1.5	2	2.5	3	3.5
Cooking time in minutes (lamb)						
Cooking time in minutes (chicken)						

See also using timetables (page 101), problems involving numbers in 'real life' (page 83), money (page 85), measures (page 87), and puzzles (page 79).

Pupils should be taught to:	As outcomes, Year 4 pupils should, for example:

Use vocabulary related to measures

Use, read and write:

- *unit, standard unit, metric unit, imperial unit...*
- names of standard metric units:
  kilometre, metre, centimetre, millimetre...
  kilogram, gram... litre, millilitre...
- names of commonly used imperial units:
  mile... pint...
- length and distance: *long, short, tall, high, low, wide, narrow, deep, shallow, thick, thin...*
  far, near, close, distance, perimeter, circumference...
- mass: *big, bigger, small, smaller, balances...*
- weight: *heavy, light, weighs...*
- capacity: *full, empty, holds...*
- and comparative words such as: *longer, longest...*

Use correctly the abbreviations:
mm (millimetre), cm (centimetre), m (metre), km (kilometre), g (gram), kg (kilogram), ml (millilitre), l (litre), ...
and cm^2 (square centimetre), m^2 (square metre).

Know and use relationships between familiar units

Know that:

1 kilometre	= 1000 metres
1 metre	= 100 centimetres or 1000 millimetres
1 centimetre	= 10 millimetres
1 kilogram	= 1000 grams
1 litre	= 1000 millilitres

Recognise the mile as a unit for measuring distance.
Know that a mile is longer than 1 km but less than 2 km.

Recognise the pint as a unit for measuring capacity.
Know that a pint is, very roughly, about half a litre.

Know the equivalent of one half, one quarter, three quarters and one tenth of 1 km, 1 m, 1 kg, 1 litre in m, cm, g and ml respectively. For example, know that:

- 500 g is one half of 1 kg;
- 75 cm is three quarters of 1 m.

Begin to write, for example:

- 1.6 m in centimetres (160 centimetres);
- 4 kg in grams (4000 grams);
- 5 litres in millilitres (5000 ml);
- 8 km in metres (8000 metres);
- 3 cm in millimetres (30 millimetres);

and vice versa.

As outcomes, Year 5 pupils should, for example:

Use, read and write, spelling correctly, the vocabulary from the previous year, and extend to:

- names of commonly used imperial units: *gallon.*

Use correctly the abbreviations:
km, m, cm, mm, kg, g, l, ml...
and cm^2, m^2 , mm^2 (square millimetre).

Know the relationships between units from the previous year.

Recognise that:

- a mile is a unit of distance, and is a bit more than 1.5 km (about 1600 metres);
- a pint is a unit of capacity, and is slightly more than half a litre (about 570 ml);
- a gallon is a unit of capacity, and is a bit less than 5 litres.

Know the equivalent of one half, one quarter, three quarters, one tenth and one hundredth of 1 metre, 1 kilometre, 1 kilogram and 1 litre in m, cm, g and ml respectively. For example, know that:

- 10 g is one hundredth of 1 kg.

Write, for example:

- 1.6 m in centimetres (160 centimetres);
- 4.5 kg in grams (4500 grams);
- 367 cm in metres (3.67 metres);
- 2500 millilitres in litres (2.5 litres).

As outcomes, Year 6 pupils should, for example:

Use, read and write, spelling correctly, the vocabulary from the previous year, and extend to:

- names of standard metric units: *tonne, centilitre...*
- names of commonly used imperial units:
  pound, ounce...
  yard, foot, inch...

Use correctly the abbreviations:
km, m, cm, mm, kg, g, l, ml, cl (centilitre)...
cm^2, m^2, mm^2
and, in science, N (newtons)...
and read the imperial abbreviations: lb and oz.

Know the relationships between units from the previous year, and extend to:

1 tonne	= 1000 kilograms
1 litre	= 100 centilitres
1 centilitre	= 10 millilitres

Know the approximate equivalence between commonly used imperial units and metric units:

1 litre	2 pints (more accurately, 1 ¾ pints)
4.5 litres	1 gallon or 8 pints
1 kilogram	2 lb (more accurately, 2.2 lb)
30 grams	1 oz
8 kilometres	5 miles

Make use of rhymes like:

A metre is just three feet three.
It's longer than a yard, you see.

Two and a quarter pounds of jam
Is round about one kilogram.

A litre of water's a pint and three quarters.

Know the equivalent of one thousandth of 1 km, 1 kg, 1 litre in m, g and ml respectively.

Convert a larger metric unit to a smaller.
For example:

- write 3.125 km in metres (3125 metres);
- write 1.25 litres in millilitres (1250 millilitres).

Begin to convert a smaller unit to a larger.
For example:

- write 750 grams in kilograms (0.75 kilograms);
- write 300 millilitres in litres (0.3 litres);
- write 3 centimetres in metres (0.03 metres).

Pupils should be taught to:	As outcomes, Year 4 pupils should, for example:
Suggest suitable units to estimate or measure length, mass or capacity	Use, read and write: *estimate...* *roughly, nearly, about, approximately...* Estimate and check, using standard units, measurements such as: • how tall a friend is; • how long/wide a playing card is; • how heavy a tennis ball is; • how much a sink holds. Respond to oral or written questions like: Would you expect: • a bungalow to be about 3 metres, 6 metres or 12 metres tall; • a big potato to be 20 g, 200 g or 2000 g; • my thumb nail to be about 1 mm, 5 mm or 10 mm wide; • a small bottle of lemonade to hold about 250 ml or 1250 ml? Suggest things you would measure in: • kilometres, metres, centimetres, millimetres... • kilograms, grams... • litres, millilitres... • miles, pints... Suggest a metric unit to measure, for example: • how far it is from London to Birmingham; • the height of a telegraph pole; • the length, breadth and thickness of a library book; • the weight of some butter in a butter dish; • the capacity of a big saucepan. **See also time (pages 98 and 100).**

As outcomes, Year 5 pupils should, for example:

Use, read and write, spelling correctly:
estimate...
roughly, nearly, about, approximately...

Estimate and check, using standard metric units, measurements such as:
- how wide/high the front fence of the school is;
- the total weight of three parcels;
- the amount of rainfall collected in a week;
- the thickness of a playing card.

Respond to oral or written questions like:
Do you think that:
- the classroom is 3 metres, 6 metres or 12 metres high;
- this crayon is about 5 mm, 55 mm or 555 mm long;
- this pear weighs about 500 g, 250 g or 100 g;
- there is 1000 ml, 500 ml or 250 ml of water in this jar?

Suggest things you would measure in:
- kilometres, metres, centimetres, millimetres...
- kilograms, grams...
- litres, millilitres...
- miles, gallons, pints...

Suggest a metric unit to measure, for example:
- the distance from Bradford to Coventry;
- your height;
- the width of a dinner plate;
- the weight of a daffodil bulb;
- the amount held by a tablespoon.

See also time (pages 99 and 101).

As outcomes, Year 6 pupils should, for example:

Use, read and write, spelling correctly:
estimate...
roughly, nearly, about, approximately...

Estimate and check, using metric or imperial units, measurements such as:
- the distance from Leeds to Liverpool;
- the weight of an egg;
- the perimeter of the classroom.

Suggest how you could measure:
- the thickness of a piece of paper;
- the weight of one grain of rice;
- the quantity of water in a raindrop;
- the thickness of the glass in a window pane.

Respond to oral or written questions like:
- Do you think this box weighs about 1 N, 5 N or 25 N?

Suggest things you would measure in:
- kilometres, metres, centimetres, millimetres...
- tonnes, kilograms, grams... newtons...
- litres, millilitres, centilitres...
- miles, gallons, pints, pounds, ounces...

Suggest an imperial or metric unit to measure, for example:
- the distance from Earth to the Moon;
- the growth of mustard and cress;
- the weight of a paper clip... of a van;
- the amount of milk in a jug... in a milk tanker.

What units of measurement might you see, for example, in:
- a TV weather forecast;
- a supermarket;
- road signs;
- a garage;
- a railway station;
- a chemist's shop...?

See also time (pages 99 and 101).

Pupils should be taught to:	As outcomes, Year 4 pupils should, for example:

Suggest suitable measuring equipment, record estimates and readings from scales to a suitable degree of accuracy

Choose a suitable measuring instrument to measure, for example:
- the length of the classroom... a small library book... a fence...
- the weight of a bag of pears... a person...
- the capacity of a bottle... a teapot...

Use a ruler to measure and draw lines to the nearest 0.5 cm.

Read measuring scales to the nearest division.
For example:

- How much water is in the measuring cylinder?

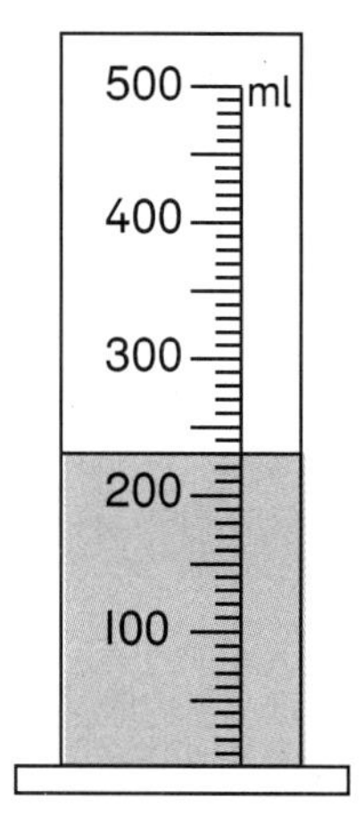

- Mr Jones is standing on the bathroom scales shown below. Roughly what measurement is shown on the scales?

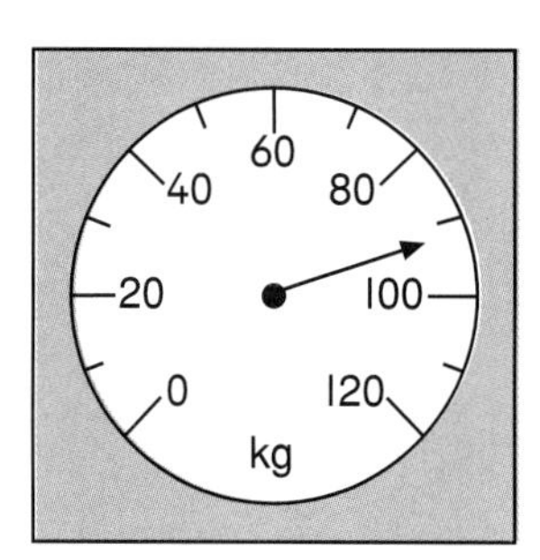

Record estimated and measured lengths in metres and centimetres in decimal form: 1.35 metres.

Record other estimates and measurements using a mix of units: for example, write '4125 grams' as '4 kilograms and 125 grams'.

Round measurements to the nearest ten or hundred units.
For example:
- I am about 157 cm tall, or 160 cm to the nearest 10 cm;
- our rabbit weighs 4690 grams, or 4700 grams to the nearest 100 grams.

As outcomes, Year 5 pupils should, for example:

Choose a suitable measuring instrument to measure, for example:
- the height of the classroom...
  the depth of the swimming pool...
- the weight of a ball of wool...
- the capacity of a tea urn...
  the capacity of a bath...

Measure and draw lines to the nearest millimetre.

Read measuring scales between divisions. For example:

- What is the distance between the two arrows?
- What is this distance in millimetres?
- What length in metres is indicated by each arrow?

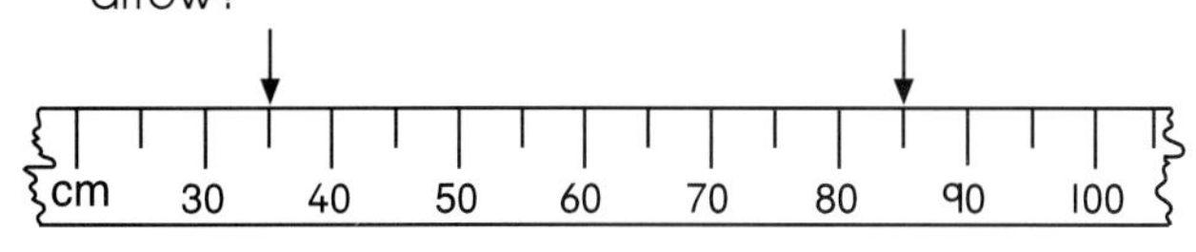

- 200 ml more water is poured into the cylinder. Mark the new water level.

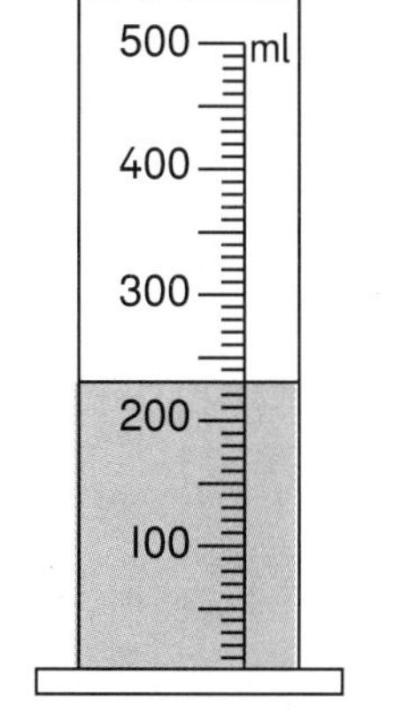

- 300 grams of flour are taken off the scales. How much flour is left?

Begin to record estimates and measurements involving halves, quarters or tenths of 1 km, 1 kg or 1 litre in decimal form: for example, record '1500 ml' as '1.5 litres', or '600 m' as '0.6 km'.

Begin to round decimal measurements to the nearest whole unit. For example:
- a saucepan holding 4275 millilitres holds 4 litres to the nearest litre;
- a 3.25 kg bag of carrots weighs 3 kg to the nearest kilogram.

As outcomes, Year 6 pupils should, for example:

Choose a suitable measuring instrument to measure, for example:
- the thickness of a rubber band...
- the width of a manhole cover...
- the weight of a lorry...
- the mass of an insect...
- the capacity of a thimble...

Read measuring scales, converting the unit to an equivalent metric unit. For example:

- How many grams of flour are on the scales?

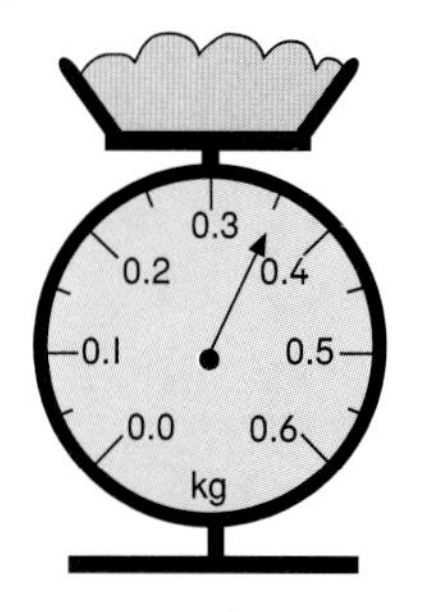

Read metric and imperial units from measuring scales that show both units. For example:

- Approximately how many litres are there in 3 gallons? Give your answer to the nearest litre.
- Approximately how many gallons are there in 7 litres? Give your answer to one decimal place.

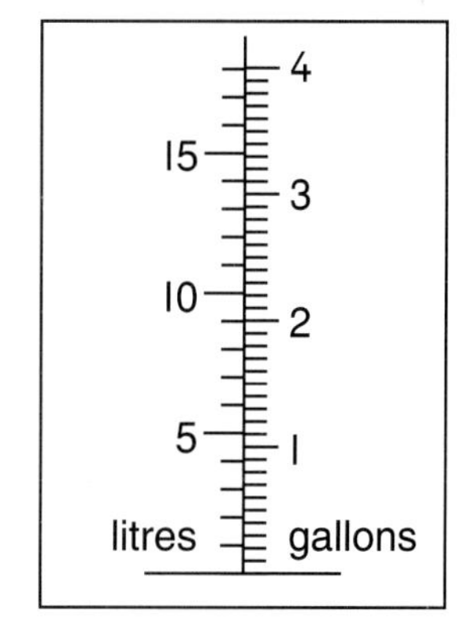

Record estimated and measured lengths, weights or capacities in decimal form: for example, write '4125 grams' as '4.125 kg'.

Round a measurement to the nearest whole unit or tenth of a unit. For example:
- 3870 grams of potatoes weigh 3.9 kg to the nearest tenth of a kilogram, or 4 kg to the nearest kilogram.

Pupils should be taught to:	As outcomes, Year 4 pupils should, for example:

Measure and calculate the perimeter and area of simple shapes

Use, read and write:
area, covers, surface, perimeter, distance, edge...
and use symbols for:
square centimetres (cm^2).

Perimeter
Respond to questions such as:

- Draw round the edge of a rectangle with your pencil. How far did your pencil travel? Measure the distance.
- Estimate then measure the perimeter of the classroom... the top of your desk... a piece of A4 paper... a regular hexagon...
- How long is the perimeter of: a 5 cm × 5 cm square... a 4 cm × 7 cm rectangle... a triangle whose sides are 10 m, 20 m, and 24 m?
- The perimeter of a square is 28 cm. What is the length of one side? Draw two rectangles with the same perimeter as the square.
- Draw different rectangles with a perimeter of 24 cm. Which has the largest area?

Find a short way to work out the perimeter of a rectangle.

Area
Find out which of two or more things has the greatest area by covering with, say, pennies, cubes, postcards, sheets of A4 paper, sheets of newspaper, squares... and counting.

Find areas by counting squares. For example:
- Find out which of two greetings cards has the greatest area by tracing on centimetre squared paper or by covering with a transparent centimetre grid.
- Each square is 1 square centimetre. What area is shaded?

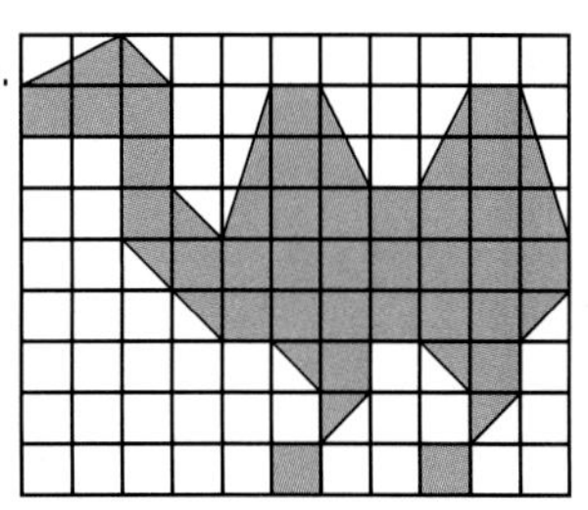

- Find different ways of halving the area of a 5 × 5 pinboard. Justify your results.

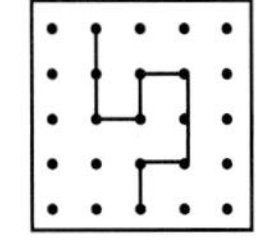 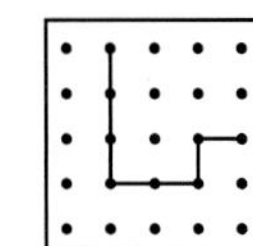 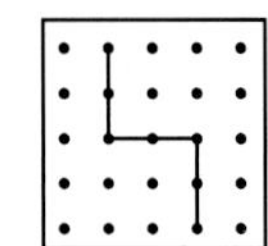 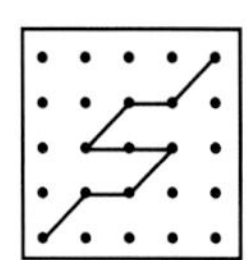

Choose a suitable unit and estimate the area of, for example:
- a postcard;
- a page of a book;
- this rectangle.

Measure and check.

Suggest areas to measure in square centimetres.

As outcomes, Year 5 pupils should, for example:

Use, read and write, spelling correctly:
area, covers, surface, perimeter, distance, edge…
and use the symbols for: *square centimetres (cm²), square metres (m²), square millimetres (mm²).*

Perimeter
Express the formula for the perimeter of a rectangle first in words, then in letters.

Work out and express in words a formula for finding the perimeter of a regular polygon.

Respond to questions such as:

- The perimeter of a rectangle is 72 cm.
  The shortest side is 9 cm.
  What is the length of the longest side?
- Draw some shapes on squared paper.
  Measure the perimeters to the nearest mm.

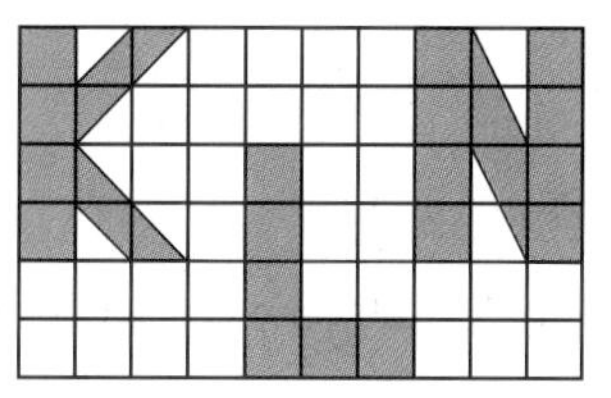

Area
Express the formula for the area of a rectangle first in words, then in letters.

Choose a suitable unit to estimate the area of, for example:
- a sheet of newspaper… the top of a desk…
- a leaf… a postage stamp…
- the top of a matchbox…
- the cover of a book… a round table mat…
- the hall floor… the swimming pool surface…

Discuss how to find the area of each one.
Measure and calculate how close the estimates were.

Respond to oral or written questions like:

- What is the approximate area of this rectangle?

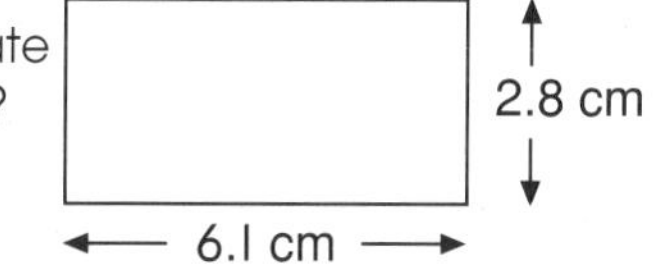

- Would you expect the area of:
  a paperback book to be 100 cm², 600 cm² or 6000 cm²;
  a bedroom floor to be 10 m² or 100 m²;
  a playing card to be 5 cm², 50 cm² or 100 cm²?

Suggest areas you would measure in mm², cm², m²…

Know that 1 square metre is 10 000 cm².
Know that 1 square centimetre is 100 mm².

As outcomes, Year 6 pupils should, for example:

Use, read and write, spelling correctly:
area, covers, surface, perimeter, distance, edge…
and use the symbols for: *square centimetres (cm²), square metres (m²), square millimetres (mm²).*

Perimeter
Calculate the perimeters of compound shapes that can be split into rectangles.

For example, find the perimeter of this shape.

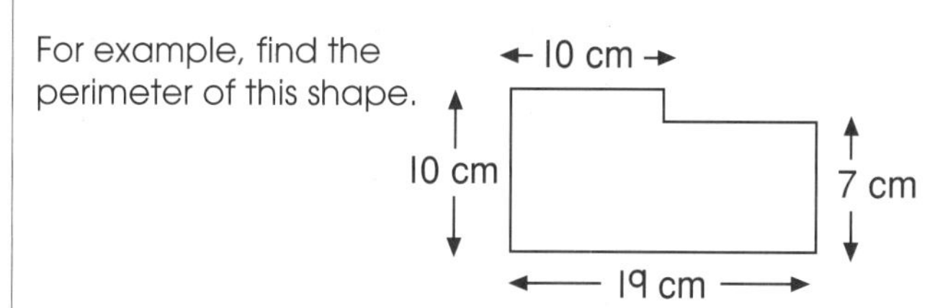

Area
Know the formula for finding the area of a rectangle.

Begin to find the areas of compound shapes that can be split into rectangles, such as this shape.

10 cm
10 cm
7 cm
19 cm

Respond to oral or written questions like:

- Find the length, breadth and height of this box.
  Use a calculator to find its surface area.

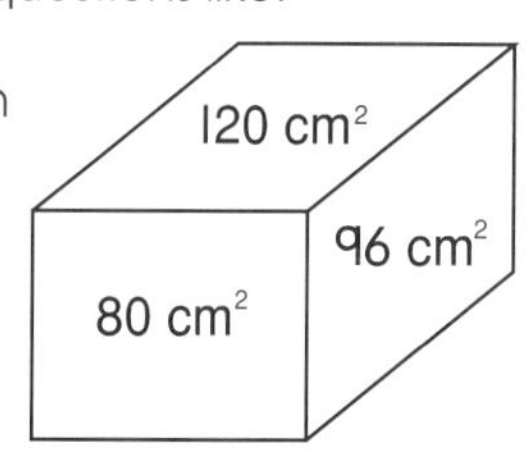

- Each of these shapes has an area of two square units. Draw some more.
  Decide which has the longest perimeter.

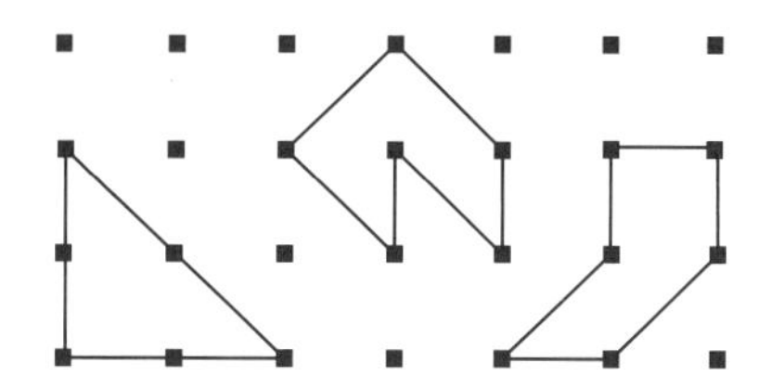

Find the area of a right-angled triangle by considering it as half of a rectangle.

Pupils should be taught to:	As outcomes, Year 4 pupils should, for example:

Use the vocabulary related to time; suggest suitable units of time to estimate or measure

Use, read and write:
names of days of the week, months and seasons...
day, week, fortnight, month, season, year, leap year, century, millennium, morning, afternoon, evening, night, midnight, noon, hour, minute, second, today, yesterday, tomorrow, weekend... am and pm...
how long ago, how long will it be to, arrive, depart...
faster, fastest, slower, slowest, takes longer, takes less time, earliest, latest...

Know and use:

1 millennium	= 1000 years
1 century	= 100 years
1 year	= 12 months or 52 weeks
1 week	= 7 days
1 day	= 24 hours
1 hour	= 60 minutes
1 minute	= 60 seconds

and the rhyme:
30 days hath September,
April, June and November.
All the rest have 31,
except in February alone
which has but 28 days clear
and 29 in each leap year.

Know their date of birth: day, month, year.

Estimate or measure, suggesting suitable units
Suggest things you would estimate or measure in:
- hours, minutes, seconds, days, weeks, months, years...

Suggest a unit to estimate or measure, for example:
- the time it will take to eat lunch...
- the time you watch TV each week...
- how long it is until the end of the year.

What measuring instrument would you use to time, for example:
- running 100 metres... cooking a cake...?

Estimate, using standard units, for example:
- how long it takes to run across the school field;
- how long it takes on the bus to the town centre;
- how long it takes to fly to Miami from London.

Use a stop watch or other timers to measure and compare times of events: for example, use a stopwatch in science to find how long it takes for water to boil, or in PE to time races.

Respond to oral or written questions like:
- Would you expect:
  to cook a soft boiled egg in 3 minutes or 30 minutes;
  to walk across the road in 1, 10 or 100 seconds?

- Have you lived more or less than 500 weeks?

As outcomes, Year 5 pupils should, for example:

Use, read and write, spelling correctly, the vocabulary from the previous year, and extend to:
decade...
digital/analogue clock, 24-hour clock, 12-hour clock.

Know and use:

1 millennium	= 1000 years
1 century	= 100 years
1 decade	= 10 years
1 year	= 12 months or 52 weeks or 365 days
1 leap year	= 366 days
1 week	= 7 days
1 day	= 24 hours
1 hour	= 60 minutes
1 minute	= 60 seconds

and the rhyme: *30 days hath September...*

Estimate or measure, suggesting suitable units
Suggest things you would estimate or measure in:
- weeks, months, years, decades, centuries...

Suggest a unit to estimate or measure, for example:
- how long it takes from planting a daffodil bulb to when it flowers;
- the age of an old yew tree.

Suggest how to measure, for example:
- how long it takes for a runner bean to grow...
- how long until your birthday...

Estimate, using standard units, for example:
- the hours of darkness in December... in June...
- how long it takes to run a marathon...
- the time each week you spend sleeping... eating...

Respond to oral or written questions like:
- Would you expect:
  to roast a chicken in 2 hours, 5 hours or 10 hours;
  to walk a mile in 15 min, 45 min or 75 min?
- Have you lived more or less than 3650 days? Than 100 000 hours?

As outcomes, Year 6 pupils should, for example:

Use, read and write, spelling correctly, the vocabulary from the previous year, and extend to:
Greenwich mean time, British summer time...

Know and use:

1 millennium	= 1000 years
1 century	= 100 years
1 decade	= 10 years
1 year	= 12 months or 52 weeks or 365 days
1 leap year	= 366 days
1 week	= 7 days
1 day	= 24 hours
1 hour	= 60 minutes
1 minute	= 60 seconds

and the rhyme: *30 days hath September...*

Pupils should be taught to:	As outcomes, Year 4 pupils should, for example:

Read the time from clocks, calendars and timetables

Read clocks and calendars

Read the time to the minute on a 12-hour digital clock and an analogue clock. Know, for example, that 4:37, or 37 minutes past 4, or 23 minutes to 5 are all equivalent.
Use am and pm.

Use this year's calendar to work out, for example:

- which day of the week is 22 June;
- the date of the third Thursday in May;
- the number of days from 27 February to 10 March;
- the number of weeks from 18 September to 13 November.

Use timetables

For example:

- Use a TV guide to work out how long favourite programmes last.

- Use the class timetable to find out how much time you spend on mathematics each day; each week; each term; each year.

- This table shows the times of buses.

8:00 am	10:30 am	1:00 pm	3:30 pm	5:00 pm

  You are at the bus stop at 2:50 pm. How long do you wait for a bus?
  The 10:30 bus is 35 minutes late. What time does it arrive?
  How long is it between the first and last bus?

- A bus takes 20 minutes between each stop.

  Complete the timetable.

High Street	11:05		1:45
Church			
Post Office		1:05	
Sports Centre			

See also problems involving time (page 88).

As outcomes, Year 5 pupils should, for example:

Read clocks
Read the time to the minute on a 24-hour digital clock. Understand 8:48 am, 8:48 pm, 08:48 and 20:48.

For example, fill in the gaps in this table.

seven o'clock in the evening	19:00 h	7:00 pm
quarter to ten in the morning		
	14:20 h	
	22:15 h	
midnight		
17 minutes past 4 in the afternoon		

Use timetables
Use a train timetable. For example:

Birmingham New Street	09:40	10:05	11:05	12:35
Birmingham International	09:50	10:15	11:15	12:45
Coventry	10:10	10:30	11:30	13:00
Leamington Spa	10:25	....	11:45	13:15
Banbury	10:45	....	12:05	....
Oxford	11:05	11:20	12:25	13:55
Reading	11:30	11:55	12:50	14:25

- What time does the 09:40 from Birmingham New Street arrive at Reading? Which is the fastest train from Birmingham New Street to Reading?
- At how many stations does the 10:15 from Birmingham International stop before it reaches Reading?
- How long does it take the 13:55 from Oxford to reach Reading?
- You have to arrive at Oxford at 2:00 pm. Which train would you catch from Coventry?
- You get to Leamington at 09:30. How long will you have to wait for a train to Reading?

See also problems involving time (page 89).

As outcomes, Year 6 pupils should, for example:

Read world time charts
Understand different times around the world.

Use a world time chart to answer questions such as:
- It is 12:00 noon in London. What time is it in Delhi, Tokyo, Hawaii, San Francisco...?
- It is 4:36 am in Sydney. What time is it in New York?

See also problems involving time (page 89).

Pupils should be taught to:

Describe and visualise 3-D and 2-D shapes; classify them according to their properties

As outcomes, Year 4 pupils should, for example:

Use, read and write the words:
pattern, shape, 2-D, two-dimensional, 3-D, three-dimensional... line, side, edge, face, surface, base, point, angle, vertex, vertices... centre, radius, diameter... net... make, build, construct, draw, sketch...
and adjectives such as: *curved, straight... regular, irregular... concave, convex... closed, open... circular, triangular, hexagonal, cylindrical, spherical... square-based, right-angled...*

Name, classify and describe 2-D and 3-D shapes:
circle, semi-circle, triangle, equilateral triangle, isosceles triangle, quadrilateral, rectangle, oblong, square, pentagon, hexagon, heptagon, octagon, polygon... cube, cuboid, pyramid, sphere, hemi-sphere, cylinder, cone, prism, tetrahedron, polyhedron...

For example:

3-D shapes
Know that in a polyhedron:
- each face is a flat surface and is a polygon;
- an edge is the straight line where two faces meet;
- a vertex is the point where three or more edges meet.

Know that a prism has two identical end faces and the same cross-section throughout its length.
Collect, name and describe examples.

2-D shapes
Know that a polygon is a closed, flat shape with three or more straight sides, and that regular polygons have all their sides and all their angles equal.

Know the angle and side properties of isosceles and equilateral triangles, and use them: for example, to make triangular patterns.

Name and classify polygons.

	triangles	quadrilaterals
regular		
irregular		

Know some of their properties. For example:

- all heptagons have seven sides;
- a quadrilateral is any shape with four straight sides;
- the square and the equilateral triangle are examples of regular polygons;
- an isosceles triangle is an example of an irregular polygon;
- a polygon can be concave or convex.

Identify particular shapes from a mixed set.
For example, which of these shapes are hexagons?

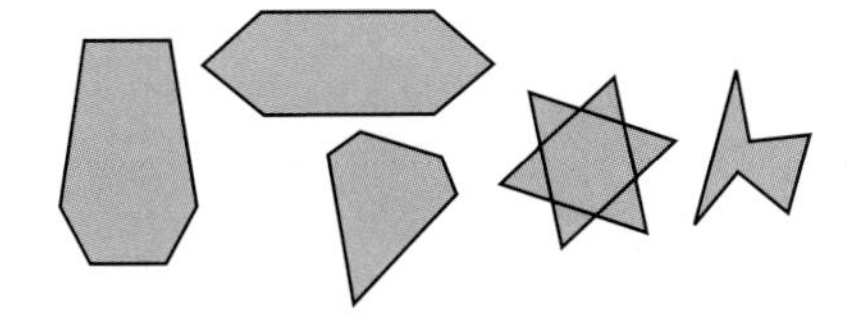

As outcomes, Year 5 pupils should, for example:

Use, read and write, spelling correctly, the vocabulary from the previous year, and extend to:
congruent...

Continue to name and describe shapes, extending to: *scalene triangle... octahedron...*

For example:

3-D shapes
Classify solids according to properties such as:
- the shapes of the faces;
- the number of faces, edges, vertices;
- whether or not any face is right-angled;
- whether the number of edges meeting at each vertex is the same or different.

2-D shapes
Recognise properties of rectangles such as:
- all four angles are right angles;
- opposite sides are equal and parallel;
- the diagonals bisect one another.

Name and classify triangles.

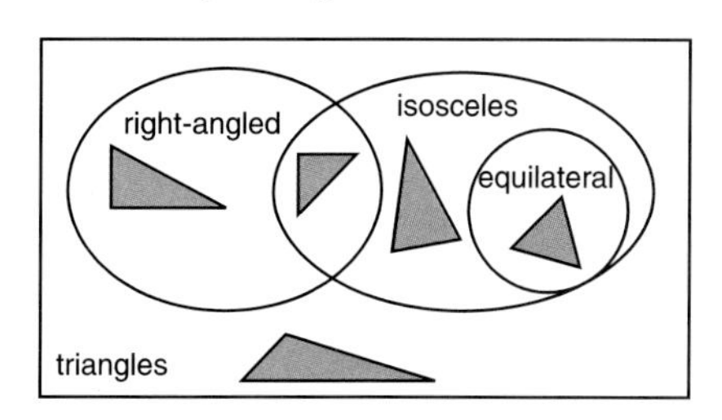

Know some of their properties. For example:
- in an equilateral triangle all three sides are equal in length and all three angles are equal in size;
- an isosceles triangle has two equal sides and two equal angles;
- in a scalene triangle no two sides or angles are equal;
- in a right-angled triangle one of the angles is a right angle.

Use a 'binary tree' computer program to sort and identify a set of 2-D shapes.

See also reflective symmetry (page 107).

As outcomes, Year 6 pupils should, for example:

Use, read and write, spelling correctly, the vocabulary from the previous year, and extend to:
concentric... tangram...
circumference, arc...

Continue to name and describe shapes, extending to: *parallelogram, rhombus, kite, trapezium... dodecahedron...*

For example:

3-D shapes
Describe properties of 3-D shapes, such as parallel or perpendicular faces or edges.

2-D shapes
Name and begin to classify quadrilaterals, using criteria such as parallel sides, equal angles, equal sides, lines of symmetry...

Know properties such as:
- a parallelogram has its opposite sides equal and parallel;
- a rhombus is a parallelogram with four equal sides;
- a rectangle has four right angles and its opposite sides are equal;
- a square is a rectangle with four equal sides;
- a trapezium has one pair of opposite parallel sides;
- a kite has two pairs of adjacent sides equal.

Begin to know properties such as:
- the diagonals of any square, rhombus or kite intersect at right angles;
- the diagonals of any square, rectangle, rhombus or parallelogram bisect one another.

See also reflective symmetry (page 107).

Pupils should be taught to:

Make shapes and patterns with increasing accuracy

As outcomes, Year 4 pupils should, for example:

Construct models, shapes and patterns with increasing accuracy. For example:

3-D shapes
Identify simple nets of 3-D shapes. For example, unfold packets which are cubes or cuboids to identify their nets.

Make polyhedra such as cubes, cuboids, pyramids and prisms, using straws and pipe cleaners to make 'skeleton' shapes, or construction kits to make 'solid' shapes...

Count the number of faces and edges. Recognise properties such as:

- all pyramids have an even number of edges;
- the number of straight edges in a prism is a multiple of 3;
- the number of faces of a pyramid is one more than the number of edges of the base;
- the number of faces of a prism is two more than the number of edges of an end face...

Visualise 3-D shapes from 2-D drawings.
For example, work out the least number of cubes needed to build these shapes.

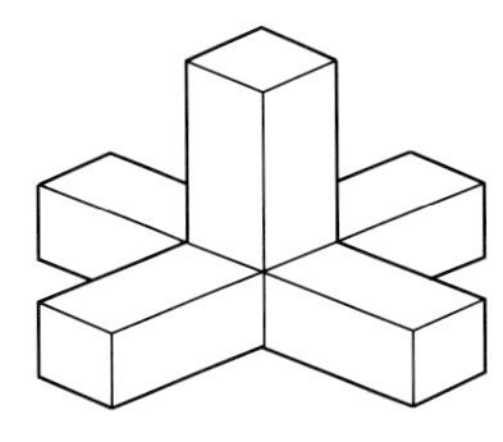

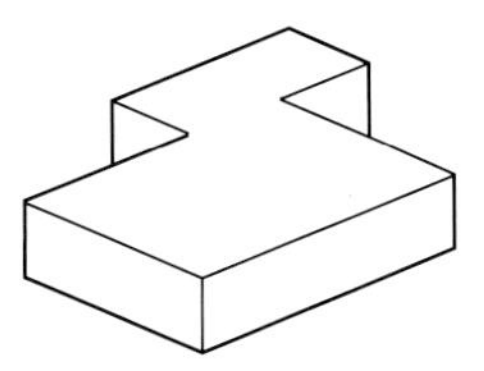

2-D shapes
Construct different polygons by paper folding or on a pinboard, and discuss properties such as lines of symmetry.

As outcomes, Year 5 pupils should, for example:

Construct models, shapes and patterns with increasing accuracy. For example:

3-D shapes

Identify the different nets for an open cube (five square faces). (The black square shows each cube's 'base'.)

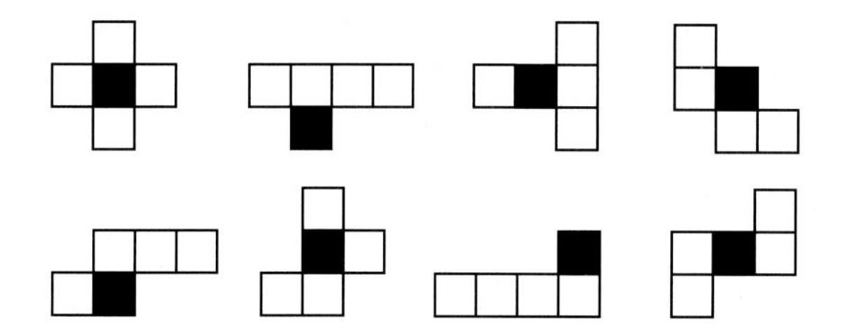

Visualise 3-D shapes from 2-D drawings.
For example, work out the least number of unit cubes needed to turn this shape into a cuboid.

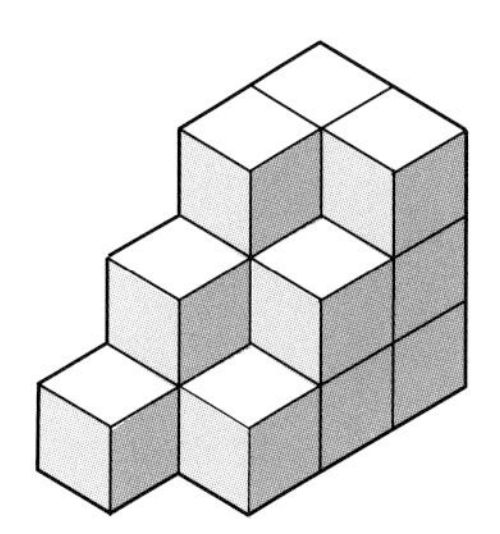

2-D shapes

Use a pinboard to make shapes.
For example, make:

- different triangles on 3×3 pinboard;
- different squares on a 5×5 pinboard.

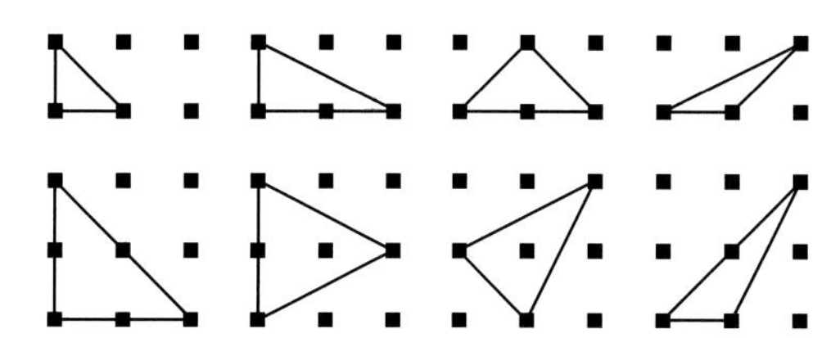

Discuss properties such as which of these triangles are scalene, or which has the greatest area.

As outcomes, Year 6 pupils should, for example:

Construct models, shapes and patterns with increasing accuracy. For example:

3-D shapes

Identify the different nets for a closed cube (six square faces).

Visualise 3-D shapes from 2-D drawings.
For example, find and justify the least number of cubes needed to cover and join the shaded faces.

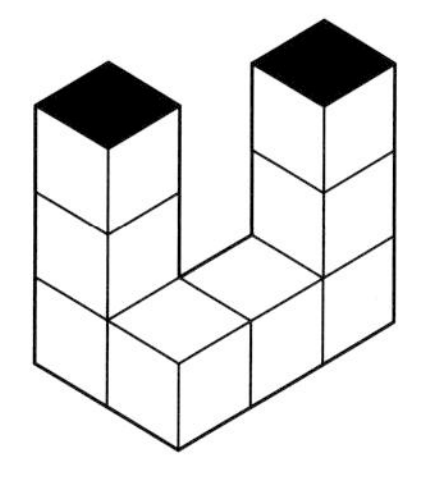

2-D shapes

Investigate the different polygons that can be made using tangram pieces.
For example, reassemble the five tangram pieces to form hexagons.

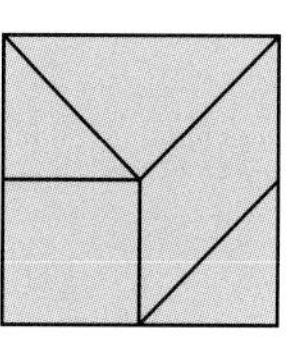

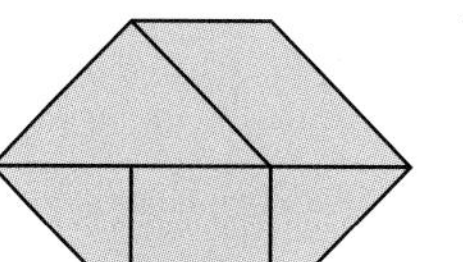

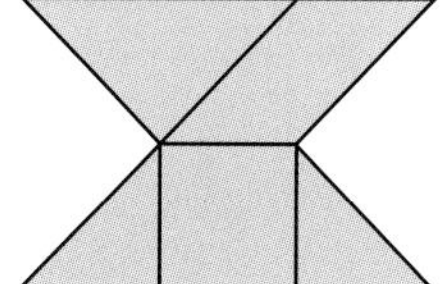

Use turtle graphics to draw polygons.
Discuss the geometric features of the shapes made.

Pupils should be taught to:

Recognise reflective symmetry in 2-D shapes, reflections and translations

As outcomes, Year 4 pupils should, for example:

Use, read and write:
mirror line, line of symmetry, line symmetry, symmetrical, reflect, reflection, translation...

Identify and sketch two or more lines of reflective symmetry, and recognise shapes with no lines of symmetry. For example:

- Identify whether designs, logos, advertisements... have a line of symmetry.
- Classify 2-D shapes according to their lines of symmetry.

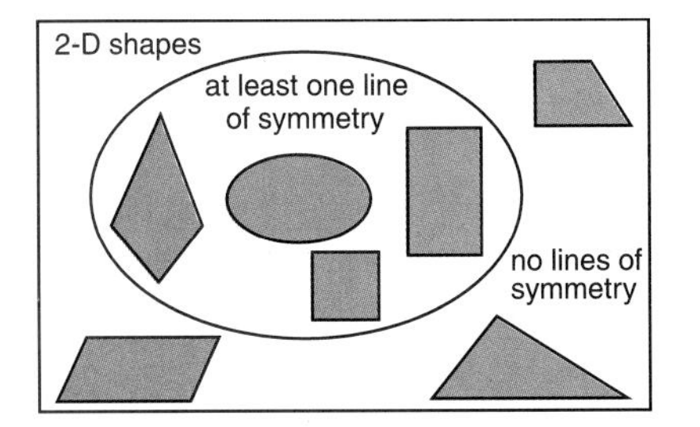

Sketch the reflection of a simple shape in a mirror line parallel to one edge, where the edges of the shape or the lines of the pattern are parallel or perpendicular to the mirror line.
For example:

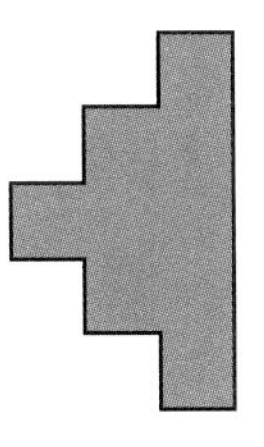

Know that equivalent points are the same (shortest) distance from the line of symmetry.

Make patterns by repeatedly translating a shape.

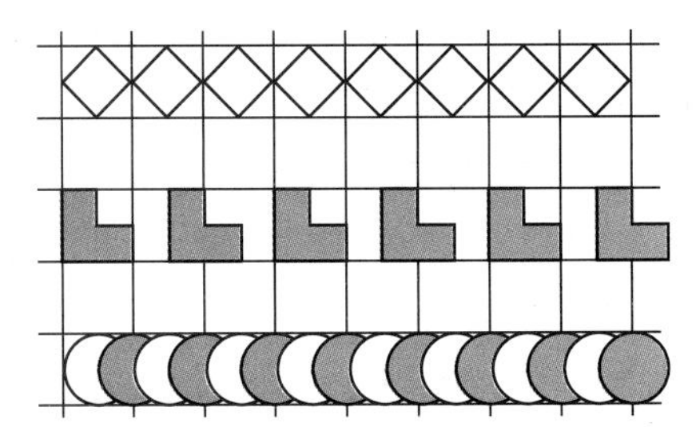

Use a computer program to:
- create a pattern and reflect it in a horizontal or vertical line;
- create a 'tile' and translate it repeatedly along a line.

Predict and discuss the patterns made.

As outcomes, Year 5 pupils should, for example:

Use, read and write, spelling correctly, the vocabulary from the previous year, and extend to:
axis of symmetry, reflective symmetry...

Recognise the number of axes of reflective symmetry in regular polygons. For example:

- Draw regular and irregular polygons on squared paper and cut them out. Test for symmetry using a mirror and by folding.
  Say which fold symmetrically more than once.

- Investigate the lines of symmetry in regular polygons.

  Know that the number of lines of symmetry in a regular polygon is equal to the number of sides, so a square has four lines of symmetry and an equilateral triangle has three.

Sketch the reflection of a simple shape in a mirror line parallel to one edge, where the edges of the shape are not all parallel or perpendicular to the mirror line.

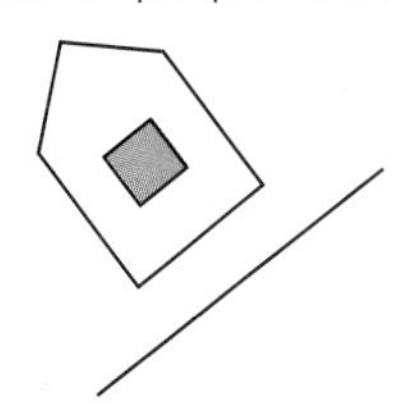

Complete symmetrical patterns on squared paper with two lines of symmetry at right angles.
For example, complete this pattern:

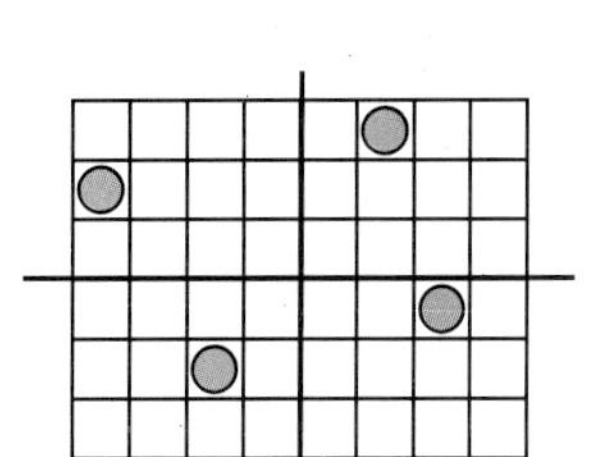

solution:

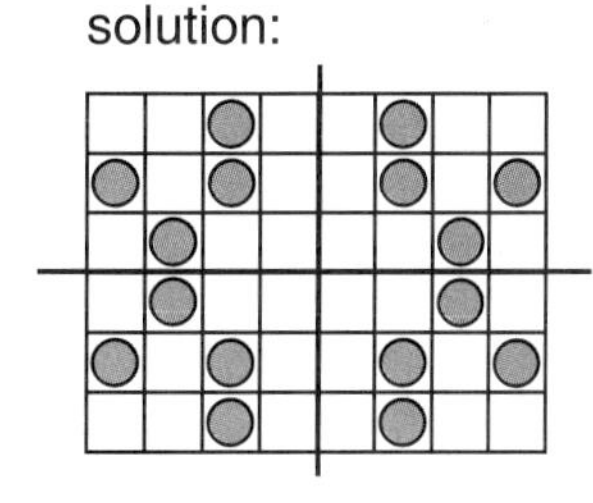

Sketch the position of a simple shape after it has been translated, say, 2 units to the left.

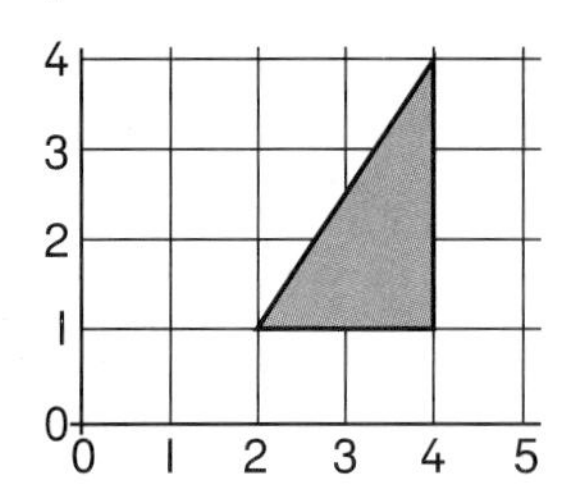

Use a computer program to create a 'tile' and use it by alternately translating the tile and its reflection along a line. Predict and discuss the patterns made.

As outcomes, Year 6 pupils should, for example:

Use, read and write, spelling correctly, the vocabulary from the previous year.

Sketch the reflection of a simple shape in a mirror line touching it at one point, where the edges of the shape are not necessarily parallel or perpendicular to the mirror line.

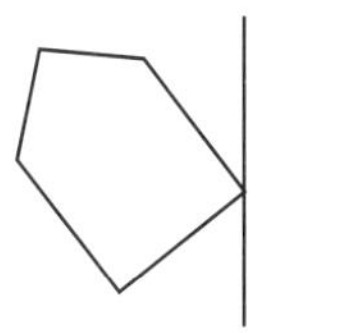

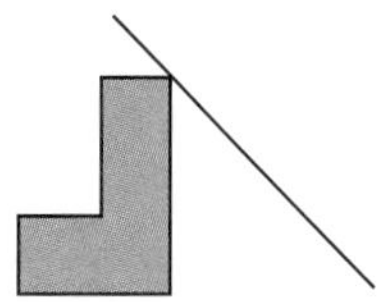

Sketch the reflection of a simple shape in two mirror lines at right angles, where the sides of the shape are parallel or perpendicular to the mirror line.

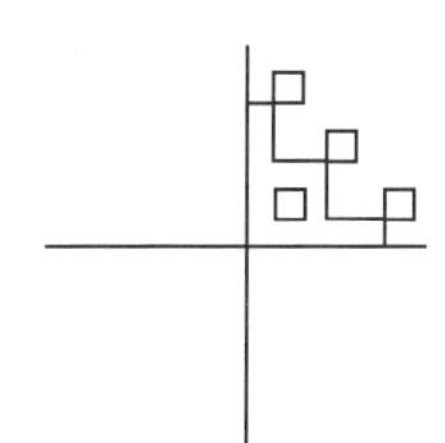

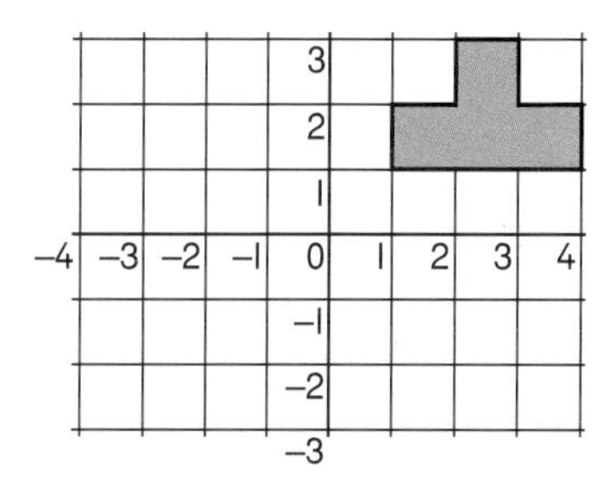

Sketch the position of a simple shape after it has been translated, say, 3 units to the right, then 2 units down.

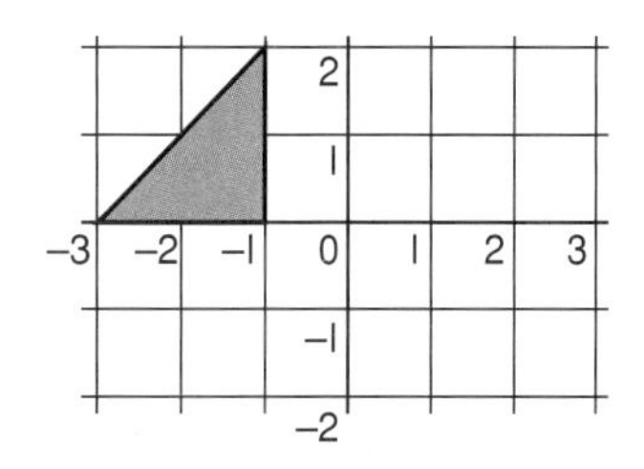

Use a computer program to transform shapes.
Predict and discuss the patterns made.

Pupils should be taught to:

Recognise positions and directions, and use co-ordinates

As outcomes, Year 4 pupils should, for example:

Use, read and write:
prepositions and everyday words to describe position and direction...
position, direction...
ascend, descend... journey, route, map, plan...
grid, row, column, origin, co-ordinates...
compass point, north, south, east, west, north-east, north-west, south-east, south-west...
horizontal, vertical, diagonal...

Describe and find the **position of a point on a grid of squares** where the lines are numbered.

Begin to understand the convention that (3, 2) describes a point found by starting from the origin (0, 0) and moving three lines across and two lines up.

Recognise that (4, 1) and (1, 4) describe different points.

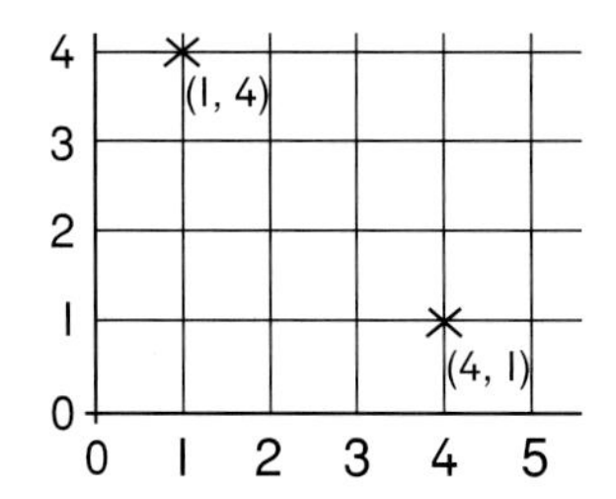

Recognise and identify simple examples of **horizontal or vertical lines** or edges in the environment. For example:
- the edge of the table is horizontal:
- the edge of the door is vertical...

Know that rows on a grid are described as horizontal, columns as vertical, and lines joining opposite corners as diagonals.

Use the eight **compass directions** N, S, E, W, NE, NW, SE, SW. For example:

- Describe a south-east route from (1, 4) as going through the points (2, 3), (3, 2), (4, 1) and (5, 0).
- Work out that to travel along the grid lines for a total distance of 5 units from the origin takes you to (0, 5), (1, 4), (2, 3), (3, 2), (4, 1) or (5, 0).
- Describe all the different routes from A to B, travelling only north-east or north-west.

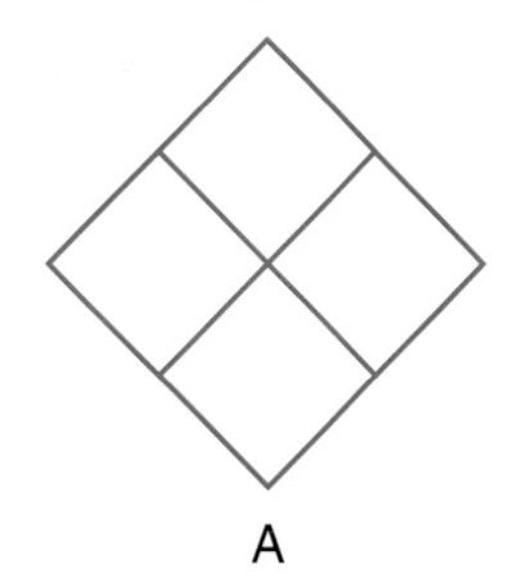

As outcomes, Year 5 pupils should, for example:

Use, read and write, spelling correctly, the vocabulary from the previous year, and extend to:
x-axis, y-axis... quadrant...
parallel, perpendicular...

Read and plot points using co-ordinates in the first quadrant.

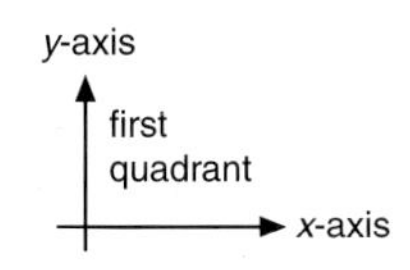

Know the convention that (3, 2) describes a point found by starting from the origin (0, 0) and moving three lines across and two lines up.

Respond to questions such as:

- These points are the co-ordinates of the vertices of a shape: (1, 5), (2, 5), (4, 3), (2, 1), (1, 1). What is the name of the shape?
- Three of the vertices of a square are (2, 1), (2, 4) and (5, 4). What are the co-ordinates of the fourth vertex?

Know that:
- **perpendicular** lines are at right angles to each other;
- **parallel** lines are the same distance apart.

Recognise and identify parallel and perpendicular lines in the environment and in regular polygons such as the square, hexagon and octagon.

Know that a **diagonal** is a straight line drawn from a vertex of a polygon to a non-adjacent vertex. For example:

- Draw all the diagonals of a shape such as a pentagon or an octagon.

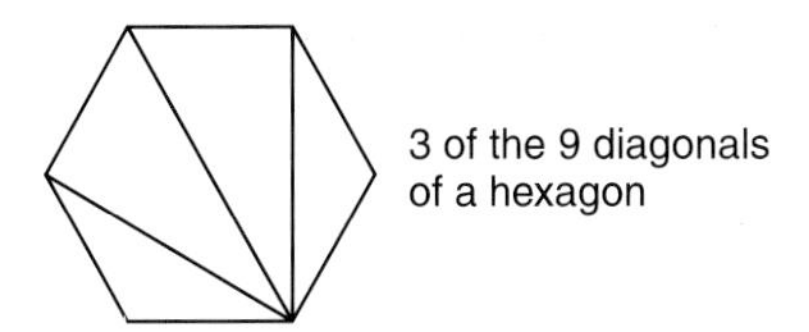
3 of the 9 diagonals of a hexagon

As outcomes, Year 6 pupils should, for example:

Use, read and write, spelling correctly, the vocabulary from the previous year, and extend to:
intersecting, intersection...
plane...

Read and plot points using co-ordinates beyond the first quadrant.

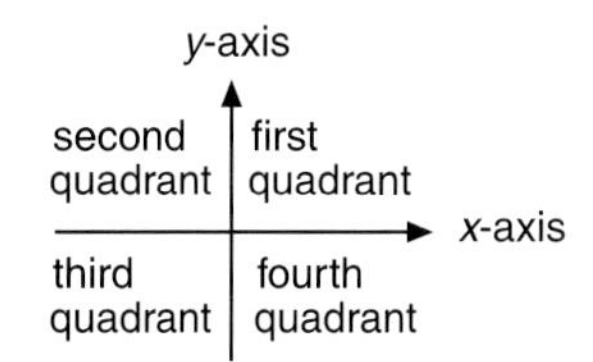

Respond to questions such as:

- The points (–1, 1), (2, 5) and (6, 2) are three of the four vertices of a square. What are the co-ordinates of the fourth vertex?
- Draw a polygon with each vertex lying in the first quadrant. Plot its reflection in the *y*-axis, and name the co-ordinates of the reflected shape.

Recognise **parallel and perpendicular lines** in quadrilaterals.

See also properties of 3-D and 2-D shapes (page 103).

Know that two lines that cross each other are called **intersecting lines**, and the point at which they cross is an intersection. For example:

- Identify all the intersections of lines drawn from 2 points to, say, 3, 4, 5... other points.

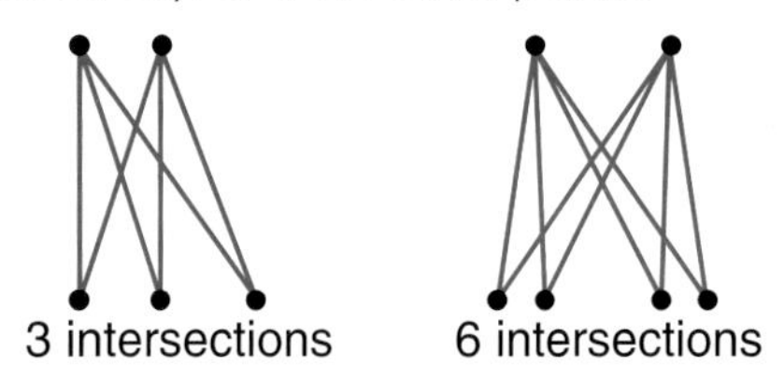

Predict the number of intersections from 2 points to 10 points.

Pupils should be taught to:

Make turns; estimate, draw and measure angles; recognise rotations

As outcomes, Year 4 pupils should, for example:

Use, read and write:
turn, rotate, whole turn, half turn, quarter turn…
angle, right angle, straight line… degree…
ruler, set square, angle measurer…

Know that angles are measured in degrees and that:

- one whole turn is 360° or four right angles;
- a quarter turn is 90° or one right angle;
- half a right angle is 45°.

Know that the angles at the corners of rectangles and squares are 90°, and that the angles of an equilateral triangle are 60°.

Make and measure clockwise and anti-clockwise turns, describing them in degrees. For example:

- Make and describe turns of 30°, 60°, 90° using the hour hand on a clock: for example, from 10 o'clock to 2 o'clock, or 5 o'clock to 7 o'clock, or 2 o'clock to 3 o'clock.
- Make and describe turns using compass directions: for example, face west, turn clockwise by 45°, and say in which direction you are facing now.
- In geography, express day-to-day changes in wind direction from, say, south-west to west in degrees.
- Work out how many degrees the pointer turns from wash to spin.

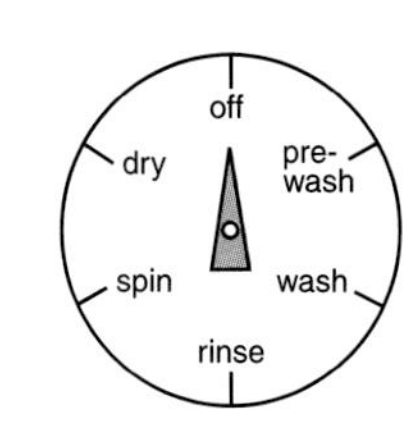

Start to order angles. For example:

- Use a 45° or 60° set square to draw and measure angles of 90°, 60°, 45° and 30°.
- Recognise which of two angles is greater: for example, that an angle of 60° is greater than an angle of 45°.
- Place in order of size a set of angles, each less than two right angles.

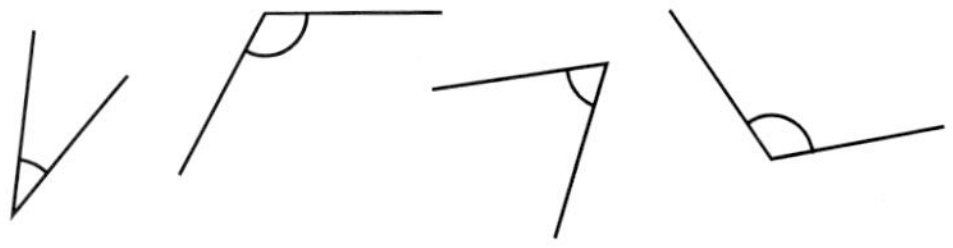

As outcomes, Year 5 pupils should, for example:

Use, read and write, spelling correctly, the vocabulary from the previous year, and extend to:
rotation...
acute, obtuse... protractor...

Make patterns by rotating shapes.

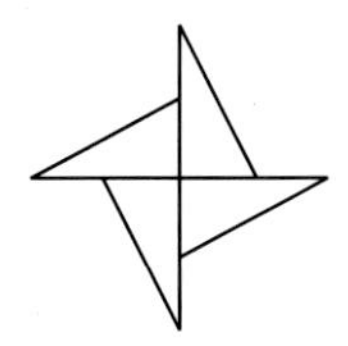

rotations of 90°

rotations of 45°

Recognise right angles and understand and use angle measure in degrees.

Begin to identify, estimate, order, measure and calculate acute, obtuse and right angles. Know that:

- an angle less than 90° is acute;
- an angle between 90° and 180° is obtuse;
- an angle of 180° is a straight line.

For example:

- Identify acute, obtuse and right angles in the classroom, and in 2-D shapes.
- Say which of these angles are acute, and which are obtuse.

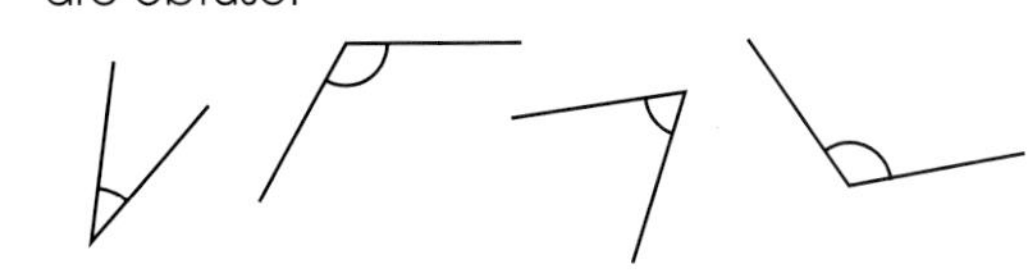

Estimate the size of each angle to the nearest 5°.

- Use a protractor to measure these angles to the nearest 5°.

- Use a protractor to draw angles of 25°, 80°, 135°.
- Calculate angles in a straight line. For example:

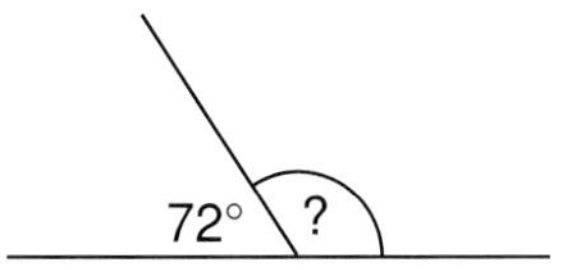

As outcomes, Year 6 pupils should, for example:

Use, read and write, spelling correctly, the vocabulary from the previous year, and extend to:
reflex...

Sketch the position of a simple shape after a rotation of 90° or 180° about a vertex.

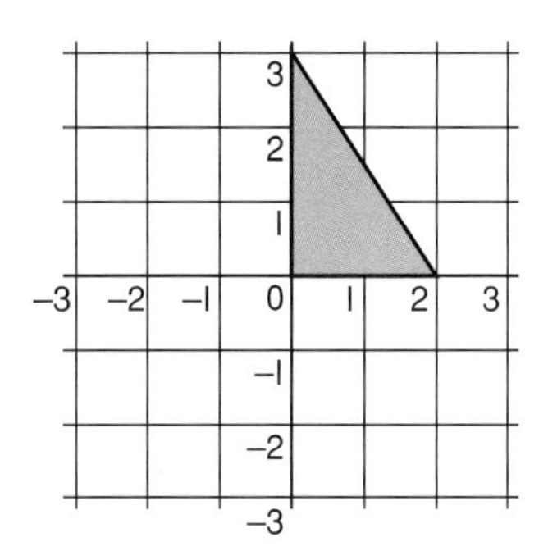

Identify, estimate, order, measure and calculate acute and obtuse angles.

For example:

- Estimate in degrees the size of each of a set of angles.
- Use a protractor to measure given angles to the nearest degree.
- Use a protractor to draw angles to the nearest degree.
- Check that the sum of the three angles of a triangle is 180° by measuring or paper folding. For example, draw and cut out a triangle. Tear off the three corners and rearrange them to make a straight line.
- Calculate the third angle of a triangle, given the other two.

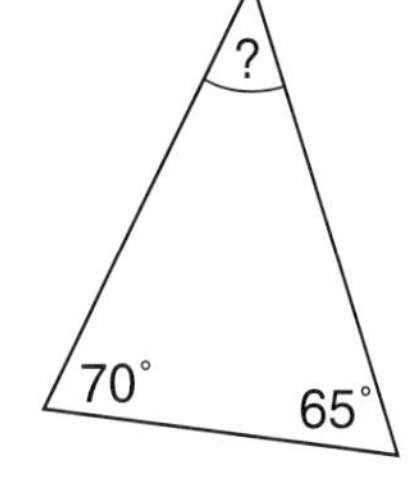

- Calculate angles at a point. For example:

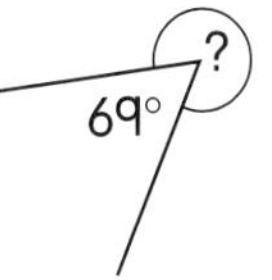

- Use a Logo procedure to explore the external angle properties of regular polygons

Pupils should be taught to:

Use the language associated with probability to discuss events, including those with equally likely outcomes

As outcomes, Year 4 pupils should, for example:

As outcomes, Year 5 pupils should, for example:

Use, read and write, spelling correctly:
fair, unfair...
likely, unlikely, likelihood...
certain, uncertain...
probable, possible, impossible...
chance, good chance, poor chance, no chance...
risk, doubt...

Use cross-curricular opportunities to discuss events which have a good chance of happening and those which have a poor chance. For example:

- Discuss statements like:
  I doubt whether I will catch the 4 o'clock bus.
  Snakes and Ladders is not a fair game – the first player has the best chance of winning.
  There is little risk of catching measles these days.

- Match one of these words to each of the statements below:

  CERTAIN LIKELY UNLIKELY IMPOSSIBLE

  a. I will watch television tonight.
  b. It will snow next Christmas.
  c. I will grow taller than my mother.
  d. It will get dark tonight.
  e. I will see Queen Victoria on my way home.

  Place the statements on this scale:

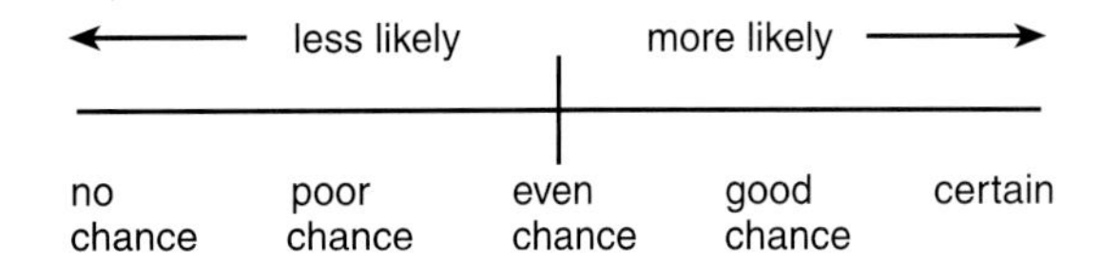

As outcomes, Year 6 pupils should, for example:

Use, read and write, spelling correctly, the vocabulary from the previous year, and extend to:
equally likely...
equal chance, even chance, fifty-fifty chance...
biased, random...

Discuss events which might have two equally likely outcomes. For example:
- a new baby is equally likely to be a boy or a girl;
- if I drop a picture postcard there is an even chance it will land picture side up;
- if I roll a dice I am just as likely to roll an even number as an odd number...

Discuss events with two or more equally likely outcomes. For example:

- Consider a 1 to 6 dice.
  What is the probability of:
  a. rolling a 4;
  b. rolling an even number;
  c. rolling a number greater than 2;
  d. rolling zero;
  e. rolling a number lying between 0 and 7?

  Place each probability on this scale.

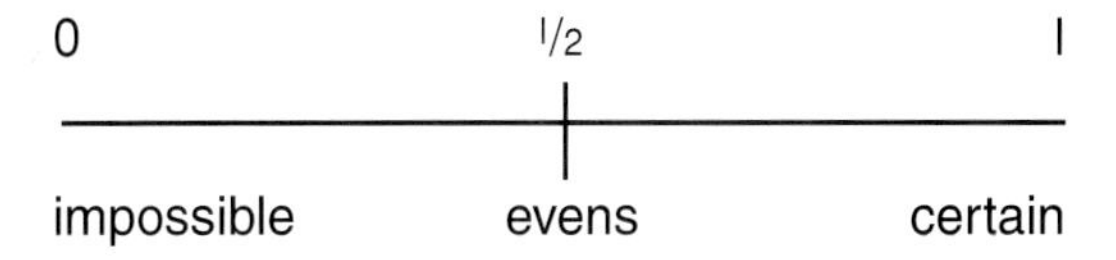

Discuss the difference between the theory of outcomes and the actual, experimental results. For example:

- Discuss outcomes when a coin is tossed.

  How many heads and how many tails might turn up if a coin is tossed 10 times, 20 times, 30 times...?

  Work in pairs and record results on squared paper. In 20 tosses, did heads and tails each come up 10 times? What happens when you combine your results with another pair?

  Discuss whether the results would be the same if the experiment were repeated.

Pupils should be taught to:

Solve a problem by collecting, organising, representing, extracting and interpreting data in tables, graphs and charts

As outcomes, Year 4 pupils should, for example:

Use, read and write:
vote, survey, questionnaire, data, count, tally, sort, set, represent... table, list, graph, chart, diagram, axes, label, title... most common or popular...

Find the answer to a question by collecting data quickly then making a **tally chart**. For example:

Do many children get measles nowadays?

Find out by asking at home who has had German measles, chicken pox, mumps, flu...
Make a tally chart.
Discuss the findings, such as the risk of catching measles, or flu.

ILLNESSES	
German measles	~~IIII~~ III
Mumps	III
Chicken pox	~~IIII~~ ~~IIII~~
Flu	~~IIII~~ ~~IIII~~ III
Measles	I

Find the answer to a question by using data collected in another subject or at home. Make a **pictogram, where the symbol represents several units**. For example:

It is said that thrushes are becoming less common. Are there any around our school?

Discuss the findings. For example:

- How many thrushes?
- How many more sparrows than thrushes?
- How many birds altogether?
- Were there many thrushes compared with other birds? Why might this be?
- How might more accurate data be collected?

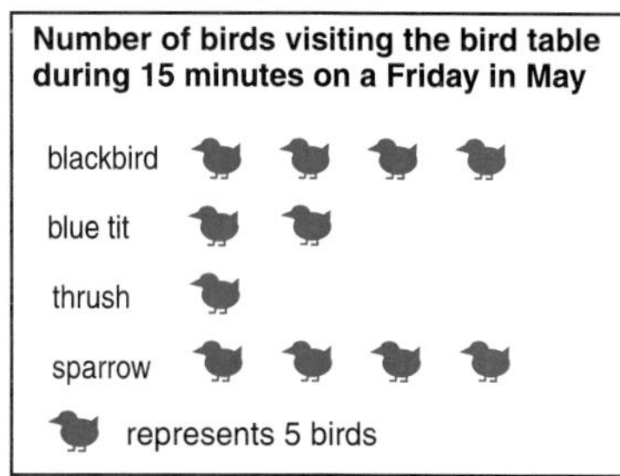

Answer a question or solve a problem by interpreting a **bar chart** with the vertical axis marked in multiples of 2, 5, 10 or 20, noting that the graph has a title, and axes are labelled. For example:

At what time of day do most people use the local bus?

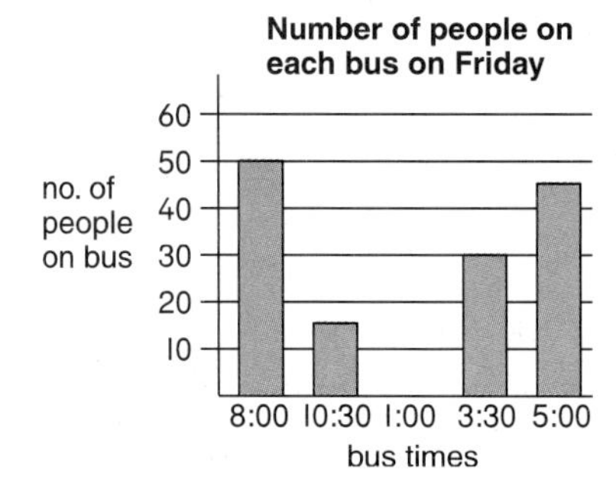

- 25 people were on the 1:00 bus. Draw in the bar.
- On a Friday, which bus is most likely to be full?
- Which bus had the fewest people on it? Why?
- What might the graph for Saturday look like?
- How often do the buses run? Do you think that the bus timetable should change? How and why?

As outcomes, Year 5 pupils should, for example:

Use, read and write, spelling correctly, the vocabulary from the previous year, and extend to: *classify, mode, maximum/minimum value, range... outcome...*

Test a hypothesis about the frequency of an event by collecting data quickly: for example, from a simple experiment, a local newspaper, a reference book, work in other subjects... Discuss a **bar chart** or **bar line chart** showing the frequency of the event and check the prediction. For example:

We think Rovers scored more than 3 goals in a quarter of their matches last season.

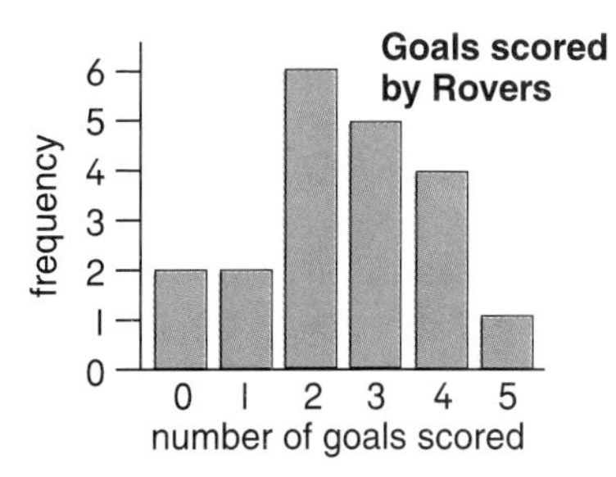

This **bar chart** shows the number of goals scored by Rovers in last season's matches. Discuss questions like:

- How many matches in total did Rovers play?
- What was the maximum number of goals Rovers scored in a match?
- In how many of their matches did Rovers score more than 3 goals?
- What was the most common number of goals (mode)?
- How likely are Rovers to score 7 goals in a match when they play in the same league this season?

You are more likely to throw a 6 on a dice than any other number. Is this true?

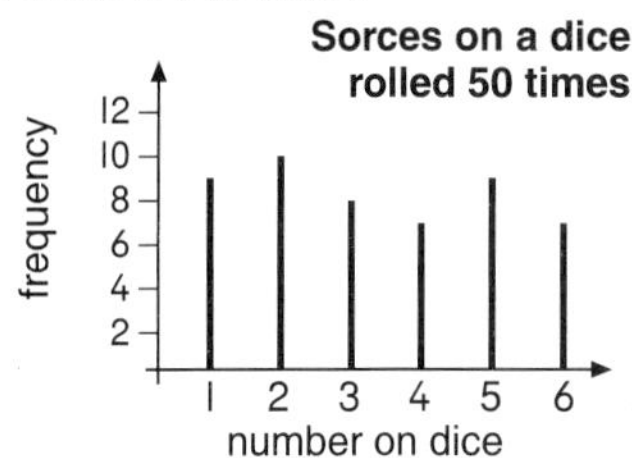

This **bar line chart** shows how many times each number was thrown when a dice was rolled 50 times. Discuss questions such as:

- Which number was rolled most often?
- Was this what you would have expected? Why?
- Do you think the next time you roll the dice you are more likely to roll a 2 than a 6? Why?
- What do you think will happen if you roll the dice 50 more times? Now try it and see.

Know that it is not appropriate to join the tops of the bars when the values in-between have no meaning: for example, a dice does not show the number 2.5.

As outcomes, Year 6 pupils should, for example:

Use, read and write, spelling correctly, the vocabulary from the previous year, and extend to: *statistics, average, distribution... median, mean...*

Test a hypothesis by drawing and discussing a **bar chart where (discrete) data are grouped**: for example, to check predictions of the most common number of:

- lengths that will be swum in a sponsored swim;
- peas in a pod;
- scores in a tables test...

We think that most of the class will get more than 30 marks in the test.

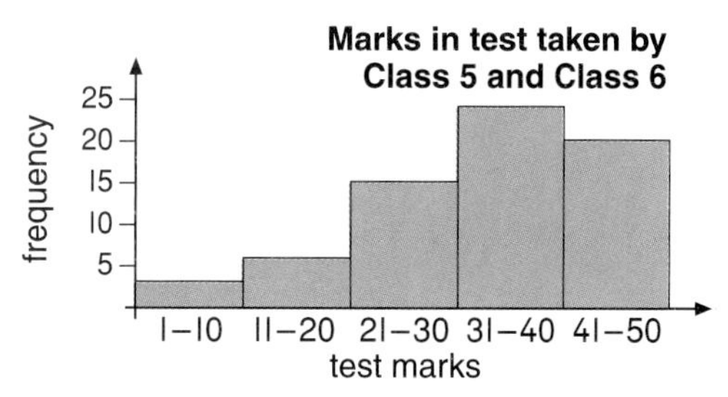

Discuss questions such as:

- What was the most common score in the test?
- How many children took the test? Estimate how many of them got fewer than half marks.
- The children who took the tables test practise recalling their tables each day for a week. They then take the same test again. Sketch a graph showing how you think the marks in the second test will be distributed.

Know that for grouped discrete data the bars may be labelled with the range that they represent but not the divisions between the bars.

Begin to interpret **simple pie charts**, such as those showing the data in a computer database.

Ages of the population of Ham village

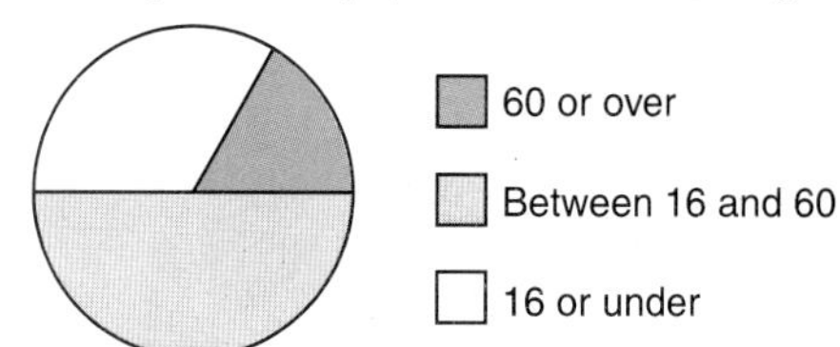

Answer questions such as:

- What fraction (percentage) of the population of Ham is 16 or under? 60 or over?
- Why do you think there are more people aged 16 or under than aged 60 or over living in Ham?

Pupils should be taught to:

Solve a problem by collecting, organising, representing, extracting and interpreting data in tables, graphs and charts (continued)

As outcomes, Year 4 pupils should, for example:

Use **sorting diagrams** such as two-way Venn and Carroll diagrams to display information about shapes or numbers.

For example:

- This **Venn diagram** records how some number cards were sorted.

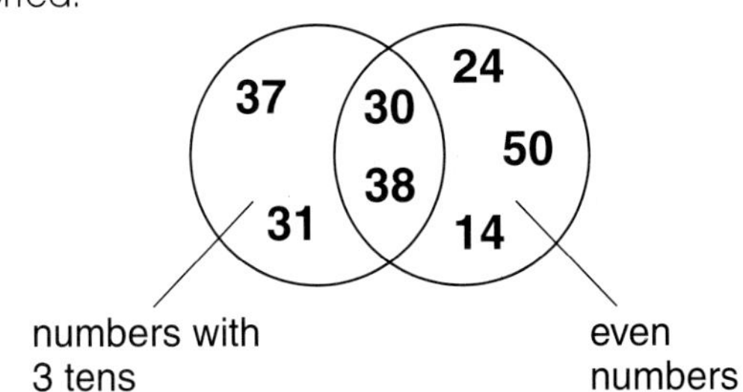

Put these numbers on the diagram: 8, 33, 36, 41.
Choose some other numbers. Add them to the diagram.

- This **Carroll diagram** records how some of the whole numbers from 20 to 39 were sorted.

	odd	not odd (even)
numbers that have 3 tens	37 31	38 30
numbers that do not have 3 tens	23 25	26 20

Add these numbers to the diagram: 24, 35.

As outcomes, Year 5 pupils should, for example:

Develop understanding of the **mode** (most common item) and the range (difference between greatest and least) of a set of data.

Test a prediction such as:
Most of our class will get 9 out of 10 questions right in a mental test and 8 out of 10 right in a spelling test.

Discuss questions like:
- How can we find out if this is true?
- What information shall we collect?
- How shall we organise it?

Make a simple **database on paper**. For example:

Scores for 10 spelling and 10 mental answers

Name	Mental test score	Spelling test score
Danny	8	9
Elizabeth	10	7
Anil	7	9

Find the most common score in each test (mode). Put the scores for one of the tests in order to find the maximum and minimum score, and the difference between them (range). Repeat for the other test. Discuss outcomes, and the extent to which the prediction was true.

Draw and interpret a **line graph**. Understand that intermediate points may or may not have meaning. For example:

- In science, investigate room temperature. For example, use an IT sensor to collect, store and retrieve room temperature in a classroom. (Points in the resulting graph are joined to show trends.)

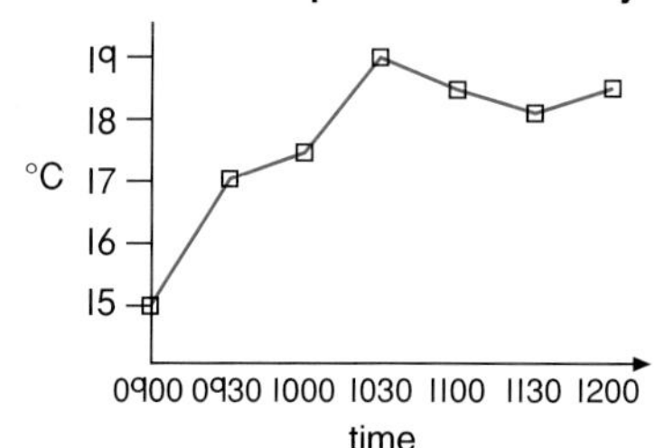

- This graph shows the level of water in a rain barrel during the month of April. Explain it by describing the pattern of rainfall throughout the month.

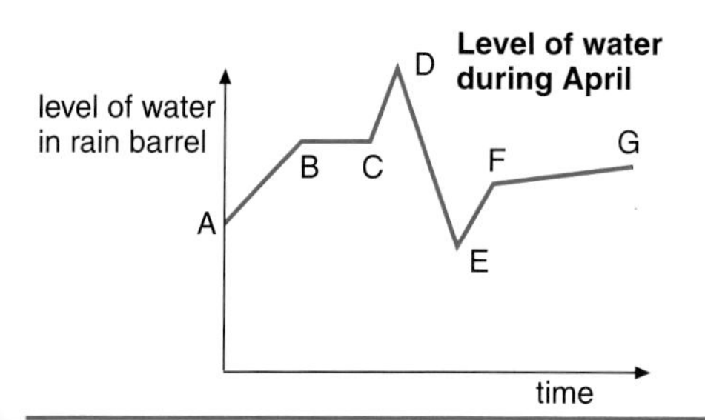

As outcomes, Year 6 pupils should, for example:

Find the **mode** and range of a simple set of data in a computer database. Begin to find the **mean** and **median**.

For example, make a simple **computer database**. Transfer the results of a spelling test and a mental test to it and then use its facilities to find out, for example:

- Who scored more than 7?
- What were the frequencies of scores of 10, 9, 8...?
- What was the most common score (the mode)?
- What was the difference between the greatest and least scores (the range)?
- What was the middle score (the median)?
- What was the mean score (the sum of all the scores divided by the total number of scores)?

In other subjects, test hypotheses by interrogating data in a **prepared computer database**, such as census data or data on road safety. For example:

Do people live longer today than 100 years ago?
Do most accidents occur when it is dark?

Use the facilities of the database to compare and contrast the presentation of data in different charts or graphs, deciding which is best for its purpose. Discuss the efficiency of a computer database compared with searching and sorting a paper database.

Begin to draw and interpret a **line graph, in which intermediate values have meaning**.
For example:

- This road sign is in miles. Use the conversion graph to rewrite the road sign in kilometres.

Darlington	15
Durham	35
Newcastle	45

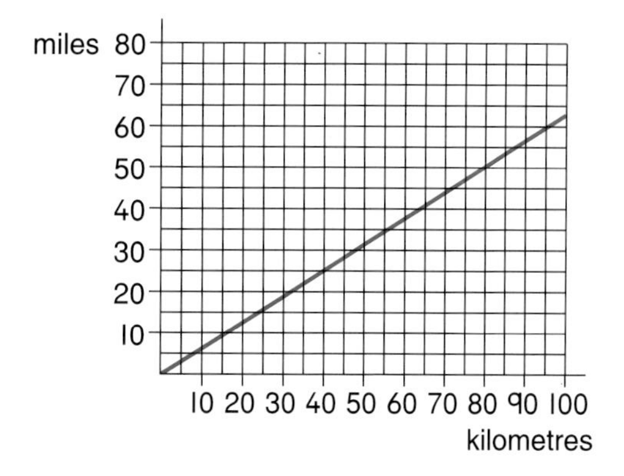

- The tourist rate for South Korea is 2000 won to £1. Construct a graph to convert pounds to won. Use the graph to find out what you get when you exchange:
  £5, £8.50, 9000 won, 13 125 won.

- Draw and use a '3 times-table' graph.